WITHDRAWN
L. R. COLLEGE LIBRARY

PLANT GALLS
AND GALL MAKERS

PLANT GALLS
AND GALL MAKERS

By

EPHRAIM PORTER FELT, D.Sc.

*Director and Chief Entomologist, Bartlett Tree Research
Laboratories; Editor (Honorary) Journal of Economic
Entomology; Formerly State Entomologist
of New York; Collaborator New
York State Museum*

Ithaca · New York

Comstock Publishing Company, Inc.

1940

581.27

F 34 p

COPYRIGHT, 1940, BY
COMSTOCK PUBLISHING COMPANY, INC.

18849

March, 1942

PRINTED IN THE UNITED STATES OF AMERICA

THE COLLEGIATE PRESS · MENASHA · WISCONSIN

PREFACE

THIS BOOK is planned to give a general idea of the immensely interesting and comparatively unknown insect galls and their producers and to facilitate the identification of the hundreds of these deformities occurring upon numerous plants in all parts of North America. It is a branch of science which appeals to the general student of nature as well as to the botanist, entomologist and ecologist.

There is an attempt to sketch in broad outlines the relations existing between gall producers and their plant hosts and to explain in some measure the mysteries of gall production. There are also brief accounts of the relationships existing in a number of plant families especially favored by gall insects. Common names have been used generally where available and technical terms have been avoided where it could be done in order to make the work more generally acceptable to the average reader. This has not materially lessened the value of the work for specialists, since the bibliography supplements the more extensive one in the earlier published "Key" and it is therefore comparatively easy to refer to the extensive literature. This book is a summation of what has been learned about insect galls of the country and may well serve as a guide to future studies in this attractive field of natural history.

This work is an extended revision, a rewritten version with much additional matter, of the author's "Key to American Insect Galls" which appeared as New York State Museum Bulletin #200 in 1917. The demand for the bulletin was so great that the edition was speedily exhausted.

The twenty odd years just passed have been marked by great additions to our knowledge of insect galls and gall producers, especially of the gall wasps on oaks, the most noteworthy contributions being made by Professor A. C. Kinsey of Indiana State University and Dr. L. H. Weld of the United States National Museum. The work of these investigators in the description of new gall insects and the light they have thrown on the previously unknown alternate generations of a number of species have contributed materially to the value of this book.

The numerous figures printed in the author's "Key to American Insect Galls" are included through the courtesy of the New York State Museum, Dr. C. C. Adams, Director. Permission has been accorded by Dr. F. E. Lutz of the American Museum of Natural History to include the long series of gall illustrations prepared under the direction of the late William Beutenmuller, a well known earlier student of gall insects. Through the courtesy of Professor A. C. Kinsey and Dr. L. H. Weld, we have been allowed to reproduce many of their photographs, there being an especially long series from Dr. Weld. The latter has also read critically the section on oak galls, a field in which he is a recognized leader.

E. PORTER FELT

Stamford, Conn.
May 1940

CONTENTS

PART I

INTRODUCTION

PART I

Introduction

NEARLY everyone has seen an insect gall. It is quite possible that one or more of these peculiar growths has aroused a certain amount of interest on the part of casual observers. Comparatively few realize that gall insects live, as it were, in a world of their own, and that they are past masters in the art of beguiling or compelling the host plant to provide food and shelter with a minimum expenditure of effort on their part. It seems absurd, from the human viewpoint, that the relatively slight irritation produced by the feeding of an aphid or plant louse, for example, should cause adjacent plant tissues to develop in such a manner as to securely protect an enemy, especially when such a course is presumably injurious rather than beneficial to the plant. This remarkable relation is true not only of one but of many of the numerous gall insects, each presenting certain similarities of structure and habit and all differing from each other in one or more essentials.

An invitation to eat and be sheltered appears too good to be true. This is especially the case if there is an abundance of food and satisfactory shelter. Nevertheless, the plant world has been extending this invitation for many centuries and although most insects have accepted so far as eating is concerned, comparatively few have fed in such a way as to secure shelter. This latter is true of the 1500 or more different kinds or species of gall producers. It would not be so peculiar if an occasional insect here and there in the long series of species and varieties was able to take advantage of plants as indicated above. It is remarkable to find that several widely different groups of insects or their close relatives, namely the plant mites, gall midges and the gall wasps, have largely mastered the problem of feeding in such a way as to secure, through the mere satisfying of the pangs of hunger, most satisfactory shelter from the elements.

A scrutiny of these shelters or galls, and some consideration of the insects which produce them, indicate that a variety of methods may be used in attaining the desired goal. It will be noted that the less highly organized gall producers, such as the plant mites and many of the insects in the larger groups of gall producers, occur in comparatively simple galls, leaf roll or pouch galls, whereas the more highly organized producers inhabit complex structures which at first sight seem unrelated to the tissues from which they have developed. A cardinal requirement is that the feeding must be so gauged as to stimulate growth without killing too many plant cells. The gall producers have learned by experience how to do this, and in the accomplishment of their purpose, actually deceive, as it were, the plant tissues adjacent to the stimulated area, and in some of the more highly developed galls, there is a close approximation to the seed and its structures, the gall maggot taking the place of the seed itself, the walls of the gall forming the protective coat and the process being perfected to such an extent in some cases that seed-like galls are actually shed in much the same way as the normal seed of the plant. Furthermore, in a number of genera of gall insects, there is a restriction to closely related plants, mostly belonging to the same plant genus and even to parts of plants and with corresponding variations in the complexity of the galls produced.

There are also the purely attractive or artistic aspects, such as varied form and striking or delicate coloration. The almost innumerable variations in the form of galls are due to the part of the plant affected and the stimulation to abnormal growth of portions of plants or of plant structures usually escaping notice. Such conditions are found in the mossy rose gall and the hedgehog gall of the oak, together with numerous remarkable deformities produced by related insects. The fresh, well-developed, creamy-white, pink spotted gall of the wool sower is one of the most beautiful of natural objects, while the delicately colored cypress "flower galls" are occasionally found in such numbers as to suggest an attractive spray of dainty flowers, structures very different from what normally occurs on bald cypress and therefore even more surprising. The yellow, red-margined leaf spot of soft maple, the product of a gall midge, is noteworthy because of its abundance and striking coloration.

GALLS AND GALL TYPES

Galls are abnormal vegetable growths resulting from the work of insects, usually immature, and other organisms. There are innumerable gradations between the apparently normal and the decidedly abnormal and as a consequence it is difficult to establish a satisfactory distinction between plant galls and deformations not worthy of classification under this term. Some would include the mere curling of leaves, and while to a certain extent this is justified, in most cases, unless the curling is pronounced, it has not been considered as a gall in this work.

There is no reason why the deformities upon plants produced by insects and other organisms should not be given names, though the best zoological practice is against the bestowal of scientific names upon plant deformations. Such designations should be applied to a characteristic animal organism and not to the product of its activities. A number of group names for galls are well established, such as oak apples, blister galls, bud galls and the like and they should be used wherever brevity and clarity can be promoted. Characteristic common names for plant galls are valuable aids in stimulating general interest and we have used these as freely as circumstances appeared to warrant.

It is very convenient to separate galls and their producers into easily distinguished groups and the following are the most useful of the descriptive terms.

Blister Galls. Many blister-like swellings of leaves are included under this term. The more conspicuous and common are the apparently fungus-filled galls occurring upon the leaves of goldenrod or solidago and aster and usually inhabited by gall midges belonging to the genus *Asteromyia*. Botanists for a time supposed these swellings were produced by a fungus, and described a number of them as species of *Rhytisma*. There are a number of less conspicuous blister galls produced by plant mites.

Bud Galls. Many deformations originate in buds. They vary from a plainly aborted bud to large swellings developed from such parts. Gall midges belonging to the genus *Asphondylia* are practically restricted to bud galls.

Bullet Galls. These are nearly solid, one-celled or monothalamous galls produced by species of gall wasps or *Disholcaspis,* mostly upon oak twigs and are suggestive in appearance of bullets.

Cecidomyia. This is a general term applied to any species referable to the gall midges or *Itonididæ* and which can not be readily assigned to more closely defined genera.

Erineum. These are the hairy or pile-like growths upon leaf surfaces produced by species of plant mites or *Eriophyidæ*.

Flower Galls. Aborted or deformed flowers or masses of flowers afford suitable conditions for many gall insects.

Fruit Galls. This term is used in a botanical sense and includes seeds as well as fruits. In many cases there is a marked deformity, though in some the fruit has a nearly normal appearance.

Leaf Galls. This term applies to all deformations definitely associated with leaves.

Leaf Spots. This is a convenient designation for some leaf galls which are more evident because of marked discoloration than on account of swelling or deformation.

Many-celled, or *polythalamous,* a term used to designate galls containing two or more young or larvae in more or less separated cells.

Oak Apples. This applies in particular to the familiar large galls on oak produced by the gall wasp genus *Amphibolips,* the large oak apple and the empty oak apple being among the best known.

One-celled or *monothalamous;* a convenient term used to designate galls inhabited by a larva or a number of larvae in one cell or cavity.

Pouch Galls. They are simply pouch-like deformities usually caused by a depression in the leaf surface, inhabited, in many cases by gall mites or aphids.

Roly-Poly Galls. These are smaller than oak apples and are easily recognized by the loose, usually oval cell within a large cavity.

Root Galls. This is simply a designation indicating the position of the gall. They vary in size, shape and location on the root system.

Rosette Galls. These are specialized types of bud galls, usually at the tip or apical, though sometimes at the base of a branchlet or axillary, and generally they consist of a central cell surrounded by a rosette of partly developed leaves.

Stem or twig galls are deformations restricted to that portion of the plant. This is generally applied to galls affecting the entire circumference of the stem or twig.

Subcortical galls. These are swellings just under the bark, usually upon one side of a stem or twig and are frequently irregular in shape.

The Principal Gall-Producers

The ability to produce plant galls has developed to a great extent in one section of the mites and among a number of widely different insects, though in certain groups of the latter, it is much more common than in others. The principal gall-producers are found among the plant mites, the plant lice, including the jumping plant lice, the gall midges and the gall wasps, the first and the last two being largely gall-producers. The tiny insects known as thrips are found in many galls in the tropical and subtropical regions.

The plant or gall mites are microscopic in size, usually pale yellowish or nearly transparent, the larger species being visible to the naked eye as little more than minute specks. These mites are easily distinguished from related forms by the slender, more or less pear-shaped body, usually with numerous transverse microscopic ridges or lines, and the presence of but four legs,— most full grown mites have eight legs. The plant mites, as suggested by their name, occur upon plants, some living freely upon the leaf surface, many in dense, felted masses of plant hairs known as erineums, others in buds, as the filbert bud gall mite, and still others may be found in a variety of pouch or pocket galls, one of the most common being the maple bladder gall. These last are really bulgings or distentions of the leaf surface, and might be classed as extreme forms of hairy leaf patches or erineums. Mite galls on leaves may be recognized by the tiny, usually hairy orifices. Many of the gall mites winter in buds or under bud scales. There are a large number of species, many undescribed. They occur upon a great variety of plants, and exhibit no such preference for certain plant genera or plant families as is found among some plant lice, the gall midges and the gall wasps.

The aphids or plant lice are represented by a number of gall makers. They are all soft bodied insects with well developed, sucking mouth parts, and when full-grown or adult, possess four membranous wings. These insects are small, usually $\frac{1}{8}$ of an inch in length or less. There are several genera which commonly produce galls, though this habit is by no means so general as in the case of the plant mites, the gall midges and the gall wasps. One gall producer, notably the *Adelges* on spruce, is best known because it produces the common cone gall upon Norway spruce. This particular species breeds year after year on the Norway spruce, though related forms have a more complicated life history, and in the case of the Sitka spruce gall on Colorado blue spruce, the alternate generation is a woolly plant louse which frequently occurs in great numbers on the needles of the Douglas fir. The genus *Adelges* is limited largely to species of spruce and fir.

There is a similar limitation of food habits with species of *Pemphigus* which produce a number of globular or other leaf deformations on poplar, the globular galls on the leaf stalks being among the more common and better known. These insects, like *Adelges*, migrate to summer hosts which, in the case of the transverse poplar gall, are mostly plants belonging to the cabbage family.

A large series of diverse leaf galls on hickory are produced by various species of *Phylloxera*, a group of plant lice best known because of the exceedingly destructive grape *Phylloxera*, an insect which has caused great damage to European vineyards and threatens serious injury to European vines grown on their own roots in California. The *Phylloxera* galls on hickory vary from comparatively small disk-like or button-like galls with a central opening guarded by plant hairs or processes, to globular swellings one-half inch in diameter, or thereabouts on the upper or lower surface of the leaf. The interior of such galls may be densely lined with young *Phylloxeras* and suggest in appearance the crystals of a geode. The very injurious hickory leaf stem galls are produced by a species of *Phylloxera*, the eggs being deposited in the old galls and on rough places on the bark and hatch just as the buds begin to start, the young *Phylloxeras* invading the buds and actually producing galls before the new tissues completely push aside the bud scales.

The jumping plant lice, *Pachypsylla*, suggest in appearance tiny Cicadas. They are represented by a number of species and occur in diverse galls upon hackberry. These galls, as in the case of the *Phylloxera* deformities, vary greatly in shape from slight swellings of the leaf blade to compound deformations of the leaf stem and typical, though less spectacular deformation of buds, each species producing a definite type of gall.

The gall midges are a large group of small, delicate flies, rarely more than ¼ of an inch long and usually much smaller. Most of these insects produce galls found on different parts of a great variety of plants. They have two, usually transparent wings with three or four veins and are remarkable for the diverse frequently long antennae or feelers, there being on these organs not only unusual structures but a wide range in the number of the antennal segments, these varying in different United States species from 6 to 41 and in the Panamanian genus *Feltomyina* there are 63 segments. The maggots or larvae are usually moderately stout, rounded at both ends and yellowish or yellowish-orange, although when young they may be nearly transparent. Most possess a characteristic, usually brown "breast bone" or "anchor process", on the under anterior part of the body. Many of the gall midge maggots are able to snap or throw themselves to a distance several times greater than their length. This is accomplished by bringing the two extremities together and then straightening suddenly, the impact throwing the small maggots an inch or more.

Although the long series of gall midges have much in common, there are a few groups deserving special mention. A considerable series of relatively simple gall midges is distinguished from others by the almost universally present crossvein and the absence of what are known as "bow whorls" on the antennae. They do not produce galls and live mostly in dead or decayed organic matter. A few in this group are remarkable because maggots produce maggots directly, that is, both the egg and the adult insects, the males and females are eliminated for an indefinite series of generations.

Most species of gall midges have peculiar structures known as "bow whorls" showing a great diversity of form and development. A relatively simple group of the "bow whorl" gall midges are characterized by a well-developed crossvein. There are comparatively few species and they, like those mentioned in the preceding paragraph, live mostly in dead, frequently dry organic matter, such as the dried galls of other insects.

There is a large series of what may be termed the hairy-veined gall midges, all relatively simple in structure and living mostly in galls produced in the softer tissues of plants, such as young leaves and developing buds. One division of these, the *Dasyneuriariæ*, have well developed teeth on the claws, while the other division, the *Ogligotrophiariæ*, are most easily recognized by the simple or untoothed claws. The gall midges in both of these divisions have similar habits.

The bud gall midges, *Asphondyliariæ*, are heavy bodied, usually moderately large, the females of the more typical species being easily recognized by the needle-like ovipositer, this organ frequently being nearly as long as the abdomen and composed of the hard substance so common in insect bodies and known as chitin. These insects occur mostly in either leaf or fruit buds of many diverse plants.

The short-horned or scaly-veined gall midges, *Lasiopterariæ*, are relatively small and most are clothed with brown and white scales. These small midges also have the three anterior veins of the wing so close to the front margin of the wing as to form, ordinarily, a broad, scaly area, easily mistaken for one rather than several veins. Many of the species produce stem galls on woody and herbaceous plants: others the peculiar blister, apparently fungous infected leaf galls on goldenrod and aster.

The long-horned gall midges, *Itonididinariæ*, present an extreme in development. The antennae of the males are frequently one-half longer than the body, held in a graceful arch above the insect, and apparently have nearly twice as many segments as in the female. It was only in the last 45 years or thereabouts that the mystery was explained. It was found that the flagellate antennal segments of the males in this group have two well-marked swellings, as compared with one of the female. There is not only this apparent doubling of the antennal segments but the "bow whorls" in the typical males are enormously developed, each whorl may have a length, equal to or greater than the length of the entire segment. Furthermore, a long series of the male long-horned gall midges have three sets of long "bow whorls", whereas another division has but two. Many of the long-horned gall midges produce leaf and fruit galls and a number are beneficial, since their maggots or larvae prey upon the gall producing species.

The gall wasps or *Cynipids* are small insects, mostly an eighth of an inch in length or less. They are primarily inhabitants of various oaks, are wasp-like or ant-like in appearance, mostly black or reddish brown, have four transparent wings with a few veins, except in a number of species producing asexual wingless females, and a stout, usually oval abdomen. The young or grubs are whitish, legless maggots not found outside the invariably completely closed galls. Both the adults and the young are most easily identified by the galls which they produce and in which they develop.

There are a number of genera with many species, such as *Acraspis* occurring in spined oak leaf galls, *Amphibolips,* the producers of oak apples, *Andricus* and the closely related *Callirhytis,* with numerous species making galls in oak twigs, *Disholcaspis,* the inhabitant of oak bullet galls, *Dryophanta,* a frequenter of buds and developing tissues, is common in woolly oak leaf galls, *Neuroterus* likewise develops in soft oak leaf galls, and *Diplolepis,* probably better known as *Rhodites,* lives only in rose galls of varied form and striking appearance. There are a number of other genera with relatively few species. The separation of the gall wasps or *Cynipids* is distinctly the work of the specialist and is not advised for the amateur.

The situation in regard to the generic names of the gall wasps is difficult. The complicated life cycle of the species with alternate generations is a serious obstacle in working out the life history and also raises problems in regard to name combinations which should be used. Doctors A. C. Kinsey and L. H. Weld have added much to our knowledge of these insects, still there has been no comprehensive study in recent years of the gall wasps of America and it is presumable that many changes are yet to be made in generic assignments. There are obvious objections to the use of trinomial or quadrinomial combinations and in this work it has been deemed best to use as a rule only binomial combinations. We have been content for the present to adhere mostly to the older, generally accepted generic names, leaving the presumably numerous changes to a time when the taxonomy of the gall wasps has been worked out more fully. The specific name under present conditions is the more reliable index to *Cynipid* identity.

INJURIOUS GALL INSECTS

A large proportion of the gall producers are of relatively little importance, though pests of the first magnitude may be found in this miscellaneous assemblage.

The fruit grower, to his sorrow, has learned of the destructive possibilities of the pear leaf blister mite, and in eastern New England and in central New York State, a few already have had experience with the leaf-curling midge of the apple. The pear midge is another pest which is of importance to the fruit grower.

Wheat growers know only too well the destructive possibilities of the Hessian fly, and in the earlier days, they were quite familiar with losses caused by the wheat midge. The clover midge prevents the growing of clover seed in large areas. These insects have exacted heavy tribute from the fruit grower and the farmer.

The gardener or horticulturist has learned through bitter experience something of what these insects can do. The rose grower has had his crop blasted by the rose midge. The violet grower has suffered severe losses from the violet midge. The chrysanthemum grower has learned of the serious results which may follow infestation by the delicate chrysanthemum midge. Outside, the gardener is tormented by the really injurious producer of the cone gall on the Norway spruce, a longer and similar gall on Colorado blue spruce, and on ornamentals he is troubled by the box leaf miner and to a less degree by the box psyllid.

The gall wasps are relatively unimportant from an economic standpoint, largely because they restrict themselves to such a great extent to oaks which are, generally speaking, not readily injured and ordinarily not held in such high esteem as the ornamentals of the greenhouse or the garden. By far the greater proportion of the gall insects occurring on oak are of negligible importance. The relatively few species, such as those producing large, irregular galls upon the smaller branches, may cause serious injury and kill good sized limbs or, in some cases, most of a tree. Such attacks are ordinarily restricted to an individual tree or a group of trees, and as a rule these conditions develop only after the insects have been able to take advantage of a series of favorable seasons or conditions, as the case may be. The numerous unsightly galls, so abundant on some oaks, are by no means the product of one season. They remain for years upon a tree and consequently a superficial examination leads to an erroneous conclusion as to the degree of infestation and the amount of injury. This is especially true of the knotty oak galls on willow oak, a common tree in portions of the south.

There is a gall midge which produces the oak pill gall. Several cases have come to notice where the galls of this insect were so abundant as to interfere seriously with leaf development and were this allowed to continue, a weakening of the tree would result. A similar condition on soft maple has been noted and in this case the injury was produced by a tiny plant mite which causes the maple bladder gall.

CERTAIN GALLS HAVE VALUE

Some insect galls are commercially valuable, though not to nearly the same extent as in earlier years. Certain oak galls have long been used in the manufacture of ink, particularly the more permanent writing fluids. The most important for this purpose is the Eurasian *Cynips gallæ-tinctoriæ*, variously known as the Aleppo gall, turkey gall, Levant gall, gall nut, gall of commerce and ink marble. It contains 65% of tannic acid and is mostly used for dying wool and skins. The Knoppern or acorn gall produced by *Cynips quercus-calycis* contains 50% of tannic acid and is next in importance to the Aleppo gall. There is a Chinese sumac gall, produced by a species of Pemphigus, closely allied to the somewhat common American *P. rhois*, that is imported in considerable quantities because of its tannin content, a characteristic also of our native gall. The air dried Chinese gall contains over 60% tannic acid and our native sumac gall about 8% less. It is probable that a number of American oak galls could be utilized to advantage were it not for the high cost of labor in this country. A gall produced by *Cynips theophrastea* was used by the Greeks as a fuel in lamps.

Insect galls are used in medicine on account of their astringent properties and a few have served as articles of food, notably that of a species of Aylax on *Salvia pomifera*, which forms an article of commerce in the Near East, and the somewhat common catmint gall, *Aylax glechomœ*. Both are said to have an agreeable taste and the sweet odor of the host plant. The insect producing the latter is well establishd in this country. Other galls are known to be edible and it is possible that they could be turned to good account when the insects are unusually abundant.

There is a black oak gall somewhat resembling wheat, identified as the deciduous oak gall, *Dryocosmus deciduus*, which is so abundant during certain years in Missouri and Arkansas that it has been fed to various domestic animals with excellent results. It is there known as "black oak wheat" and "wheat mast" and is eagerly devoured by chickens, and turkeys, as well as cattle, hogs and sheep. This gall or a very similar one is readily eaten by grouse. There are other galls, possibly many, which are acceptable food for birds.

Honeydew Producing Galls

The honeydew producing galls occur in the early summer in sufficient numbers to attract hosts of honey-gathering insects, such as bees and flies.

The ribbed bud gall, *Callirhytis gemmaria*, somewhat frequently attracts attention because of the numerous insects swarming in early summer in badly infested trees. Dr. L. H. Weld states that these galls when young secrete honeydew from a gland at the apex.

The wool sower, *Callirhytis seminator*, has a distinctly sticky surface when fresh and Messrs W. T. Davis, G. B. Engelhardt and C. Schaeffer have observed droplets of a very sticky substance on this gall.

A number of other galls are known to produce honeydew, as for example *Callirhytis carmelensis*, *C. balanaspis*, a gall deeply imbedded in the acorn cup beside the acorn, *C. balanopsis*, *C. balanosa*, *C. balanoides*, *C. congregator*, and *C. perditor* (U. S. Nat. Mus. Proc. v. 61, art. 19, 1922).

In addition to the above the bud galls of *Andricus atractans*, *Disholcaspis monticola*, *D. chrysolepidis*, *D. eldoradensis* and *Neuroterus vernus* are also known to produce more or less honeydew which attracts various insects.

Later a number of pip galls of the fall form of *Callirhytis operator* were collected under a badly infested oak which had been full of bees the greater part of the preceding summer. It was stated that in the early part of the season a sweet substance exuded from the edge of the acorn cups, presumably from the galls. The observations of Dr. Weld indicate that one is often guided to the smaller, inconspicuous galls by noticing ants and wasps which have been attracted by the honeydew.

The production of honeydew by galls appears to be somewhat common. Dr. J. Bequaert has compiled a list of 16 European species (Brooklyn Ent. Soc. Bul., 19:102-104, 1924) which have been definitely associated with honeydew production and also calls attention (page 107) to an African Cecidomyid gall which excretes upon its surface great quantities of a sweet liquid attractive to large numbers of ants. Several *Caryomyia* galls on hickory leaves have a distinctly sticky surface, evidently caused by an excretion of honeydew or a fluid of that general nature.

It would appear from the above that the production of honeydew by certain insect galls, particularly bud galls, is somewhat common and may be rather general. The liquid may be simply an excessive, possibly modified plant excretion, such as is produced by the opening buds and to some extent by other tissues of various plants. There have been attempts to explain this phenomenon as a result of natural selection, and as possibly affording some protection to the plant, though such an interpretation is open to serious doubt.

A striking illustration of the amount and value of honeydew secreted by galls has been recorded by Dr. Weld.* Galls, presumably those of *Dishol-caspis eldoradensis* on *Quercus lobata,* are so abundant in one section of California and produce so much honeydew that bees may store from 30 to 40 pounds of honey per hive collected from this source. The flow commences about the middle of August and continues into October or November, the late production being especially valuable since it encourages the bees to raise large quantities of late brood, thus putting the colonies in the best condition for early queen raising. The production of honeydew is so abundant that some years the bees are not able to care for it and entire trees look greasy with the liquid. The honey-producing glands of the galls appear to be correlated with the extra-floral nectaries present on many plants, and although they occur upon an abnormal structure the secretion is a pure plant product.

Dr. Weld also refers to the honey ants in the Garden of the Gods in Colorado which gather honeydew from galls on nearby scrub oaks at night and carry it to their underground chambers where it is stored in the greatly distended abdomens of special workers.

How Galls Are Produced

Plant galls and the insects which produce them have aroused lively interest in the relations existing between the plant and the producer. There

* *Brooklyn Ent. Soc. Bul.* 20:175-179, 1925. *Amer. Bee Jour.,* Oct., 1925, p. 469.

have been attempts to prove a reciprocal relation in that the plant as well as the insect benefits. There may be a few cases where this is true, but ordinarily there is no benefit, but rather, injury to the host plant.

The causes which produce plant galls have also been the subject of much speculation and study. It is evident that the gall is not produced except as a portion of a plant may be affected by some agency, in most cases, the gall insect. The effect of the producer upon the plant may be largely mechanical, as in the case of cambium borers which, by girdling a stem or branch, interrupt the flow of sap and the incidental mechanical disturbance results in the local production of many cells—really wound tissue—and an enlargement known as a plant gall. There are relatively few deformities of plants produced in this manner.

An evident type of injury is caused by a number of gall insects which attack definite portions of plants and apparently do not materially affect the structure of other parts, except as these may be changed by the failure of certain plant organs or parts of organs to develop normally. There is, for example, the pear midge, the maggots of which develop at the expense of the seeds and incidentally produce some malformation and prevent the normal development of the fruit, or as with the gall midge developing in the fruit of the wild cherry and producing comparatively little change in the protective layers surrounding the stone or seed. The same condition is seen in a number of bud galls, the producers developing at the expense of the forming, tender portions within, and as a consequence, the parts below are frequently stunted or greatly reduced and the aborted stem tip and the massed rudimentary structures form the well known rosette galls, such as those commonly found on the tips of willow and goldenrod shoots. In these cases, the gall maker lives at the expense of the growing tip of the bud and the normal foliage is represented by a cabbage-like whorl of stunted leaves surrounding the gall itself.

A number of gall insects occupy cells in apparently normal stems or twigs and produce little or no enlargement of the infested part of the plant. There are a series of gall midges which develop in apparently normal willow twigs, several species of gall wasps which are found under similar conditions in oak twigs and a few which occur in apparently normal herbaceous stems.

A large number of comparatively simple plant galls result from local irritation. It may be in the egg of certain sawflies; it may be the effect of the young or larvae of other gall makers. It can not be explained as a purely mechanical injury. Most of the galls in this group are characterized by local swellings and a greater or less deformation of the affected part of the plant, though the distortion is not great enough to conceal the nature of the part affected, and usually the deformation itself varies to a marked extent in size or shape—sometimes both, dependent in large measure upon the degree of infestation.

Examples of this *indeterminate* type of gall may be seen in the velvety or pile-like spots on leaves produced by plant mites and the slightly swollen leaf spots of the pear blister mite. The pocket or pouch galls are simply distortions and extensions of the leaf surface, although superficially they may appear to be totally different from the normal leaf area from which they develop. This is also seen in the thickenings and bulgings of leaves produced by the feeding of plant lice, and the same processes are carried to a greater degree in the pouch galls inhabited by plant lice, as for example the elm pouch gall, or even the more highly developed pouch galls of the sumach leaf. In all of these cases there is a definite stimulation or irritation of the plant cells upon which the gall producers feed, and also—and this is important—plant cells adjacent to those which have been directly affected by the gall makers. This latter condition is strikingly illustrated in the thickened midrib gall of the ash. The maggots do not score the surface of the leaf. Apparently their secretions along the upper surface of the midrib stimulate the plant cell layers upon which the larvae rest, and the deeper layers in turn react to the stimulus, the thickness and the length of the gall being proportional to the number of maggots occurring upon the leaf.

There are a long series of galls which develop in such a way as to show little connection between the deformity and the parts of the plant from which they grow. Some of these galls originate in buds, others in apparently normal bark surfaces, and many in leaves. These *determinate* galls, as they may be termed, have a somewhat definite size and structure and the plant tissues appear dominated to a great extent by the stimulus or irritation of the gall maker. The production of these galls is dependent upon the availability of sufficient meristematic or plastic tissue to permit the growth of the deformity from cells which would otherwise develop into normal plant structure, as for example, a portion of a leaf. The stimulus or irritation must be sufficient to produce marked changes in cell structure or arrangement and a great increase in the number of plant cells as compared with what would be produced normally. The form of the gall has little or no relation to the normal structure of the tissues from which it develops. It is believed that the structure of such galls can be understood best by regarding them as insectean adventitious buds, and analogous to the adventitious buds which originate somewhat commonly in the bark tissues of many trees and shrubs. Such buds are known to be produced, though this is not so generally recognized, by leaves of various plants, especially ferns. Gall insects in producing such deformations provide the necessary stimulus, while the cells are still in a plastic condition. There is, during the development of the gall, as in the case of those with less definite structure, a great increase in the number of plant cells and, in addition, a greater or less differentiation between the inner nutritious layers in direct contact with the gall producers, and the outer layers, which are largely of a protective nature.

The general structure is analogous to that of a seed, the gall maker occupying the place of the seed, the nutritive coats next to the gall chamber being analogous to those adjacent to or organically connected with the embryo of the seed, and they in turn are surrounded by protective and sometimes fantastically ornamented outer layers. These might be termed gall buds. There may be real significance in the lobed splitting of the hickory leaf stem gall with its suggestion of the more perfectly divided shuck of the hickory nut. There is much of this same type of structure to be seen in a number of hickory leaf galls produced by other species of Phylloxera. The hickory nuts, as well as many other nuts or seeds, ripen and naturally free themselves from the part of the plant on which they develop. The same thing is found in a number of galls, as for example, the hickory tube gall, produced by a gall midge and ripening and falling in much the same way as a plant seed. This is found also in a considerable series of oak galls. The jumping "flea seeds" of western oaks are in a way "insect seeds", organisms developed as a blind response of plant cells to continuous or repeated stimulation by an insect.

It can not be held that the production of such galls benefits the plants upon which they occur. These adventitious "gall buds" make nutrition levies upon the vigor of the host plant in the production of a growth following the general developmental lines of a seed with its protective coats and yet controlled or manipulated into a nearly independent organism for the benefit of an insect.

BIOLOGY OR LIFE HISTORY OF GALL PRODUCERS

Much that is interesting may be learned from the study of the biology or life history and habits of the gall producers.

Plant Mites. The plant mites, really not insects, have a relatively simple life history as illustrated by the habits of the pear blister mite, a tiny pest which winters under the bud scales, attacks the young leaves as they begin to appear, and continues to breed throughout much of the season if tender foliage is available. This general life circle is typical for many of the mites which produce leaf deformations such as pouch or pocket galls, and the long series of pile or velvety deformations known as erineums and due to an excessive development of plant hairs. The filbert bud mite differs in that it attacks the leaf tissues while in the bud and prevents development after the infested buds have attained approximately twice their normal size. In early spring, literally thousands of the minute, yellowish mites may be found in the blasted buds.

Plant Lice. A number of the gall producing plant lice or aphids have complicated life histories, the grape phylloxera, for example, produces galls upon the leaves and there is also a subterranean form on root galls. This insect is exceedingly injurious to the European or wine grape, although comparatively harmless to our native grapes. The related phylloxeras are well known on account of the numerous leaf galls on hickory early in the season and at least one produces galls on pecan throughout the growing season. One of the most injurious species, well known on account of the large, irregular galls on the leaf stems and young twigs, winters as inconspicuous, dull yellowish eggs upon rough places in the bark, the eggs hatching and the young phylloxeras entering the partly opened buds and producing galls before the leaves issue from the buds. The gall producing species of *Adelges* have a complicated life history, ordinarily migrating from one food plant to another. This is true of the insect producing the Sitka spruce gall, which has an alternate series of generations of woolly aphids on foliage of the Douglas fir. The insect producing the cone gall on Norway spruce occurs only on spruce,

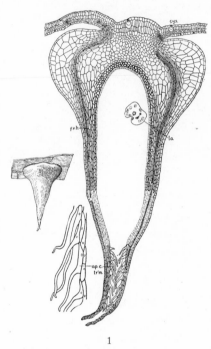

1

FIG. 1.—Gall of *Cecidomyia unguicola,* note the enormous increase in the number of plant cells as compared with the normal leaf tissues seen at the top and on either side of the base of the gall, an approximately forty fold increase in the bulk of the plant tissues. Note also the large cavity and the evident differentiation into layers of cells as shown in the enlarged section. (*After Wells*).

there being no alternate host plant. The species of *Pemphigus,* well known because of the conspicuous leaf stem galls on poplar, migrate to summer hosts, returning to the poplars in the fall. This is also true of several of the gall producing aphids occurring on elm and is seen in two species producing characteristic galls upon witch hazel, these migrating for the summer to birch and in one case, the maker of the spiny witch hazel gall, produces gall-like ridges on the leaves of birch, with a most interesting series of diverse appearing generations on this latter host. We have, among the gall producing plant lice, both alternations of series of generations and alternations of host plants.

Gall Midges. The long series of gall midges present great diversities in life histories. Many winter in the galls and issue therefrom in the spring. A few desert the galls in the spring and enter the soil just prior to changing to the adult, and a great many species issue from the galls, especially the softer leaf and fruit tissues, drop to the earth and remain, in some cases, for the greater part of the season and even to the following spring before producing adults. The life cycle may vary in length from a few weeks, as in the case of the Hessian fly, to a full year for a large proportion of the species. A considerable series of gall midges do not produce plant deformities. They live in dead or decaying organic matter, and in one group, *Miastor* and its allies,

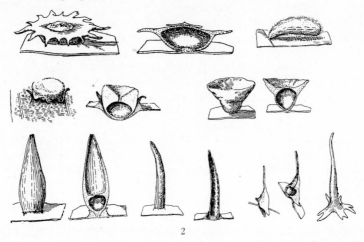

2

Fig. 2.—Diverse hickory leaf galls produced by gall midges, presumably belonging to the genus *Caryomyia*. The producers of these have not been reared and there is the possibility that some are aberrant forms of known hickory leaf galls. (*After Wells*).

we have a most interesting phenomenon known as pedogenesis, or the production of maggots by maggots through a series of generations, the normal pupal and adult stages and the production of eggs being eliminated for a period. These insects are found on various trees under bark in an incipient stage of decay.

The production of living maggots, ovoviviparousness, by the female of the Indian *Thurauia chilkeansis* has been recorded by M. S. Mani of the Indian Museum at Calcutta.

Another series preys upon the gall producing maggots, and still another, as in the case of the gall wasps, may take advantage of conditions and depend upon others for the production of gall tissue in which they can live. The number of generations in some of the more rapidly developing gall midges appears to be limited, mostly by the presence or absence of suitable plant tissues. The Hessian fly, for example, is capable of producing five or six generations in a season, though ordinarily there is a large spring and a good-sized fall generation, the intervening hot, dry months being periods of comparative inactivity.

Gall Midges and Other Organisms. The relation of gall insects to other organisms is complex. Several of the more recent discoveries in this field are briefly noted below.

There is an interesting record of the Indian *Microdiplosis pongamiœ*, which produces a peculiar polyp-like gall on a native grass, *Pongamia glabra*, serving as a carrier for the plant mite, *Eriophyes cheriana*, which also occurs in the same gall. The transfer appears advantageous to both species since they are considered producers by Mani.

Certain plant deformities, designated as ambrosia galls, show a somewhat definite relation between the gall midge larva and an ambrosial fungus. This, as worked out by Dr. W. M. Docters Van Leeuwen in the East Indian gall on *Symplocos fasciculata* produced by *Asphondylia bursaria*, is substantially as follows. A few ambrosial spores are placed in the plant tissues when the needle-like ovipositor is used to insert the egg. The larva issues in four or five days, attaches itself shortly to the wall of the developing gall and remains unchanged for many months. The ambrosia spores begin to develop in five to six weeks after being placed with the gall midge egg in the plant tissues and the fungus eventually fills the entire cavity of the gall except the part occupied by the still slightly developed larva, which in due time feeds and develops upon the ambrosial growth. The relation appears to be similar to that existing between the ambrosia beetles and the ambrosia upon which their grubs develop. The method used by the gall midge in obtaining and transferring the ambrosial spores from one plant to another has yet to be explained.

Ambrosia has been observed in a number of European galls produced by species of *Asphondylia* and *Lasioptera* upon a considerable variety of plants. The writer recalls seeing an ambrosia-like growth in some *Asphondylia* and *Lasioptera* galls in this country. It is probably somewhat common. The relation of the gall midge larva to the fungus and the part the latter plays, if any, in the development of the gall are both worthy of investigation.

Gall Wasps. The gall wasps are highly specialized with marked restrictions in hosts, by far the greater proportion occurring in oak, relatively few in rose and brambles, and with occasional forms in other species of plants. The life cycle may be completed in a few weeks in the case of many of the early spring sexual forms or generations, represented by males and females, developing in the soft tissues of buds and leaves while the agamic or female form or generation may require several months to even three or possibly four years before it completes the life cycle. This latter is known to be true of at least one of the species producing oak twig galls, and may be true of a number of others. The differences between the two generations are so marked that they were considered in earlier years as belonging to different genera. A serious hindrance to the recognition of the relationships lies in the fact the two forms or generations are known for relatively few species, and due to the prolonged life cycle and the difficulty of establishing the connection between the very dissimilar galls usually produced by different generations, it will be many years before this puzzling complex can be worked out satisfactorily. There are guest flies or inquilines among the gall wasps more commonly than in the gall midges.

Gall-makers are opportunists. It is well known that a very large portion of the plant galls are started when the affected parts are developing. It is to be expected that the parts of a swelling bud, a young leaf or a shooting stem would respond more readily and to a greater degree to irritation of one kind or another than would the same parts after they have become more fully developed. Plastic tissues are greatly favored by gall-producers, and only a little consideration is necessary to a recognition of the fact that there must be a close relation between the development of the gall insect and the part of the plant it attacks.

The above is well illustrated in the case of the spruce gall aphid, a species which winters as tiny, black young on the twigs. They complete their growth in early spring and deposit masses of eggs in white woolly matter, at the bases of the buds. The eggs hatch at the time the young leaves begin to appear, and the tiny aphids establish themselves only at the bases of developing leaves which have become swollen to some extent by the earlier feeding of the mother louse at the base of the buds, and the pineapple-like gall results. This means a close correlation between the plant louse and the developing tissues, since otherwise the chances are much against the successful production of galls.

There are a long series of hickory leaf galls, produced by closely related plant lice, belonging to the genus *Phylloxera*. These all appear on the northern hickories in the spring, while the leaves are still in a plastic condition, and yet a closely related species upon a pecan, a southern tree, produces galls even in a northern latitude throughout much of the summer. The explanation is presumably found in the continuous production of leaves upon the pecan throughout most of the summer. In other words, all of these insects depend largely upon leaf tissue in a soft or rapidly growing condition. This is also indicated by the producer of the maple leaf spot. This insect occurs on soft maple, a tree which produces new leaves throughout much of the season. The almost invisible or transparent maggot is found much of the time when fresh maple leaves occur.

Another striking instance of the close correlation between development of plant tissues and the appearance of a gall insect is found in the pear midge. This tiny insect deposits its eggs in the partly-opened pear blossoms, the maggots developing in the young fruit, and in early summer, drop to the ground where they remain until they change to flies at about the time the pear trees are blooming the following season. Any considerable deviation from this schedule would be fatal to the pear midge.

Similar relations exist between the Hessian fly and its preferred hosts, different varieties of wheat and certain grasses. It develops successfully upon some wheats and upon others is unable to maintain itself, presumably because of the stiffer or harder straw, due to the greater amount of silica in the stem. There is also a close relation between the appearance of large numbers of the Hessian fly and the development of the young wheat plants in the fall or in the spring. It has been shown that the flight period is closely restricted and that by regulating the time of sowing in the fall, it is possible to avoid infestation and consequent injury by the pest. On the other hand, an abundance of acceptable plants during the normal flight period is most apt to result in general infestation, and in some cases, complete loss of the crop. This latter is due in large measure to the general prevalence of the insect and its ability to survive in relatively small numbers upon less acceptable food plants and its great prolificacy, which latter makes possible the quick development of a general infestation when conditions are favorable.

The same principles apply to most gall producers. Many of the gall wasps must lay their eggs in the buds of oaks and a number of species are known to occur in the late fall, winter, or very early spring, and lay their eggs at a time when seasonal conditions are ordinarily considered unfavorable to insect activities. The gall wasps appearing at the inclement season of the year are all females, a development which might be construed as economic, since only one sex is exposed to these unusual hazards, the more normal generation, composed of males and females developing during milder weather. See the list of known agamic and bisexual species in America, p. 22. It is an extraordinary adaptation found in comparatively few insects. In this group, as in others, there is a marked tendency to attack the more tender tissues. The softer the parts are when attacked, the greater the probability of a large gall being produced. There is a large series of gall wasps which develop in the buds, in a number of cases, not even permitting the opening of the bud. A great proportion of the galls known commonly as leaf or twig galls, start in the buds. The same thing is seen in gall midges, though to a less extent. There is one gall midge genus, *Asphondylia*, which practically limits itself to the buds of various plants.

ALTERNATION OF GENERATIONS

It is a general rule in nature that like produces like. There are some marked exceptions to this, especially in the gall wasps or *Cynipidæ*, insects where a number of species exhibit what is known as alternation of generations, namely, that succeeding generations are unlike both as to adults and the galls inhabited by the young. The third generation is identical with the first and has the same habits. The difference between succeeding generations is so great that earlier naturalists saw no relationship between the two and placed the insects in different genera. Investigators of the present day would do the same had not the identity of the two been established by closely following the development from one to the other and then to the third generation.

The peculiar relationship existing between certain gall wasps was suspected by Basset, an American, in 1873 and demonstrated two years later by Dr. Adler. The latter, after years of patient investigation and rearing, has summarized his work in a volume of such general interest that a translation has appeared under the title, "Alternating Generations." His studies were confined to European species. Subsequent investigators have found the same true in American forms. For example, the common oak potato gall and the somewhat abundant noxious oak gall both produce alternating generations which develop in similar though decidedly smaller deformations. The gall wasp issuing from the oak wart gall, a blister-like swelling in the leaf, deposits eggs in the bark of roots and produces a root gall at the basal portion of the tree. The light brown, woolly flower gall of what has been called the wool sower is followed in the next generation by the production of seed-like kernels beside the acorns. The succulent oak gall or roly-poly produces the wasp which causes a solid, waxy, leaf gall. One of the most remarkable is found in the oak hedgehog gall which, in the alternate generation, develops in small oval cells in the leaf scales and growing points of the buds. Similar differences in habits between the two generations are found, as suggested above, in European species. The galls of one generation may be conspicuous and common, while those of the other may be uncommon or so inconspicuous as to be generally overlooked. In the case of the oak hedgehog gall, the gall produced by the alternating generation appears so immature and drops so quickly that it is rarely collected.

The two generations differ in that one is composed of both males and females and is therefore known as the perfect generation, while the other is limited to females. The latter usually appears in early spring when conditions are unfavorable to insect activity and the galls develop rapidly. The perfect generation, the one with both males and females, issues during the summer, frequently in early summer, and the development of the young is comparatively slow. This suggests that the elimination of the male in the early spring or female generation is an advantage to the species, since all the flies produce eggs and furthermore the low temperature prevailing at that season would make it difficult for the insects to find mates, were that necessary.

Investigations in Europe show that a relatively large number of oak gall wasps have alternating generations. There are probably more than 600 oak galls occurring upon American oaks and as yet the direct connection between the two generations has been established for relatively few. This complex life history greatly increases the difficulties of understanding all about this very interesting group and for the present a satisfactory classification or grouping of these various forms can not be made. The continued existence of this long series of mysteries—they can hardly be called anything else— is a perpetual challenge to the nature lovers of America.

Alternation of generations is by no means peculiar to the gall wasps, but it appears to be more general in this group than among other insects. There are, among plant lice, a number of cases where there is a true alternation of generations except that these alternations are of a somewhat indefinite series of generations, the transformation from one to the other being dependent, to a large extent, upon the ability of the food plant to support the insects and to seasonal changes. Moreover, some of our plant lice not only have an alternation of generations, but an alternation of food plants, one species migrating back and forth from such dissimilar hosts as birch and witchhazel and producing upon each a characteristic deformity. Certain small gall midges also have an alternation of series of generations in that some possess the peculiar ability in the maggot or larval stage to produce an indefinite series of maggots, flies eventually appearing as though there had been no such extraordinary departure from the general habits of their associates.

THE KNOWN AGAMIC AND BI-SEXUAL FORMS OF AMERICAN GALL WASPS

Acraspis gemula Bass.
  var. *gemula* Bass.
  Agamic form, *prinoides* Beutm.
    Gall, globular, spined, monothalamous, on leaves.
    Adults, Dec.
  Bi-sexual form, *gemula* Bass.
    Gall, egg-shaped, in buds or surrounded by deformed bracts.
    Adults, May.
    On *Q. prinoides.*
Acraspis pezomachoides O.S.
  var. *erinacei* Beutm.
  Agamic form, *erinacei* Beutm.
    Gall, globose, naked or spiny, on leaves.
    Adults, Oct.-Jan.
  Bi-sexual form, *bicolens* Kins.
    Gall, seed-like, egg-shaped, in buds.
    Adults, May.
    On *Q. alba.*
Andricus clavigerus O.S.
  Agamic form, *clavigerus* O.S.
    Irregular, ovoid, horned, woody twig or branch galls, dia. 1-3 cm.
    Adults in May.
  Bi-sexual form,
    Inconspicuous, narrowly oval blister galls on the underside of the leaves, along mid-vein, length 2 mm.
    Adults in June.
    On *Q. phellos.*
Andricus palustris O.S.
  Agamic form, *compressus* Gill.
    Gall small, globular, dia. 2-3 mm., on under surface of leaf, pinkish, wax-like, solid.
    Adults, April or early May.
  Bi-sexual form, *palustris* O.S.
    Gall hollow, succulent, dia. 3-12 mm., singly or in clusters on young buds, aments, petioles and leaf blades.
    Adults, mid-May to June 4.

On *Q. coccinea, Q. falcata, Q. palustris, Q. phellos, Q. rubra, Q. velu-tina, Q. ilicifolia, Q. imbricaria, Q. marilandica.*

Callirhytis futilis O.S.

Agamic form, *radicicola* D.T.

Gall, larval cells in scurfy bark of roots.

Adults, April.

Bi-sexual form, *futilis* O.S.

Gall, blister-like, subglobular swellings on the leaf blade.

Adults, June to July.

On *Q. alba, Q. bicolor, Q. prinoides, Q. prinus, Q. stellata.*

Callirhytis operator O.S.

Agamic form, *operatola* Bass.

Gall, seed-like galls at base of nut, inside cup.

Adults, May.

Bi-sexal form, *operator* Bass.

Gall, large woolly.

On *Q. rubra, Q. coccinea, Q. nigra* and *Q. ilicifolia.*

Cynips fulvicollis Fitch

Agamic form, *fulvicollis* Fitch.

Gall, globular, smooth to pubescent, on leaves.

Adults, Nov. Dec.

Bi-sexual form, *pallipes* Bass.

Gall, egg-shaped, inside buds or deformed or dwarfed leaf clusters.

Adults, April, May.

On *Q. alba, Q. michauxii*

Cynips echinus O.S.

var. *douglasii* Ashm.

Agamic form, *douglasii* Ashm.

Gall, squash-shaped, 5-11 short projections, on leaves.

Adults, Nov.

Bi-sexual form, *lobata* McCracken & Egbert

Gall, spherical, short, soft spines, on twigs.

Adults, April.

On *Q. lobata.*

Cynips echinus O.S.

var. *vicina* Kins.

Agamic form, *vicina* Kins.

Gall, smaller than var. *echinus,* otherwise indistinguishable, on leaves.

Adults, midwinter.

Bi-sexual form, *incepta* Kins.

Gall, closely resembling others, on twigs.

Adults, April.

On *Q. douglasii.*

Cynips echinus O.S.

Agamic form, *echinus* O.S.

Gall, spherical, 20-60, spiny projections, color red, on leaves.

Adults, Nov.

Bi-sexual form, *ribes* Kins.

Gall spherical or ovoid with low indefinite ridges and short, soft spines, on twigs.

Adults, April.

On *Q. douglassi.*

Cynips echinus O.S.

var. *schulthessæ* Kins.

Agamic form, *schulthessæ* Kins.

Gall, bowl or vase-shaped, subcyclindrical or cone-shaped, a narrowed base, yellow or pinkish, on leaves.

Adults, midwinter.

Bi-sexual form, *atrata* Kins.

Gall nearly spherical, few irregularities, no spines, on twigs.

Adults, May.

On *Q. durata, Q. dumosa.*

Neuroterus batatus Fitch

Agamic form, *batatus* Fitch

Gall, tuber-like, irregular, polythalamous stem swellings.

Adults, April, May.

Bi-sexual form, *bisexualis* Kins.

Galls, moderate sized swellings of young stems and petioles.

Adults, June.

On *Q. alba.*

Neuroterus batatus var. *prini* Kins.

Agamic form, *deprini* Kins.

Gall as described for agamic forms on *Q. prinus.*

Adults, April.

Bi-sexual form, *prini* Kins.

Gall similar to that of *noxiosus* form *vernalis* on *Q. prinus.*

Adults, June, July.

Neuroterus noxiosus Bass.

Agamic form, *noxiosus* Bass.

Gall, irregular, elongate woody swellings of young stems and sometimes petioles.

Adults, late March to early May.

Bi-sexual form, *vernalis* Kins.

Gall, nearly as above.

Adults, June to July.

On *Q. prinus, Q. bicolor.*

Neuroterus tectus Bass.

Agamic form, *abundans* Kins.

Gall, most likely similar to bisexual generation, but on mid-vein of leaf.

Adults, April and May.

Bi-sexual form, *tectus* Bass.

Gall, small swellings of the stems of flower clusters, of petioles or of young stems.

Adults, June.

On *Q. prinoides*.

Plagiotrochus cornigerus O.S.

Agamic form, *cornigerus* O.S.

Irregular, ovoid, horned woody twig and branch galls, dia. 1-3 cm.

Adults in April.

Bi-sexual form,

Ovoid, whitish leaf galls, 1.5-2.5 mm. long., along midrib or major veins.

Adults in July.

On *Q. rubra, Q. palustris, Q. imbricaria, Q. ilicifolia*.

Plagiotrochus punctatus Bass.

Agamic form, *punctatus* Bass.

Irregular, ovoid, woody twig and branch gall, dia. 1-3 cm.

Adults in April.

Bi-sexual form,

Blister-like leaf galls, on or near veins, length 1-2 mm.

On *Q. rubra*.

INSECT AND FUNGOUS GALLS

A considerable proportion of the peculiar growths found upon plants are caused by insects and yet a number are due to fungous growths, notably the black knot upon plum and the cedar apple upon red cedar with its peculiar cedar-rust spots which develop upon apple foliage.

An interesting fact is that a number of galls produced by insects were in earlier years supposed to be caused by fungus. This is particularly true of the numerous blister-like thickenings on the leaves of solidago and aster, known for many years to botanists as *Rhytisma solidaginis* and *Rhytisma asteris* respectively, and by them supposed to be caused by a fungus which produces very similar spots upon the foliage of other plants. More recently it has developed that the flower-like gall upon cypress, likewise attributed by botanists to a fungus, proves to be the work of a gall midge, though the somewhat bell-shaped, flower-like enlargement is most suggestive of fungous growth.

THE DISTRIBUTION AND ABUNDANCE OF GALL INSECTS

It is well known that insects producing galls upon plants are frequently very local. The extensive collecting of Professor A. C. Kinsey indicates that solitary oaks or oaks on the edges of forests are more likely to be infested with gall insects than those in normal woodland areas. Dr. L. H.

Weld states that the gall wasps or Cynipids "almost never fly and most likely never travel more than a very short distance." It is well known that the female or agamic generations of certain species of gall wasps are wingless and are unable to travel any distance. The gall wasps are presumably not strong flyers, and this is certainly true of the gall-producing aphids or plant lice. This last does not make impossible wide distribution by air currents. During the summer of 1927, the author systematically collected insects on the roof of the State Education Building at Albany, N.Y. The wide gutters were by far the best collecting ground, although they were 125 feet above the sidewalk and well above the tops of adjacent trees. In the course of this work, six species of gall wasps, kindly identified by Dr. L. H. Weld, were taken, namely *Trigonaspis radicola* Ashm., *Andricus ostensackenii* Bass., *Andricus petiolicola* Bass., *Holocynips badia* Bass., *Holocynips maxima* Weld, and *Gonaspis potentillæ* Gill. All but the last are well recognized oak species, and since there were probably no oaks within a mile of the building, one is forced to conclude that the insects must have flown or drifted in wind currents, and in view of the presumably limited flight ability of these insects, it is believed that convectional currents and wind drift, rather than flight, were the main factors in raising the insects to that height, and carrying them to such a considerable distance from oaks. One of the species, *H. badia* Bass., produces a root gall and had not been recorded previously from the state of New York. A similar condition is suggested by the finding on the same roof of a number of *Adelges sp.*, probably *A. abietis* Linn., the producers of the very common cone gall on Norway spruce. These insects probably drifted a mile or more, since there were no spruces in the near vicinity of the Education Building.

It seems probable that wind drift rather than flight is an important factor in distributing a number of gall insects. This is supported by the observations of Professor Kinsey in relation to the generally greater infestation upon oaks standing in the open or on the edge of the woods. Such trees are more exposed to winds and insects at a distance and drifting at a moderate height would pass through these before coming to the trees behind or beyond, and these more exposed trees would therefore be more likely to become infested.

The probability of extended, though presumably exceptional wind drift of these small insects is suggested by the world-wide or nearly world-wide distribution, subject to the local occurrence of acceptable hosts, of a number of tropical and subtropical species. The dissemination of such forms may also be brought about through commercial activities, but these hardly account for all spread of this character. The most suggestive occurrence in this connection was the discovery in Utah, in 1914, of a species of *Aplonyx,* a genus previously not known to occur outside of the Mediterranean area, and living upon widely distributed, though closely related plant hosts.

There are not only a large number of different species of gall insects but occasionally some become exceedingly abundant. Sometimes large oaks may have their smaller branches almost covered with the giant bead-like swellings of the gouty oak gall or that of a closely related species, in which case a single tree may easily support over 500,000 gall wasps. The same condition is true of a number of other gall wasps producing oak twig deformities and in the case of some which at times yield a sweet liquid or honeydew, the infested tree may be literally alive, as it were, with hosts of flies and bees attracted by the unusual abundance of sweets. These latter insects are sometimes so numerous as to make a perceptible humming or "roaring" of sufficient magnitude to attract notice from the casual observer. The tumid leaf swellings of *Neuroterus irregularis* are occasionally so abundant as to weigh down oak branches much as though they bore a fair crop of well-developed apples.

Among economic species, the well known Hessian fly frequently becomes numerous enough to destroy large areas of wheat, the sorghum midge and the clover midge make it nearly impossible to grow the seed of these plants in certain sections, while the rose midge, the violet midge and the chrysanthemum midge are greenhouse species known only too well to the florist. The ornamental box along the Atlantic coast is sometimes so generally infested with the recently introduced box midge as to result in badly discolored foliage and even the ruin of these highly prized ornamentals.

The richness of the relatively unexplored gall producing fauna is illustrated by the work of Dr. L. H. Weld in the somewhat unfavorable Chicago area, so far as collecting deformities produced by gall wasps is concerned. He found 124 species in that section and secured field notes on 30 other galls either not determined or not reared.

The exhaustive and recently published studies of Dr. A. C. Kinsey have resulted in discovering a number of the alternate generations in American gall wasps and the demonstration of many local varieties heretofore unsuspected.

The work of the author and his associates when at Albany, N.Y., resulted in finding some 400 gall midge species in that area, though not all of these produced galls.

There is still much to be done in this large and most fascinating field.

Gall Insects in Different Parts of the World

The marked abundance of certain groups of gall insects and the decided preferences for a few plant families or even plant genera are not confined to any one section of the world, though as might be expected some groups are more abundant in the tropics than in temperate regions and plants preferred in one section are not favorites in another.

Generally speaking, gall midges, gall wasps and the gall mites are the predominant gall-producers in different sections of the world, though there are some marked variations as will be seen by the following tabulation:

TABLE 1. IMPORTANT GROUPS OF GALL-PRODUCERS SHOWING THE NUMBER OF SPECIES
KNOWN IN DIFFERENT SECTIONS OF THE WORLD

	GALL MITES	PSYL-LIDS	APHIDS	GALL MIDGES	GALL WASPS	THRIPS	TOTAL
Asia	130	42	47	176	102	53	.708
D. E. I.	355	145	62	535*	27**	124	1536
So. Europe	263	38	172	398	262		1446
No. America	162	11	47	682	444		1441
M. Europe	196	40	96	325	125	1	1131
Moravia	68	13	42	99	73		327
So. & Cent. America	19	20	10	127	6	1	1341†

* Figures for Diptera only available.   † Galls listed.
** Figures for Hymenoptera only available.

The figures for the Dutch East Indies, South Europe and North America
are fairly comparable, since approximately the same number of species
are known in each of these areas. It will be noted that in North America
there are relatively fewer gall mites known than in the other two sections,
whereas in the Dutch East Indies there is a relatively large number of
jumping plant lice or Psyllids and thrips, and in southern Europe a considerable proportion of gall midges. These relationships are influenced
somewhat by the flora, since most gall producers are rather closely limited
as to food plants, and in addition there is the well known tendency of
collectors to specialize or restrict themselves to certain groups.

The relations obtaining between gall producers and the plant families
which are favored by them are illustrated in the following tabulation:

TABLE 2. GALL INSECT PREFERENCES FOR CERTAIN PLANT FAMILIES INDICATED BY
THE SPECIES LISTED FROM DIFFERENT SECTIONS OF THE WORLD

PLANT FAMILIES	ASIA	D.E.I.	So. EUROPE	NORTH AMERICA	MORAVIA	So. & CENT. AMERICA
Pine	17		84	47	14	
Grass	44	17	188	60	4	6
Willow	71		569	115	117	2
Walnut	4	3	7	65	1	
Birch	9		110	34	12	
Beech	304	9	993	419	143	16
Elm	207	125	65	37	19	7
Rose	109	14	499	130	113	14
Laurel	53	48	8	3		36
Spurge	129	129	43	6		48
Maple	17		80	48	11	
Vine	40	37	44	35		8
Verbena	58	39	3	8		32
Acanthus	47	47	3			2
Madder	91	71	160	5	12	39
Composite	181	33	660	182	41	164
Total Species	708	1536	1446	1441	327	1341†

† Galls listed.

The data in the above tabulations are based upon seven important, comprehensive works on gall insects, namely:

Asia: Les Zoocécidies des Plantes d'Afrique, d'Asie et d'Oceanie, by C. Houard, vol.
1 & 2, 1922.

D. E. I.: The Zoocecidia of the Netherlands East Indies, by Mrs. J. Docters van
Leeuwen-Reijvaan and Dr. W. M. Docters van Leeuwen.

M. Europe: Die Pflanzengallen, Mittel- und Nordeuropas, by H. Ross, Jena, 1911.

So. Europe: Les Zoocécidies des Plantes d'Europe et du Bassin de la Méditerranée, by C. Houard, vol. 1 & 2, 1908, 1909.

North America: Key to American Insect Galls, by E. P. Felt, New York State Museum Bulletin 200, 1918.

Moravia: Moravské Hálky (Zoocecidia), by Emil Bayer, 1914.

So. & Cent. America: Les Zoocécidies des Plantes de l'Amérique du Sud et de l'Amerique Centrale, by C. Houard, 1933.

It will be seen that gall insects exhibit marked variations in preferences for plant families in different sections of the world, this being especially well shown in the tabulations for the Dutch East Indies, Europe and America, with the total species in each so nearly the same that the differences are expressed almost exactly by variations in the number of species for each of these regions, though a part of these are probably due to the variations in methods and more skillful or thorough collecting in some families than in others. It may be noted that in the Dutch East Indies and practically so in South and Central America, no gall makers are recorded from the pine, willow, birch and maple families, whereas the willow in particular is a favorite in both Europe and North America. On the other hand, there are proportionately a much larger number of galls upon members of the elm family in the Dutch East Indies than in either Europe or America, though this total is exceeded by that recorded for the plants of Africa, Asia and Oceania.

GALL INSECT PREFERENCES FOR HOST PLANTS IN AMERICA

The obvious limitation of many gall midges to a relatively few host plants, especially those with numerous closely allied species, such as the willows, oaks, goldenrods and asters and the great diversity of both structure and food habits among gall midges, all suggest interesting lines of study. There are more than 2000 American insect galls, over one third, or 805 being produced by gall wasps, and a somewhat larger proportion, nearly 700 being the work of gall midges. The remaining plant galls are the product of other four-winged flies or *Hymenoptera,* mostly sawflies and joint worms, certain two-winged flies or *Diptera,* a few beetles or *Coleoptera* and moths or *Lepidoptera* and the true bugs or *Hemiptera,* about 80 of these last being aphids or the closely related jumping plant lice or Psyllids. A considerable number of plant galls, namely 181, are produced by the microscopic plant mites or *Eriophyidæ* and a number result from fungus infections.

The gall wasps or *Cynipidæ* present a most interesting condition so far as the selection of host plants is concerned. They attack plants referable to only six botanical families and assignable to less than 20 plant genera. There is, however, a most striking restriction in food habits, since nearly 750 live at the expense of members of the beech family, *Fagaceæ,* which for this group practically means the oaks, since only one of this large number has been reared from chestnut.

The relation of the 805 Cynipid galls to various parts of the tree is interesting, 41 occur in root galls, 45 in bud galls, nearly 175 in woody galls of the twigs, branches and trunk, over 275 in leaf galls, 21 in flower galls and 34 in galls of the acorn or the acorn cup. In other words, the large gall wasp fauna dependent upon the oaks levies through the agency of one or more species upon practically every part of the host.

The next most obvious restriction among the gall wasps is seen in the 62 galls upon members of the rose family or *Rosaceæ*, there being 50 such galls recorded from the various species of rose, 7 from bramble and 4 from cinquefoil. Some 17 Cynipid galls have been recorded from the *Compositæ*, these few species occur mostly singly and in relatively small numbers upon a few rather closely related plant genera, and in addition one species each is known to attack plants in the heath, sapodilla and mint families.

The gall midges or *Itonididæ* produce about 700 plant galls, they being found in 69 of the 78 plant families known to be attacked by gall insects or mites of one kind or another. These little midges produce 49 galls in the willow family, 37 of these upon willow; 39 attack plants of the beech family (37 of these being upon the oaks); 56 species produce galls upon members of the rose family, 25 upon plants belonging to the pulse family; 21 form galls on members of the vine or grape family and 172 may be found upon various composite plants. The most obvious restriction of the species, aside from those mentioned above, is the 54 galls occurring upon various species of goldenrod or solidago, 5 being flower galls, 23 being bud galls, 17 leaf and 9 stem or root galls. There are some 24 aster galls, 5 in flowers or buds, 13 of the peculiar leaf blister galls of *Asteromyia* which are almost entirely limited to aster and solidago, and 6 occurring in the stems. Marked restrictions in food habits are also seen in certain gall midge genera, such as the numerous species of *Rhabdophaga* on willow, *Caryomyia* on hickory, *Cincticornia* on oak and to a less marked extent, *Diarthronomyia* on *Artemisia*. It is evident that the gall midges are more general in their food habits than the gall wasps.

The plant lice or aphids occur upon a great variety of plants, though the gall-making forms are found upon relatively few, the most evident food preference being in the genus *Phylloxera* with its 29 species producing deformities on hickories, the several species of *Pemphigus* on poplar and the closely related species of *Adelges* on spruce. The nearly allied jumping plant lice or Psyllids present a similar condition in the genus *Pachypsylla* with their numerous galls upon hackberry or *Celtis*.

The microscopic plant mites or *Eriophyidæ* have been associated with 158 galls or deformations upon 38 of the 78 plant families, the larger number of deformations being in the willow, the beech, the rose and the maple families. Galls produced by plant mites are relatively simple in structure, are characterized by abnormal hairy growths known as *Erineums* and frequently originate in the bud, sometimes persisting as bud galls, though in most cases the leaves develop and the deformation is simply a

TABULATION OF PLANTS AND AMERICAN INSECT GALLS

PLANTS		CLASSES OF GALL MAKERS, NUMBER OF SPECIES					
Family	Genera	Gall Wasp	Midge	Aphid	Other Insects	Mite	Fungus
Fern	1		1				
Gnetaceae	1		2				
Pine	8		30	8	3	2	1
Grass	27		14		20	7	
Sedge	3		3	1			
Rush	1			1			
Lily	7	1	10				
Iris	1				1		
Yam	1		1				
Orchid	2		2		1		
Willow	2		49	7	33	7	
Sweet Gale	1		2			2	
Walnut	2		16	32		8	
Birch	5		7	1	6	19	
Beech	4	740*	39		3	16	
Elm	7		23	16	1	3	
Birthwort	1		1			1	
Buckwheat	4		4		2		
Goosefoot	5		14		3		
Amaranth	1		2				
Pokeweed	1		1				
Four O'Clock	1		1				
Crowfoot	4		7		1	3	
Laurel	4		4	3		1	
Magnolia	2		3	1			
Poppy	1		1				
Mustard	5		5		1		
Caper	1		1				
Red Orpine	1					1	
Saxifrage	2		6			3	
Witch-Hazel	2		5	2	1	1	
Plane Tree	2		1			1	
Rose	16	41	56		13	23	2
Pulse	19	1	25		5	1	
Geranium	1		1			1	
Flax	1				1		
Caltrop	2		3				
Rue	1					3	
Spurge	4		5			11	
Box	1		1	1			
Cashew	2		7	1	1	4	
Holly	2		2	1			
Stafftree	2		3			1	
Maple	1		11		3	26	
Jewel-weed	1		4		1		
Buckthorn	1		2		1	1	
Vine	3		21	1	7	3	
Linden	1		4		1	3	
Mallow	5		6		4	1	
St. John's-Wort	1		3			1	
Violet	1		3			1	
Loasa	1		1				
Cactus	1		4				
Oleaster	1		1				
Myrtle	1		2				
Primrose	2		1			1	
Evening Primrose	2		1		1		
Parsley	3		3				
Dogwood	3		8			3	
Heath	5	3	7	1	1	1	
Leadwort	1					1	
Sapodilla	1	1					
Ebony	1			1		1	
Storax	1						1
Olive	1		9	1		4	
Logania	1		1				
Dogbane	1		2				
Milkweed	1		3				
Convolvulus	3		3		1		
Borage	1		1				
Vervain	3		6			1	
Mint	14	1	18		1	1	
Nightshade	3		2		2	1	
Figwort	6		6			2	
Bignonia	2		2				
Madder	3		2		1	3	
Honeysuckle	5		17			2	
Lobelia	1		1				
Gourd	1		2				
Composite	47	17	172		23	6	
Total	291	805	687	79	143	181	4

* All but 9 of these occur on oaks.

sack-like or pouch gall with a hair-guarded orifice, or only a thickly haired, sometimes brightly colored area or *Erineum.*

A few other gall makers deserve mention. The joint worms are limited largely to the stems of grasses and grains, while the rather closely related seed wasps develop in the seeds of different plants. The galls produced by various beetles are largely the result of mechanical causes, certain *Lepidoptera,* especially the genus *Gnorimoschema,* inhabit the stems of various composites, usually producing somewhat fusiform enlargements.

Natural Checks

Gall insects live such protected lives that one would naturally think they would be comparatively immune from various natural checks and to a certain extent this is possibly true.

Unfavorable weather conditions at the time adults are abroad in large numbers and of necessity compelled to find suitable food plants within a short period, must result in the death of many of these fragile insects, especially the more delicate ones, such as the gall midges. The gall wasps appear to have developed a method of minimizing this danger through the alternation of generations, the wingless females of the agamous generation appearing ordinarily in late fall, winter or early spring when weather conditions would probably be fatal to winged flies, since the winds would most likely sweep the insects from their food plants.

All of these insects must find not only suitable food plants but plants in a condition favorable to infestation, the latter requirement at times probably accounting for great reductions in the numbers of these insects. The mere fact that many species are very local, such as the gall wasps producing various knotty oak galls or the plant lice inhabiting deformities on witchhazel or poplar, to mention a few rather common cases, indicates that this must be a somewhat potent factor in checking the normal increase in numbers.

Many gall insects, in spite of their protection by plant growths of various thickness, are quite subject to attack by insect parasites. This is particularly marked in the case of many gall midges and gall-making aphids and is by no means uncommon among the gall wasps. Considerable series of parasites belonging to different species and genera have been reared from gall midges.

The development of the true gall makers is also interfered with to some extent by the presence in the deformities of guest flies or inquilines which, while they may not attack the gall insects directly, undoubtedly live upon the nourishment in the gall and to a certain extent reduce the amount available for the producers.

Gall insects are also subject to attack by a number of predators. This is particularly true of the gall midges and the gall-making aphids. There is a considerable series, for example, of gall midge larvae which actually prey upon their gall-making cousins instead of producing galls for themselves. These little predators also attack a number of species of plant lice, some being gall-makers.

There are records of birds eating insect galls, notably the oak pill gall and also of mammals feeding upon them, though probably only to a limited extent. Some of the smaller, warm blooded animals prey upon the larvae of gall insects and in certain cases obtain a very acceptable addition to their more usual fare. The larger oak apple, for example, under certain conditions, proves attractive to gray squirrels, the gall being opened, and the large, plump larvae carefully extracted. The stem galls of solidago are frequently emptied of their contents. Mr. W. T. Davis of Staten Island has found many of the galls produced by *Gnorimoschema gallæsolidaginis* which had evidently been eaten into by a mouse. It is quite probable that the galls of related species suffer from such attacks. Woodpeckers are known to drill the globular ball galls of *Eurosta solidaginis* and mice not only attack these, but gnaw into the rose root galls of *Diplolepis radicum,* in a search for the maggots (Davis, Bull. Bkln. Ent. Soc. 26:120-122, 1931).

The deciduous oak gall is very abundant on black oak in some sections, and in Missouri affords a generally recognized food for cattle, hogs, sheep, turkeys and chickens, it being so common that it has won for itself local names, such as "black oak wheat" and "wheat mast." A chemical analysis shows that this gall possesses a relatively high food value. (Ent. Soc. Wash. Proc. 5:151-152.)

COLLECTING GALLS AND STUDYING GALL INSECTS

The collection and study of plant galls is easy and fascinating. The specimens may be found at all times of the year and those with woody tissues require no special preparation if one simply desires to make a collection. The softer galls, such as deformed fruits, swollen buds and modified leaves, require more careful treatment, if they are to be preserved satisfactorily. Many of the leaf galls can be treated in much the same way as ordinary herbarium specimens or they may be slipped into manila envelopes and simply allowed to dry. Fruit galls and the softer leaf galls must as a rule be kept in alcohol or some other liquid preservative. All specimens should bear a label giving the locality, date and the name of the plant.

Some care is necessary to distinguish between true gall makers and similar guest flies or inquilines, or in the case of gall midges, between gall makers and frequently associated enemies. The rearing of an insect from a gall does not always prove that it is the gall producer. Usually there is but one species which causes a certain gall, though occasionally one may be found where there are possibly two or more species commonly inhabiting the same gall or a very similar gall. The occurrence of a gall upon the leaf and upon the shoot does not necessarily indicate the work of more than one species. The location of the gall in relation to the structure of the plant depends in some species upon the part where the gall producer lays its eggs, and to some extent upon the rapidity of growth of the infested parts. A few gall insects produce galls either on the flowers, on the leaves or on the younger part of the stem. A certain amount of variation in the form and appearance of the gall produced by one species may be expected, particularly when the deformities occur upon different parts of the plant.

The secret of rearing gall insects lies in delaying when possible the collection of the galls until just before the insects are ready to emerge and then keeping the galls under as nearly normal conditions as possible. There are many gall insects which issue as adults directly from the gall itself, and it is comparatively easy to rear these in large numbers by placing the galls in handy containers such as fruit jars or preserve tumblers with a covering of fine cheesecloth to prevent the insects escaping. There should be some provision for maintaining an approximately normal amount of moisture. This may be a little clean sand, or even pieces of blotting paper, periodically moistened, care being taken to prevent excessive drying or a supersaturated condition. Here is an opportunity for the exercise of discretion. There are a number of galls from which the insects issue in early spring, and it is from these that gall insects are most easily reared. Knowledge of the approximate date when the insects appear is also helpful.

Galls collected in the fall which must be carried over winter before the insects develop, should be kept under approximately normal winter conditions through the cold weather. The jars or glasses containing them may be put in a large box and this partly buried in the soil or under leaves so as to minimize temperature extremes and at the same time afford protection from invasion by mice or other natural enemies. Dr. Weld, who has had extensive experience in rearing gall wasps, states that in some cases the galls may become so hard as to prevent the insects emerging, and with such species he advises cutting the galls open and allowing the insects restricted freedom until they have colored normally. He finds that two winters often pass before the gall wasps appear, and some may issue each spring for several years.

There are many gall insects which leave the galls and undergo their final transformations in the soil. This is particularly true of those which produce fruit galls and the softer leaf galls. The same kind of breeding glasses or containers may be used and so far as possible there should be in the bottom of the vessel a layer of soil or material approaching in its characteristics that in which the insect ordinarily transforms. If soil is used, it is generally advisable to sterilize it, preferably with moist heat, in order to avoid the possibility of its containing insects or other forms which might be confused with or be injurious to the gall producers. Those gall insects which transform shortly after they enter the soil are easier to rear than the species which do not complete the change to the adult for a number of months or nearly a year. In the case of these latter, it is important to keep the breeding jars under as nearly normal conditions as possible, and for those which pass the winter in the soil, it is advisable to provide for approximately normal winter conditions as described for species hibernating in the galls. Some species winter in the galls, and the larvae, before changing to adults, leave the galls and enter the soil. It is well to provide for this condition in preparing breeding jars.

Gall insects are small and fragile and cannot be studied successfully without a good microscope, considerable technical skill, a moderately good collection and a special library or collection of articles on the group. Ordinarily, most gall insects can be preserved best by killing the insects with cyanide fumes or chloroform. Before the specimens dry, they should be impaled on fine insect pins or attached with a good adhesive to slender insect points, or put in vials with a little cotton to prevent shaking about. The last method is usually best for gall midges prior to study or identification. Specimens treated in this way can be kept for years. They should be cleared and mounted in Canada balsam or other media before attempting more detailed systematic studies.

PART II

KEY TO THE GALLS OF THE VARIOUS PLANT FAMILIES

PART II

Key to the Galls of the Various Plant Families

IT is easier to recognize most of these deformities by first identifying the plant and we have therefore grouped the galls first by their hosts and then followed an arrangement which seemed best adapted to ready identification in the different plant families. In most of the more important families there is a brief summation of the more interesting or significant data.

Ferns *(Polypodiaceæ)*

Bladder Fern *(Cystopteris fragilis)*

Root gall midge.....................................*Cecidomyia sp.*

Gnetum Family *(Gnetaceæ)*

Ephedra trifurca

Fusiform twig gall, length ½ inch, midge. Fig. 3.   *Lasioptera ephedræ Ckll.*
Irregular, subcortical, resinous gall, midge.   *Lasioptera ephedricola Ckll.*

Pine Family *(Pinaceæ)*

The resinous fluids of evergreens, especially the pines, would seem to afford a considerable degree of protection from gall insects. This is by no means true of a number of gall midges, several species of which have become adapted for existence in the pitch saturated cells of the twigs. The orange red maggots of the pitch midge appear to injure the inner bark and promote a more or less constant flow of pitch, which latter collects in good sized masses on the smaller twigs and affords a measurably secure and apparently a satisfactory shelter for the maggots. These latter have the posterior spiracles armed or guarded by unusually thick, horny processes, presumably an adaptation to existence in this unusual medium.

The pine needles are also attacked by gall midges, the common pine needle gall consisting merely of enlarged, apposed swellings at the base of a bundle of needles, the reddish larva developing in an oval hollow between them. Several similar, though considerably larger pine needle galls are produced by western species. The larva of one gall midge occurs at the base of the needles, producing no swelling but causing a considerable drop of needles of the white and Scotch pines.

The seeds of fir and of the bald cypress of the south are both attacked by gall midges and in some cases a considerable proportion of the seed is destroyed. The juniper berry midge, a western species, lives in the seeds of this tree.

The southern cypress is rather commonly attacked by a twig gall maker which produces a somewhat fusiform enlargement about half an inch long. A section of this swelling shows that the attack probably originated while the tissues were still in the bud, there being a number of maggots distributed throughout the swelling. This tree is also attacked by the cypress flower gall midge, which latter produces a somewhat vase shaped, whitish or pinkish gall, which, in contrast with the dark cypress foliage, suggests very

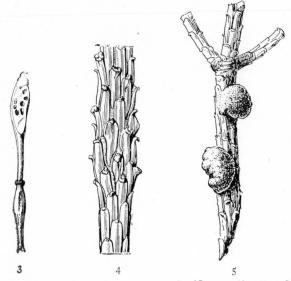

3   4   5

(Courtesy New York State Museum)

Fig. 3.—*Lasioptera ephedræ*, two galls, one in section.
Fig. 4.—Gouty pine midge, *Retinodiplosis inopis*, typical enlargement of twig.
Fig. 5.—Pitch midge, *Retinodiplosis resinicola*, typical pitch exudations.

strongly indeed a cluster of beautiful flowers. This growth early attracted the notice of botanists and for a time was supposed to be caused by a fungus.

There are a number of plant lice which produce galls. One of the very common and somewhat destructive forms is known as the spruce cone gall aphid, an insect which has proved generally injurious to Norway spruce in recent years. The gall produced by this insect is a somewhat conical swelling, one-half to three-quarters of an inch long and thickly set with rudimentary needles. At the base of each of these needles, there is a cell inhabited by gall aphids. The infestation occurs when the shoot is developing. The feeding of the mother louse at the base of the buds produces swellings in the lower part of the developing leaves and it is only on these needles that the young can establish themselves and produce galls. The mother louse in this case produces conditions favorable to the young. The attack results in an aborted growth which seriously interferes with circulation and usually results in the death of the twig beyond the affected part. A gall midge occasionally attacks spruce tips and produces dwarfing of the needles and a swelling of the affected part of the twig.

Galls of Evergreen Trees *(Coniferæ)*
Pine *(Pinus)*

Reared from pine cones....................*Asynapta hopkinsi* Felt

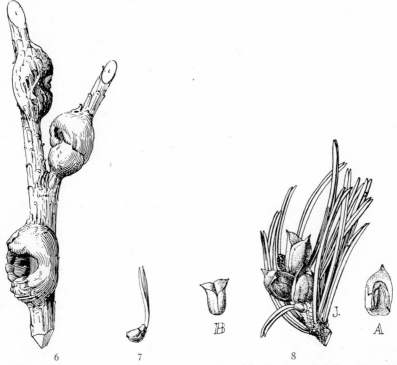

6   7   8
(Courtesy New York State Museum)

FIG. 6.—Pitch midge, *Retinodiplosis sp.*, scars on *Pinus taeda*, probably the work of a gall midge.

FIG. 7.—Pine needle gall, *Cecidomyia pinirigidæ*, typical swelling at base of leaf.

FIG. 8.—Pine needle gall, *Thecodiplosis cockerelli*, deformed needles on *Pinus edulis*.

Reared from pitch masses in summer or swollen twigs

On pitch pine ....Pitch midge, *Retinodiplosis resinicola* O.S.
In swollen twigs ......Gouty pitch pine midge, *Retinodiplosis inopis* O.S.
On white pine ....Banded pitch midge, *Retinodiplosis albitarsis* Felt
On long-leaf pine ......Southern pitch midge, *Retinodiplosis palustris* Felt
On Monterey pine. Western pitch midge, *Retinodiplosis resinicoloides* Wlms.

Reared from swollen needles or needle bundles, midges, early summer

On scrub pine.........................*Janetiella coloradensis* Felt
On pitch pine.............Pine needle gall, *Cecidomyia pinirigidæ* Pack.

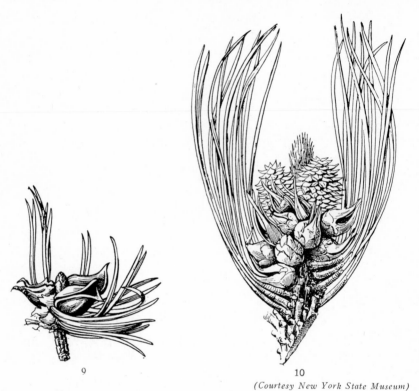

9

10

(Courtesy New York State Museum)

Fig. 9.—Pine bud gall, *Contarinia coloradensis.*
Fig. 10.—Pine bud gall, *Contarinia coloradensis,* cluster of galls on *Pinus scopulorum.*

On *P. edulis*...........................*Thecodiplosis cockerelli* Felt
On stone pine.............Pine bud gall, *Contarinia coloradensis* Felt
On Monterey pine...............*Thecodiplosis piniradiatæ* Sn. & Mlls.

PLATE 1—CYNIPID GALLS. 1, Gall on oak, of *Andricus petiolicolus* Bass. (*After Thompson*). 2, Gall on oak, of *Andricus flocci* Walsh. (*After Thompson*). 3, Gall of *Harmolita sp.* on Hilaria. (*After W. W. Jones*). 4, Oak wool gall, *Andricus flocci Walsh.* (*After Thompson*). 5, Gall on oak, of *Andricus ostensackeni* Bass. (*After Thompson*). 6, Poplar leaf stem gall, *Pemphigus populitransversus.* (*After Essig*). 7, Gall on oak, of *Andricus perditor* Bass. (*After Thompson*). 8, Galls on oak, of *Callirhytis ventricosus* Bass. Single gall and a typical cluster. (*After Stebbins*). 9, Horned oak gall, *Plagiotrochus cornigerus* O.S. on pin oak.

PLATE 1

Courtesy N. Y. State Museum

On white and Scotch pines, at base of apparently normal leaf bundles and
  causing a heavy leaf fall, summer, midge . . . .
  . . . . .Pine needle midge, *Itonida pinifoliæ* Felt
Aborted buds or leaf growths on short-leaved and Jeffrey pines . . . .
  . . . .*Eriophyes sp.*
Twig swellings or none, with pitted cavities and a tiny black pin-hole open-
  ing, scale insect, pitch and scrub pines . . . .
  . . . .*Matsucoccus matsumuræ* Kuw.
Reared from pine cones . . . . .Pine cone midge, *Asynapta hopkinsi* Felt

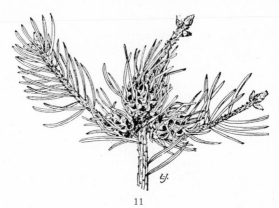

11

(Courtesy New York State Museum)

Fig. 11.—Spruce cone gall, *Adelges abietis*.

Spruce *(Picea)*

Swollen twigs or leaves simulating the gall of *Adelges similis*, early summer,
  . . . . .Spruce gall midge, *Phytophaga piceæ* Felt
Cone-like swellings on Norway spruce, aphid, early summer . . . .
  . . . . .Spruce cone gall, *Adelges abietis* Linn
Cone-like, loose, terminal gall with needles not much dwarfed and thicker
  than normal, length ¾ to 1¾ inches, aphid, on Norway, white, red,
  black, Colorado blue and Englemann spruce, early summer . . . . . .
  . . . .*Adelges floccus* Patch
Short cone-like galls, needles greatly reduced, length about ½ inch on *P.
  mariana,* aphid, early summer . . . .*Adelges consolidatus* Patch
Cone-like, russet-colored, subapical galls, with rudimentary needles, length
  about 1 inch, on *P. alba,* aphid, early summer. .*Adelges lariciatus* Patch
Cone-shaped, length ¾ to over 1 inch, each needle swollen in the middle
  and concave on the inner axillary surface, on blue spruce, aphid, early
  summer . . . .*Adelges montanus* Gill.
Cone-like, reddish or purplish gall, with needles bract-like, length about
  1 inch, on white, black and red spruce, aphid early summer . . . . .
  . . . .*Pineus pinifoliæ* Fitch

Similar terminal galls on black and red spruce.......*Pineus floccus* Patch
Conical swelling, length 2½ inches, on Colorado blue spruce, aphid, early
    summer................Long spruce cone gall, *Adelges cooleyi* Gill.
Long spruce gall similar to preceding, on Norway, white, black, Colorado
    and red spruce, aphid, early summer............*Adelges similis* Gill.
Loose terminal galls on Norway, white, red, black, Colorado blue and
    Engelmann spruce..........................*Pineus similis* Gill.
Apical bud gall, early summer.................................
...................Spruce bud midge, *Rhabdophaga swainei* Felt

Fir *(Abies)*

Reared from seeds, Fig. 12....Fir seed midge, *Dasyneura canadensis* Felt
Bud galls and leaf swellings, early summer.......................
.......................Spruce gall midge, *Phytophaga tsugæ* Felt
Leaf swellings of balsam fir, early summer......................
...............Balsam gall midge, *Cecidomyia balsamicola*, Lintn.

12 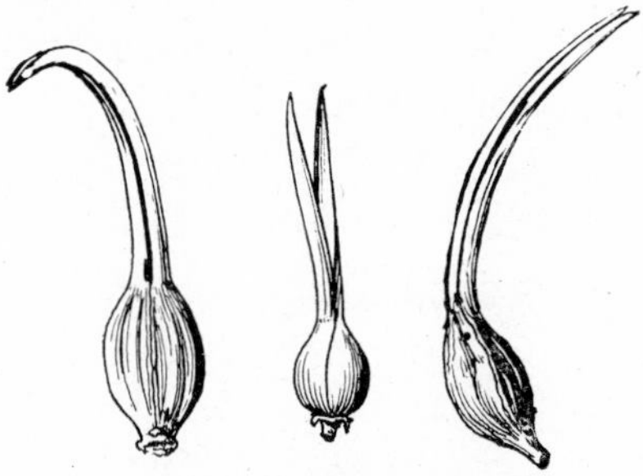   13

(Courtesy New York State Museum)

Fig. 12.—Fir seed midge, *Dasyneura canadensis*, infested cone.
Fig. 13.—Pine needle midge, *Janetiella coloradensis*, deformed needles on *Pinus virginiana.*

Douglas Fir *(Pseudotsuga)*

Needles with flattened, greenish later yellowish swellings, ⅕ inch long,
    midge ....*Cecidomyia sp.*

Bald Cypress *(Taxodium)*

Thick-walled, modified seeds, Fig. 14...........................
...................Cypress seed midge, *Retinodiplosis taxodii* Felt
Fusiform twig swelling, midge................................
...................Cypress twig gall, *Thecodiplosis ananassi* Riley
Flower-shaped whitish gall, midge, Fig. 15......................
.......................Cypress flower gall, *Itonida anthici* Felt

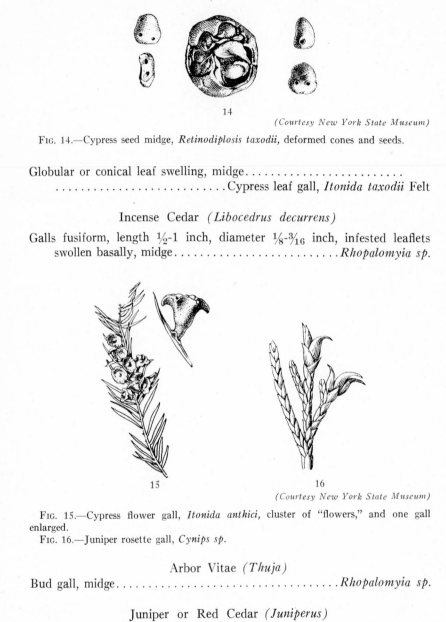

14

(Courtesy New York State Museum)

Fig. 14.—Cypress seed midge, *Retinodiplosis taxodii,* deformed cones and seeds.

Globular or conical leaf swelling, midge.........................
...........................Cypress leaf gall, *Itonida taxodii* Felt

Incense Cedar *(Libocedrus decurrens)*

Galls fusiform, length ½-1 inch, diameter ⅛-³⁄₁₆ inch, infested leaflets swollen basally, midge.........................*Rhopalomyia sp.*

15   16

(Courtesy New York State Museum)

Fig. 15.—Cypress flower gall, *Itonida anthici,* cluster of "flowers," and one gall enlarged.
Fig. 16.—Juniper rosette gall, *Cynips sp.*

Arbor Vitae *(Thuja)*

Bud gall, midge...................................*Rhopalomyia sp.*

Juniper or Red Cedar *(Juniperus)*

Enlarged fruit and purplish bud gall............................
.................Juniper berry midge, *Walshomyia juniperina* Felt
Thick-walled, reddish bud gall, at maturity the tip splits into four or more

irregular lobes, length ½ inch, diameter ⅛ inch on *J. monosperum,
J. utahensis*, midge...................*Rhopalomyia sabinæ* Felt
Oval, apical, slightly yellowish bud gall, very closely resembling normal
buds, on *J. scopulorum*, midge............*Walshomyia insignis* Felt
Reddish, conical gall, midge..............................
.....................Juniper cone gall, *Oligotrophus betheli* Felt
Flower-like, greenish, thickened leaf scales, gall wasp. Fig. 16.......
................................Juniper rosette gall, *Cynips sp.*
Prickly burr-like bud galls, midge...............*Allomyia juniperi* Felt

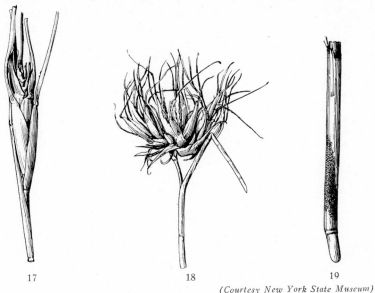

17   18   19

(Courtesy New York State Museum)

FIG. 17.—False spike midge, *Asteromyia agrostis,* deformed head of *Distichlis.*
FIG. 18.—Gall of sedge psyllid, *Livia maculipennis.*
FIG. 19.—Black sheath midge, *Lasioptera inustorum,* a portion of the stem shows
the blackened sheath.

Tips of young twigs killed, no swelling.........................
......................Juniper midge, *Contarinia juniperina* Felt
Deformed twigs and needles, the latter swollen and with small processes or
warts, on *J. communis*, mite........*Eriophyes quadrisetus* F. Thom.
Twig enlargements with a gelatinous growth in June, fungus........
.................Cedar apple, *Gymnosporangium globosum* Farl.

Mountain or Rock Cedar *(Sabina)*

Inconspicuous, usually brownish swellings of apical buds, midge.....
......................................*Phytophaga sabinæ* Felt
Oval, thin-walled, reddish bud gall, midge. Pl. 40 (1).............
......................................*Walshomyia texana* Felt

Thick-walled, reddish bud gall, at maturity the tip splits into four or more irregular lobes, length ½ inch, diameter ⅛ inch, midge........
......................................*Rhopalomyia sabinæ* Felt
Oval twig swelling, diameter about ⅙ inch, beetle..*Zeugonyx sabinæ* Notm.

Grass Galls *(Gramineæ)* and Sedges *(Cyperaceæ)*

A number of gall insects attack grasses and sedges. The structure of these plants practically limits attack to the seeds, the heads, the stems, leaf sheaths and roots.

The Hessian fly is one of the best known gall midges. The larva develops usually between the sheath and the stem, rarely producing much of a deformity, though weakening the plants and sometimes destroying the crop. The sorghum midge is common in the seed of its host plant.

The wheat jointworm gall develops in the stems and occasionally causes serious injury, though as a rule the insects are not especially destructive. The heads of grasses may be aborted by an early attack and a short tip with a mass of rudimentary leaves results. This condition may be produced by several gall midges, by a jumping plant louse, or psyllid, or even by a small red mite, the latter affecting a number of grasses.

There are probably a considerable number of grass and sedge infesting gall insects which are not known, due to the comparatively little study which has been given to these plants and the insects affecting them.

Deformed Heads or Aborted Buds

Muhlenbergia and spike grass, midge. Figs. 17, 21..*Asteromyia agrostis* O.S.
Crab grass, fly...........False spike grass fly, *Chlorops graminea* Coq.
Drop-seed rush grass, spike grass, triple-awned grass. Fig. 20. ......
.......................Grass gall mite, *Siteroptes carnea* Bks.
Spike grass, length 1½ inches, fly ....
............False spike grass fly, *Anthracophaga distichliæ* Mall.
Wheat, rye, blasted heads or grains ....
...................Wheat midge, *Thecodiplosis mosellana* Gehin
Triticum, "cockle heads," eel worm...........*Tylenchus tritici* Steinb.
Brome grass, enlarged, oval spikes, length 1½ inches, mite, ...
......................................*Eriophyes tenuis* Nal.
Hilaria, fusiform bud gall, ¾ to 1½ inches long ....
............*Harmolita sp.,* also *Systole sp., Siteroptes carnea* Bks.

PLATE 2—INSECT GALLS. 1, Gall on *Mimosa biuncifera,* of *Tanaostigmodes howardi* Ashm., *(After Weld).* 2, Gall on *Mimosa biuncifera,* of *Tanaostigmodes howardi* Ashm., 3, Gall on *Mimosa biuncifera,* producer unknown, Dipterous. 4, Woolly blossom gall, *Callirhytis operator* O.S. Spring form. *(After Thompson).* 5, Fall form of *Callirhytis operator* O.S. 6, Gall of sexual generation of the Gouty oak gall, *Plagiotrochus punctatus* Bass. 7, Oak flower gall, *Callirhytis pulchra* Bass. *(After Thompson).* 8, Gall on oak, of *Callirhytis scitula* Bass. *(After Thompson).* 9, Scrub oak club gall, *Callirhytis similis* Bass. *(After Thompson).*

PLATE 2

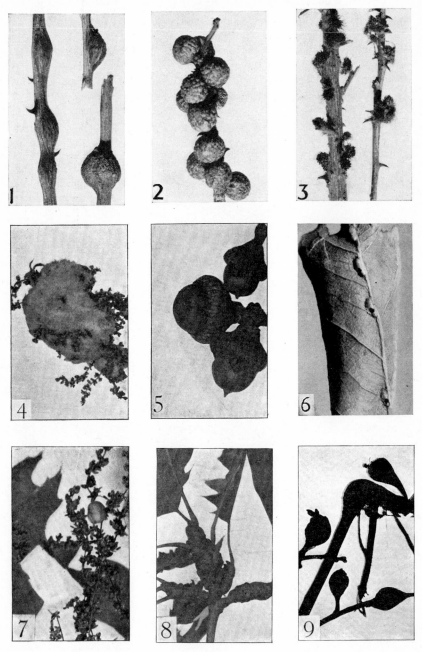

Courtesy N. Y. State Museum

Hilaria, irregular, bud-like swellings, joint worm. Pl. 1 (3)........
....*Harmolita sp.*
Brome grass and wild rye.....................*Siteroptes carnea* Bks.
Wild rye, apical bud galls, midge ....*Asteromyia sp.*
Phragmites, presumably a deformed head....*Asteromyia phragmites* Felt
Rush, length 1½ to 2 inches. Fig 18 ....
.......................Sedge Psyllid, *Livia maculipennis* Fitch
Sedge, length ¼ inch, midge...............*Hormomyia caudata* Felt

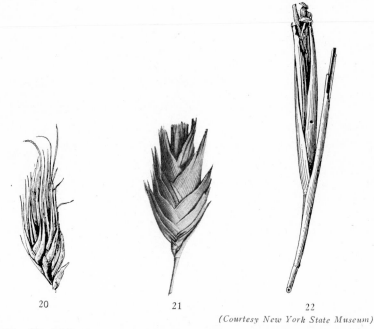

20   21   22

(Courtesy New York State Museum)

Fɪɢ. 20.—Aborted head of *Aristida purpurea,* caused by a mite, *Siteroptes carnea.*
Fɪɢ. 21.—Deformed head of *Muhlenbergia,* the work of *Asteromyia agrostis.*
Fɪɢ. 22.—Work of wheat joint worm, *Isosoma grande.*

In Stems, Sometimes Swollen or Blackened, or Leaf Sheath

Wheat, under leaf sheath, barley, couch or quitch grass and wild rye,
      midge. Fig. 23..............Hessian fly, *Phytophaga destructor* Say
Blackened leaf sheath of Panicum. Fig. 19......................
.................Black-sheath midge, *Lasioptera inustorum* Felt
Meadow grass, joint worm...................................
...............*Harmolita poæ* Ph. & Em., *H. poophila* Ph. & Em.
Wheat stems, somewhat swollen. Fig. 22........................
....................Wheat joint worm, *Isosoma grande* Riley
                    Wheat stem sawfly, *Cephus pygmœus* Linn.
                    Wheat stem maggot, *Oscinus carbonaria* Lw.

Western grass stem sawfly, *Cephus cinctus* Nort.
Trachelus tabidus Fabr.
Wheat, deformed leaf sheaths. Pl. 4 (6).......................
............Wheat sheath joint worm, *Harmolita vaginicolum* Doane
Barley...................Barley joint worm, *Harmolita hordei* Harr.
Rye......................Rye joint worm, *Harmolita secale* Fitch
Cephus cinctus Nort.
Trachelus tabidus Fabr.
Bent grass, swellings ½ inch long............................
...................Grass joint worm, *Harmolita agrostidis* How.
Fescue grass...... (also *Hordeum jubatum*), *Harmolita festucæ* Ph. & Em.
Cephus cinctus Nort.

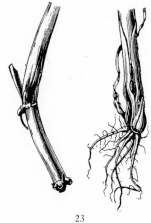 

23

24

(Courtesy New York State Museum)

FIG. 23.—Wheat stems infested by the Hessian fly, *Phytophaga destructor*.
FIG. 24.—Head of *Dulichium* infested by *Thecodiplosis dulichii*, affected spikelets on either side, a normal one in the middle. (*After Wells*).

Muhlenbergia, fusiform enlargements............*Chlorops ingrata* Will.
Red top...
Red top borers, *Eurytomocharis eragrostidis* How., *E. triodiœ* How.
Barnyard grass..........Grass crown midge, *Lasioptera echinocloa* Felt
Timothy.................................:...*Harmolita albomaculata*
Brome grass..
........Grass joint worm, *Harmolita bromi* How., *H. bromicola* How.
Orchard grass, in stems.............*Harmolita dactylicola* Ph. & Em.
Hair grass, *Aira*..............................*Cephus cinctus* Nort.
Wild rye, galls in second or third internode....................
.............................*Harmolita elymicola* Ph. & Em.
Carex, Juncus, infesting leaf sheath, midge...................
.............................*Procystiphora coloradensis* Felt
P. junci Felt

Wild rye, galls inconspicuous, near head.......................
.............................*Harmolita elymivora* Ph. & Em.
Harmolita hesperus Ph. & Em.
Cenchrus, oval, pointed swellings near tips of branching stems........
....*Lasioptera sp.*

25

26

(Courtesy New York State Museum)

FIG. 25.—Root gall of *Dasyneura torontoensis.*
FIG. 26.—*Dioscorea* stem gall, *Cecidomyia sp.*

Reared from Seeds

Wheat, rye...............Wheat midge, *Thecodiplosis mosellana* Gehin
Sorghum, Johnson grass, bristly fox-tail grass, tall red-top.........
.....................Sorghum midge, *Contarinia sorghicola* Coq.
Fox-tail grass..................Grass seed midge, *Itonida setariae* Felt
Stenodiplosis geniculata Reut.
Dasyneura alopecuri Reut.
Sedge, *Dulichium.* Fig. 24....Sedge fruit midge, *Thecodiplosis dulichii* Felt

Lily and Iris Galls *(Liliaceæ Iridaceæ)*

Comparatively few gall insects are known to attack plants of these families, well deserved favorites with lovers of the beautiful. There is little peculiar, aside possibly from the fact that three of the few listed are found in the roots.

Lilium auratum
Reared from scarcely thickened stems   *Neolasioptera hibisci* Felt

Oakesia
Yellowish blister leaf gall, midge.....................*Cecidomyia sp.*

Yucca
Occurring in pods.............Yucca pod midge, *Dasyneura yuccæ* Felt

False Solomon's Seal *(Smilacina)*
Deformed berries, midge...................*Asphondylia smilacinæ* Felt
Root gall, midge...........................*Dasyneura smilacinæ* Bish.

Miaanthemum
Brown blister leaf gall, midge..........................*Cecidomyia sp.*
Root gall, length ¼ inch, midge. Fig. 25.......*Dasyneura torontoensis* Felt

Solomon's Seal *(Polygonatum)*
Blister leaf gall, midge..............................*Cecidomyia sp.*
Irregularly oval, blister stem galls, diameter ¼ inch, midge........
.................................*Dasyneura smilacinæ* Bish.

Green Brier *(Smilax)*
Oval blister leaf spots, midge. Pl. 7 (7)...........................
...................Smilax blister, *Camptoneuromyia rubifolia* Felt
Young rolled leaves, midge. .Smilax leaf midge, *Dasyneura smilacifolia* Felt
Green knotty stem swelling, gall wasp...........................
....................Smilax stem gall, *Diastrophus smilacis* Ashm.

Fleur-de-Lis *(Iris)*
Green leaf gall, length ½ to ¾ inches. Pl. 4 (2)................
........................Iris leaf gall, *Agromyza laterella* Zett.

Dioscoreaceæ
Yam *(Dioscorea)*
Irregular warty gall, stem midge. Fig. 26......................
........................*Dioscorea* stem gall, *Cecidomyia sp.*

Orchids (*Orchidaceæ*)
Cattleya
Irregular root galls, midge, Orchid root gall. *Parallelodiplosis cattleyæ* Moll.
Spherical or conical pseudo-bulbs...............................
..................Orchid bud gall, *Eurytoma orchidearum* Westw.

Hookera or Triteleia *(brodiæa)*
Flower stalk swelling, 1¼ to 1½ inches, diameter ½ inch, midge....
....*Cecidomyia sp.*

Willow Family (Salicaceæ)

Willows of a number of species and with similar characteristics may be found in almost any wet place. Like goldenrod they are favorites with a long series of gall insects.

The willow apple galls and the closely related deformations produced by certain small gall flies are sometimes exceedingly abundant on the leaves. These are globular or oval, greenish, yellowish or reddish swellings, with a diameter approximating one-quarter to one-half an inch and are the work of several species of sawflies. The eggs are tucked into the young leaves with the saw-like ovipositor of the mother insect. The galls of some of these sawflies are rather symmetrically arranged upon the leaves. The development of sawfly galls is well advanced before the eggs hatch, probably the result of a chemical stimulus produced either by fluids injected at the time of oviposition, or, more probably, by the contents of the eggs, themselves.

Sawfly galls each contain a greenish, many footed false caterpillar or sawfly larva which becomes full grown in the fall and leaves the gall for shelter in soft wood, pithy stems or the like, and transforms to the fly early the following spring.

The beaked willow gall, the pine cone gall, and the willow cabbage gall,

27   28
(Courtesy New York State Museum)

FIG. 27.—Beaked willow gall, *Phytophaga rigidae.*
FIG. 28.—Pine cone gall, *Rhabdophaga strobiloides.*

are very common tip deformities produced by allied gall midges; in the case of the latter two the producers are closely related. The galls of any one of these three may be found on most of the shoots in one or more willow clumps. There is little in the general appearance of the first named to suggest a modified bud gall, yet the shriveled, open tip and the maggot deep in the cavity indicate somewhat earlier or deeper attack than in the case

PLATE 3—INSECT GALLS. 1, Oak leaf seed gall, *Dryocosmus deciduus* Bass. (*After Thompson*). 2, Gall on oak, *Andricus formosus* Bass. (*After Weld*). 3, Oak rosette gall, *Cynips frondosa* Bass. (*After Thompson*). 4, Gall on oak, of *Cynips glandulosus* Riley. (*After Thompson*). 5, Gall of grape Phylloxera, *Phylloxera vitifoliæ* Fitch. (*After Britton*). 6, Gall on *Lactuca, Aulacidea podagræ* Bass. (*After Thompson*). 7, Willow egg gall, *Euura ovum* Walsh. (*After Thompson*). 8, Gall on willow, of *Pontania desmodioides* Walsh. (*After Thompson*). 9, Willow apple gall, *Pontania pomum* Walsh. (*After Thompson*).

PLATE 3

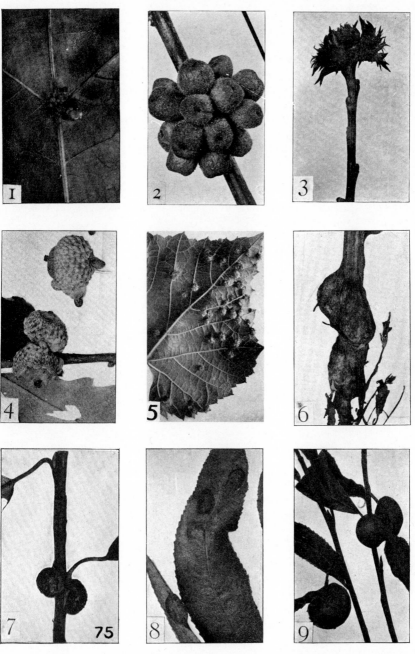

Courtesy N. Y. State Museum

of the familiar rosette galls, such as the pine cone gall and the willow cabbage gall. In the first named the attack appears to be deeper and in the developing tip of the wood rather than among the forming leaves, as in the case of the latter two.

The willow beaked gall maggot is very subject to parasitic attack and not infrequently one may find a number of partly developed, more rounded galls, since the growth of the gall stopped with the death of the producer larva and its consequent inability to continue the stimulation necessary for subsequent development. Sometimes this occurs so early as to check the growth of the gall when the walls are rather soft and as a consequence there is a slight shriveling or wrinkling as the tissues harden, producing a somewhat puzzling variation until the cause for the difference becomes apparent.

The potato gall of the willow, an irregular potato shaped swelling, usually an inch or so in diameter, is rather common on the small twigs in many localities. This gall, unlike those just mentioned, contains a number of maggots, each in an individual cell.

Willow shoots grow very rapidly and in some cases the development of the cane is so quick that a primarily bud infestation becomes a twig gall. This is well shown in the case of the wheat ear gall, so called because of its resemblance to a wheat head. The parent midge lays eggs or places them so that a series of lateral buds are infested while the shoot is only partly developed, and as a consequence the affected part of the cane fails to grow normally and buds which should be several inches apart remain in a crowded condition, the maggots developing in a cell near the base of each. The willows support many very similar species of gall midges.

It is probable that many other willow shoot galls have their inception in the bud. This location is favored by a number of willow gall midges and some saw flies.

It is easy to rear the producers of many willow galls if the infested parts are collected in early spring and kept in a reasonably moist container, such as a glass jar covered with fine netting. Protect glass breeding jars from the direct rays of the sun, otherwise the insects may be killed by high temperatures.

Groups of willows occasionally have the foliage greatly deformed by curious filamentous growths—the work of tiny gall mites. Related gall mites also produce numerous small pocket or capsule galls, they being so numerous at times as to give a granular aspect to the leaves.

Willow *(Salix)*
Bud Galls

Fusiform, beaked, length 1 inch, midge, winter, early spring.
Fig. 27 . . . . Beaked willow gall, *Phytophaga rigidæ* O.S.
Narrowly oval, slightly beaked, length 1 inch, midge . . . .
. . . . *Rhabdophaga coloradensis* Felt

Occur in buds, midges.................*Rhabdophaga latebrosa* Felt
Rhabdophaga gnaphalioides Felt
Rhabdophaga gemmœ Felt
Dasyneura gemmœ Felt
Dasyneura californica Felt
Rhabdophaga essigi Felt
Enlarged lateral bud, sawfly.....................*Euura gemma* Walsh
Blasted willow tips, midge. Pl. 12 (3)..................*Cecidomyia sp.*

Rosette Galls, midge, early spring and summer
Pine cone-like gall, length 1 to 1¼ inches. Fig. 28................
.................Pine cone gall, *Rhabdophaga strobiloides* Walsh
Rhabdophaga persimilis Felt
Open rosette gall. . Willow cabbage gall, *Rhabdophaga brassicoides* Walsh
Pl. 11 (7)........................*Rhabdophaga rhodoides* Felt

29 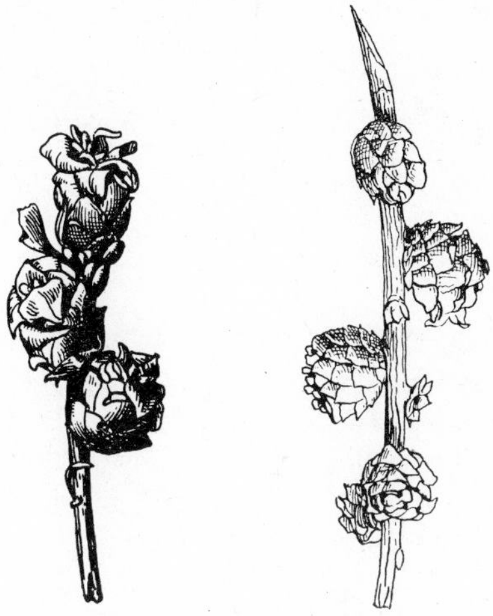   30
(Courtesy New York State Museum)

FIG. 29.—Clustered willow galls of *Phytophaga walshii*.
FIG. 30.—Clustered willow gall of *Rhabdophaga racemi*.

Small rosette gall in small willow................................
....................Cabbage gall, *Rhabdophaga normaniana* Felt
Spongy or clustered rosette gall. Fig. 29........*Phytophaga walshii* Felt
Clustered rosette galls. Fig 30................................
.................Clustered willow gall, *Rhabdophaga racemi* Felt

Leaf Rolls or Folds, midges, spring
Pod-like swelling or curled leaves Pl. 10 (2).......................
..................Willow pod midge, *Dasyneura salicifolia* Felt

Closely rolled terminal leaves...............*Rhabdophaga plicta* Felt

Capsule or Pocket Galls, plant mites, spring and summer

Irregularly hemispherical, greenish-yellow pocket galls on either surface
of black willow leaf......................*Eriophyes semen* Walsh
Filamentous leaf structure..................*Eriophyes œnigma* Walsh
A number of other capsule or pocket galls are produced by undescribed
species of *Eriophyes*. Pl. 16 (8)........?*Eriophyes œnigma* Walsh

Leaf Galls

Ovoid, yellowish, red-spotted blister gall, diameter $\frac{1}{10}$ to $\frac{1}{8}$ inch, most
evident on under surface, gall midge, summer................
.................Willow blister gall, *Oligotrophus salicifolius* Felt

31    32
(Courtesy New York State Museum)

Fig. 31.—Willow pea gall, *Pontania pisum.*
Fig. 32.—Willow apple gall, *Pontania pomum.*

Flattish yellow-green, length $\frac{1}{4}$ to $\frac{1}{2}$ inch, sawfly, spring. Pl. 3 (8)...
.................................*Pontania desmodioides* Walsh
Similar to preceding, only one gall on the leaf, sawfly, spring........
.................................*Pontania californica* Marl.
Similar to preceding, more robust, nearly spherical, sawfly, spring....
.................................*Pontania gracilis* Marl.
Similar to preceding, smaller, mostly on lower surface, sawfly, spring..
.................................*Pontania parva* Cress
Yellowish, red-spotted gall, diameter .1 inch, midge, summer Pl. 10(6)
.............Willow-lipped gall, *Trishormomyia verruca* Walsh
Conical petiole gall, length $\frac{1}{4}$ to $\frac{1}{3}$ inch, sawfly.................
.................................*Euura cosensii* Rohw.
Conical, on petioles of branches producing pistillate catkins, on *S. serissima,*
sawfly, spring.........................*Euura serissimæ* Rohw.
Petiole or midrib enlargement, spherical to ovoid, dimensions $\frac{1}{4}$ to $\frac{1}{2}$
inch, on *S. lucida,* sawfly, spring...........*Pontania lucidæ* Rohw.
Globular, smooth, fleshy, midrib gall, 2 to 6 in a row, diameter $\frac{1}{4}$ inch,
sawfly, spring...........................*Pontania monile* Marl.

Ovate, reddish gall in rows on either side of midrib, length ¼ to ⅜
 inch, sawfly, spring...................... *Pontania hyalina* Nort.
Pea-like, pale yellowish gall, on underside of leaf, diameter ¼ inch, sawfly,
 spring. Fig. 31............Willow pea gall, *Pontania pisum* Walsh
Rounded, yellowish-green, rosy cheeked gall, diameter ½ inch, sawfly,
 spring. Pl. 3 (9). Fig. 32...Willow apple gall, *Pontania pomum* Walsh
Very similar, on *S. petiolaris* .... *Pontania petiolaridis* Rohw.
Ovate, smooth, fleshy leaf gall, length ⅓ inch, on *S. longifolia*, sawfly,
 spring................................. *Pontania bruneri* Marl.

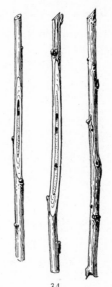

33   34
(Courtesy New York State Museum)

Fig. 33.—Willow potato gall, *Rhabdophaga batatus,* typical enlargement.
Fig. 34.—Gall of *Rhabdophaga caulicola.*

Spherical leaf gall extending from midrib almost to margin, average
 diameter ½ inch, on *S. humilis*, sawfly, spring...............
 .... *Pontania crassicornis* Rohw.
Globose, commonly paired, red or pink, yellowish or green below, on *S.
 californica,* sawfly, spring............... *Pontania resinicola* Marl.
Pyriform, usually solitary, thin-walled, broadly attached, on *S. californica,*
 sawfly, spring...................... *Pontania pyriformis* Marl.
Midvein swelling, length ⅛ inch, sawfly, spring............. *Euura sp.*
Apparently pouch leaf galls, mite............. *Cecidobia salicicola* Banks

Twig Galls
Narrowly oval, slightly beaked, apical, length 1 inch, midge........
 .... *Rhabdophaga coloradensis* Felt

Irregular, ovid or subglobular galls, diameter ½ to 1 inch, midge, spring
    and summer, Fig. 33..Willow potato gall, *Rhabdophaga batatus* Walsh
Reared from same gall midge................*Asynapta saliciperda* Felt
                                    Rhabdophaga ramuscula Felt

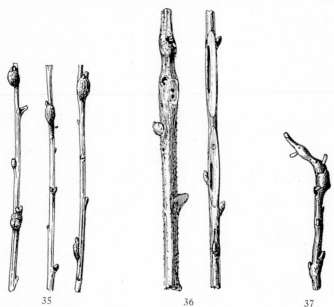

35   36   37

(Courtesy New York State Museum)

Fig. 35.—Scarred willow gall, *Phytophaga tumidosæ.*
Fig. 36.—Willow stems infested by *Sackenomyia packardi,* one in section.
Fig. 37.—Willow twig infested by *Sackenomyia porteræ.*

Irregular "wheat-ear" swelling ½ to 1½ inches, midge, spring and sum-
    mer. Pl. 12 (4).....Wheat-ear gall, *Rhabdophaga triticoides* Walsh
Nodula gall at base of twigs, length ⅓ inch, midge, spring and summer
    Pl. 11 (9).........Nodule willow gall, *Rhabdophaga nodula* Felt
Irregularly enlarged twigs of basket willow, midge, spring and summer.
    Pl. 12 (2)...........Basket willow gall, *Rhabdophaga salicis* Shrk.
Subglobose galls, the surface scarred, diameter ⅙ inch, midge, summer
    Fig. 35..............Scarred willow gall, *Phytophaga tumidosæ* Felt

PLATE 4—INSECT GALLS. 1, Dipterous gall, probably *Agromyza* on Clematis. (*After Thompson*). 2, Iris leaf gall, *Agromyza laterella* Zett. (*After Thompson*). 3, Poplar twig gall, *Agromyza schineri* Giraud. 4, Goldenrod root-stalk gall, *Eurosta reticulata* Snow. (*After Thompson*). 5, Goldenrod root-stalk gall, *Eutreta sparsa* Wied. (*After Thompson*). 6, Wheat sheath joint worm, *Isosoma vaginicolum* Doane. (*After Doane*). 7, Locust twig gall, *Ecdytolopha inscitiana* Zell. (*After Thompson*). 8, Scarred golden-rod gall, *Eucosma scudderiana* Clem. (*After Thompson*). 9, Irregular, subglobose grape leaf gall, showing a slight swelling on the upper surface and a globose enlargement be-neath. *?Coleophora sp.* (*After Clarke*).

PLATE 4

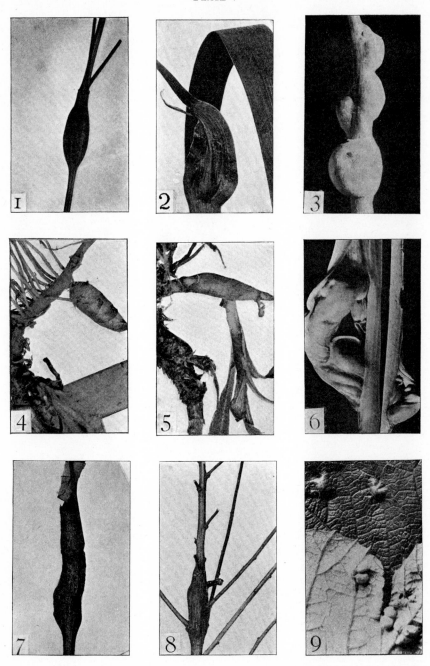

Courtesy N. Y. State Museum

Subglobular gall attached to twig, with dead area on one side, diameter ⅖ inch. Pl. 11 (8)....................*Rhabdophaga globosa* Felt
Irregularly elongated, ovate, reddish brown, spongy twig gall, length ½ to ⅘ inch, spring, sawfly. Pl. 3 ((7)......................
...........................Willow egg gall, *Euura ovum* Walsh
Globose constricted twig swellings, diameter ¾ inch, beetle, spring...
....*Agrilus politus* Say
Ovate twig swelling, length 2 inches, beetle, spring..*Saperda concolor* Lec.

38   39
(Courtesy New York State Museum)

Fig. 38.—Willow stem infested by *Rhabdophaga podagræ.*
Fig. 39.—Willow stem infested by *Rhabdophaga cornuta.*

Irregular branch and trunk swellings, beetle, spring...............
..............Mottled willow borer, *Cryptorhynchus lapathi* Linn.
Irregularly oval, subcortical twig swellings, length ⅛ inch, fly, spring
......................................*Agromyza salicis* Mall.
Irregularly swollen, frequently twisted, length ¼ inch, sawfly, spring..
....*Euura sp.*
Slightly enlarged or slender twigs, midges—A somewhat long series has

been reared. They can be identified only by rearing and studying
the insects.........................*Phytophaga timberlakei* Felt
Phytophaga americana Felt
Phytophaga caulicola Felt
Phytophaga perocculta Ckll.
Phytophaga latipennis Felt
Dasyneura corticis Felt
Fig. 34. *Rhabdophaga caulicola* Felt
Fig. 38. *Rhabdophaga podagræ* Felt
Fig. 39. *Rhabdophaga cornuta* Walsh
Asphondylia salictaria Felt
Fig. 36. *Sackenomyia packardi* Felt
Fig. 37. *Sackenomyia porteræ* Ckll.

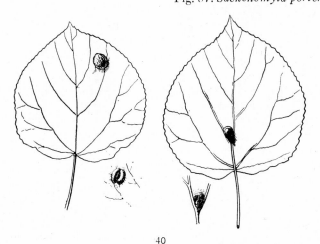

40

(Courtesy New York State Museum)

Fig. 40.—Two types of subglobular leaf galls on poplar, *Cecidomyia sp.*

Gradual twig swelling, length ½ to 1½ inches, sawflies,..........
....*Euura nodus* Walsh
Gradual twig swelling, length 3-5 inches......*Euura macgillivrayi* Rohw.
Basally an abrupt swelling..................*Euura propinquus* Rohw.

Poplar *(Populus)*

The poplars are related to the willows and like them support a number
of gall insects, though not nearly so many.

The vagabond poplar gall is a common and conspicuous deformity of
the poplar. It is the work of a plant louse which attacks the leaves in the
early spring, transforming them into irregular, greatly reduced, lobular,
hollow masses within which the plant lice develop. These are green at
first, turning black in midsummer and remaining upon the trees throughout the winter, unsightly evidence of insect attack.

The ribbed petiole gall of poplar is a peculiar oval swelling about the size of a pea, which develops at the base of the leaf blade. It is the work of a small caterpillar. The galls are occasionally abundant upon individual trees, though not particularly injurious.

Poplar leaf stems are frequently attacked by plant lice which produce globose swellings about half an inch in diameter, each with a conspicuous transverse slit across the face, the point where the two portions of the abnormal growth have failed to fuse. The gall is hollow and, in its early development, alive with plant lice. These insects are exceedingly common upon individual trees or groups of trees, a large proportion of the leaves being affected at times.

Poplar leaves also support a series of gall midges which produce reddish,

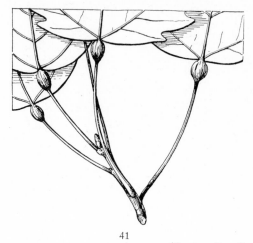

41

(Courtesy New York State Museum)

Fig. 41.—Ribbed petiole gall, *Ectoedemia populella.*

more or less globular swellings. These are sometimes abundant, though not numerous enough to cause material damage.

Enlarged buds, larvae deep red, on western balsam, midge. . . . .
. . . . *?Rhabdophaga sp.*
Irregular, granulated, woody bud enlargements, diameter 1½ to 2½ inches, mite. . . . . *Eriophyes sp.*
Irregularly globose, tomentose bud masses, diameter ¼ to ½ inch on Balm-of-Gilead, mite. . . . . *Eriophyes populi* Nal.
Irregular masses of globose galls at base of leaf stem, mite. Pl. 16 (3).
. . . . *?Eriophyes populi* Nal.
Ovate twig swellings, cracking the second season, on large toothed and quaking aspens, beetle. . . . . *Mecas ornata* Say
Spindle-shaped swellings on small branches of young trees, quaking aspens, boring caterpillar. . . . . *Memythrus tricinctus* Harr.

Irregular angular petiole or twig galls, length ½ inch, midge........
....*Cecidomyia sp.*
Oval twig gall, length 1½ to 2 inches, beetle......*Saperda populnea* Linn.
Irregular branch and trunk swellings, mostly on smaller stems, beetle
..............Mottled willow borer, *Cryptorhynchus lapathi* Linn.
Irregular oval swellings on smaller twigs, length ⅛ inch............
........................Poplar twig gall, *Agromyza schineri* Gir.
Irregular one-celled, blister galls, mostly on upper surface, light colored,
    on large-toothed poplar, midge........*Cecidomyia irregularis* Steb.
Oval petiole galls with transverse openings and near middle of leaf stem,
    aphid, summer. Pl. 1 (6)...............................
..........Poplar leaf-stem gall, *Pemphigus populitransversus* Riley

42   43
(Courtesy New York State Museum)

FIG. 42.—Vagabond poplar gall, *Mordwilkoja vagabunda.*
FIG. 43.—Midvein poplar leaf gall, *Cecidomyia sp.*

Globose ridged petiole gall, diameter ¼ inch, caterpillar. Fig. 41.....
.................Ribbed petiole gall, *Ectoedemia populella* Busck
Twisted, subglobular galls with oblique openings at base of cottonwood
    leaves, diameter ¼ to ½ inch, aphid....*Pemphigus populicaulis* Fitch
Subglobular leaf galls, midges, summer........*Dicrodiplosis populi* Felt
                                    Mycodiplosis populifolia Felt
                                    Rhizomyia absobrina Felt
Globose leaf gall on Balm-of-Gilead, gall midge. Pl. 7 (2).........
....*Cecidomyia sp.*

Light red coxcomb-like gall on mid-vein, aphid..................
....*Pemphigus populi-venæ* Fitch
Marginal leaf rolls or folds, greenish or purplish.........*Cecidomyia sp.*
Irregularly folded, convolute deformed leaves, diameter 2 inches, aphid,
      summer. Fig. 42......Vagabond gall, *Mordwilkoja vagabunda* Walsh
Pinkish pod-like gall on Lombardy poplar, diameter ½ inch, aphid, sum-
      mer......................Purse leaf gall, *Pemphigus affinis* Kalt

44

(Courtesy New York State Museum)

Fig. 44.—Work of sweet fern midge, *Janetiella asplenifolia.*

PLATE 5—MIDGE GALLS. 1, Ash leaves inhabited by *Arthrocnodax sambucifolia* Felt, the deformation probably produced by a mite, *Eriophyes sp. (After Thompson).* 2, Cone-flower gall of *Asphondylia conspicua* O.S. 3, Sunflower purse gall, *Asphondylia globulus* O.S. *(After Weld).* 4, Adherent capsule gall on solidago, inhabited by the nun midge, *Asphondylia monacha* O.S. and *Camptoneuromyia adhesa* Felt. 5, Gall of nun midge, *Asphondylia monacha* O.S., on narrow-leaved goldenrod. 6, Cactus infested by *Asphondylia opuntiæ* Felt. *(After Essig).* 7, Gall of *Asteromyia sp.* on *Aster (Ionactis) lineariifolius. (After Clarke).* 8, Blister gall of ? *Caryomyia species* on hickory. 9, Gall of spruce bud midge, *Rhabdophaga swainei* Felt. *(After Swaine).*

PLATE 5

Courtesy N. Y. State Museum

Globose, red and yellowish, clustered leaf galls, usually near the base and on underside, diameter ⅕ inch, on quaking aspen, aphid.......
......................................*Pemphigus rileyi* Steb.
There are a number of leaf galls and leaf "piles" or erineums produced by unnamed species of mites.........................*Eriophyes sp.*

Sweet Gale Family *(Myricaceæ)*

Wax myrtle *(Myrica cerifer)*
Wax Myrtle, bud galls, midge, spring..............*Itonida myricæ* Felt

Sweet fern *(Myrica asplenifolia)*
Fleshy vein folds, ⅙ inch, summer. Fig. 44.....................
...................Sweet fern midge, *Janetiella asplenifolia* Felt
Bud gall, with rudimentary, linear leaves, diameter ¼ inch, mite....
....*Eriophyes sp.*

Bayberry *(Myrica carolinensis)*
Bayberry leaves, badly deformed, mite, summer. Pl. 15 (6)..*Eriophyes sp.*

Walnut Family *(Juglandaceæ)*

The numerous galls to be found upon hickory leaves offer a most interesting field to both the casual enquirer and the trained investigator. The hickories are characteristic North American trees, differing relatively little among themselves and as might be expected, are hosts to a long series of gall producers.

Most of the leaf galls on hickories are produced by plant lice or gall aphids and gall midges. The numerous deformities, some 29, produced by the gall aphids are easily recognized by the ever present opening, usually guarded by hairy lobes, on either the upper or lower surface of the leaf. Within there are many pale yellowish or whitish, usually wingless plant lice which later develop wings when the galls are nearly grown and are about to crack open.

The galls produced by midges may be recognized because there is no such opening as in the case of the Phylloxera galls and within is a nearly transparent or yellowish maggot or larva. The maggots, though securely walled in by the growth of the gall, are not protected from natural enemies and many are killed by parasitic maggots which occasionally may be seen firmly attached to the side of the gall maker and slowly sapping the strength of its victim.

The hickory Phylloxeras are closely related to the grape Phylloxera, a pest of American origin which brought disaster to many European vineyards and is regarded as a potential danger to European grapes in California growing upon their own roots. These hickory Phylloxera galls develop earlier than the hickory midge galls, except in the case of certain species which occur upon pecan, these latter breeding throughout the season. The

Phylloxeras of the hickories inhabit a great variety of galls upon the leaf and leaf stems, ranging in form from disk-like or button-like galls on the leaf to frequently globular, sometimes conical deformities, varying in color from pale green to bright pink, and ranging in size from about $\frac{1}{8}$ to $\frac{1}{2}$ of an inch in diameter. The leaf stem and twig galls usually occur in irregular swollen masses which may grow to such an extent as to prevent the development of the leaf and even kill portions of the twig. The interior of a Phylloxera gall is most interesting and resembles nothing so much as the geode of the mineralogist, the numerous young plant lice crowded upon the inner surface suggesting the crystals of the mineral.

The eggs of the hickory leaf stem gall aphid may be found in winter in rough places on the twigs and especially in old galls. The eggs hatch and the young Phylloxeras crawl to the buds and enter between the loosened bud scales. The stimulation by the tiny gall lice results in a great production of plant tissues and a well formed gall before the foliage breaks out of the bud.

Most of the midge galls on hickory are produced by peculiar insects which are known as hickory midges or *Caryomyia*. They winter in the galls, flying the latter part of May and deposit eggs on the under side of the young leaves. The eggs are pale whitish, about $\frac{1}{100}$ of an inch long and are scattered among the plant hairs to the number of 50 or 500 on individual leaflets. The female crawls slowly over the leaf, feeling the surface in a somewhat spasmodic manner. After a moment the ovipositor is held firmly against the leaf and shortly an egg is deposited, the act taking about a second. The location of the young gall is indicated upon the upper surface by a slight discoloration near the point of attachment, and underneath there is a small cell containing the gall maker. The cell gradually enlarges and pushes through the leaf surface, the dried, brown fragments of which are frequently seen at the base of the gall and sometimes hanging from its tip. Nearly three weeks after the eggs are laid the larger galls may have a diameter of about $\frac{1}{16}$ of an inch. The development of these galls is much slower than in the case of the Phylloxera galls on hickory, and continues well toward the end of September.

Midge galls vary greatly in appearance. There is a disk-like flattened gall, approaching in shape and size the more common and better known "spangle galls" of the oak, some of which may be produced by a gall midge. Many of the midge galls are globular and in color may be greenish-white, pale green or even purple. They may be either smooth or hairy, solitary or thickly clustered, some have greatly produced points or beaks and are therefore flask-shaped, and others taper gently from the base to the slender tip, the shape being suggestive of a cow's horn. There is also the very common tube gall. A few of these hickory leaf galls secrete honeydew and have a distinctly sticky or adhesive surface.

Butternut *(Juglans cinerea)*

Folded crinkled leaves, midge..........................*Cecidomyia sp.*

Brown velvety pile on leaf stalks or veins, mite...........*Eriophyes sp.*
Button-shaped pocket leaf gall, mite....................*Eriophyes sp.*

Black Walnut *(Juglans nigra)*

A pile and leaf blister, mite.................*Eriophyes tristriatus* Nal.
Brown velvety pile on leaf stalks and veins, mite. .*Eriophyes acaulis* Walsh
Green warty pocket leaf gall, diameter ¼ inch, mite........*Eriophyes sp.*

Walnut, heartnut *(Juglans)*

A broad, lobulate green or reddish open pouch leaf deformation ¼ to ½
    inch wide and ½ to ¾ inch long, between the veins on the upper leaf
    surface, the concavity dense, whitish, woolly. The structure suggests
    the coxcomb elm gall. Later the deformed areas turn blackish with
    variable yellow margins, plant mite................*Eriophyes sp.*

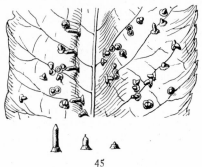

45

(Courtesy New York State Museum)

Fig. 45.—Hickory tube gall, *Caryomyia tubicola,* showing a group of galls and
below several stages in profile. See also Fig. 2 on page 17 for diversified forms.

Hickory *(Carya)*

Leaf rolls or vein angles

Narrowly inrolled pecan leaves, mite....................*Eriophyes sp.*
Small galls in the angles of lateral veins, mite.............*Eriophyes sp.*
Marginal, narrow, leaf roll, mite. Pl. 15 (4)..............*Eriophyes sp.*

Leaf blisters

Irregular greenish or blackish leaf blister, midge.........*Cecidomyia sp.*

Tube galls

Cylindrical, greenish, oblique leaf gall, length ¼ inch, midge, summer.
    Fig. 45.................Hickory tube gall, *Caryomyia tubicola* O.S.
Similar but longer, curved, tapering, midge, summer.......*Cecidomyia sp.*

Conical leaf galls with no orifice

Subglobular leaf gall with long spur, length $\frac{1}{6}$ inch, midge, summer. Pl. 6 (2, 3)...............Hickory seed gall, *Caryomyia caryæcola* O.S.
Conical thin-walled greenish or reddish leaf gall, length $\frac{1}{10}$ inch, midge, summer........Conical hickory gall, *Caryomyia sanguinolenta* O.S.

Conical or globose leaf galls with distinct orifice and containing aphids

Galls more or less conical above and beneath, opening on the upper surface, both nipples surrounded at the apex by a fringe of long filaments, walls thin, more or less transparent, diameter $\frac{1}{5}$ to $\frac{1}{2}$ inch, height $\frac{1}{6}$ to $\frac{1}{4}$ inch, aphid, summer...........*Phylloxera caryæseptem* Shim.
Similar to the preceding with both cones very much elongated, slender and toothlike, length of cones $\frac{1}{8}$ to $\frac{1}{3}$ inch, diameter $\frac{1}{12}$ to $\frac{1}{6}$ inch, aphid, summer........*Phylloxera caryæseptem* Shim. var. *perforans* Perg.
Galls conical above, opening on the upper surface, flat beneath, splitting into several bracts when mature, with slender filaments at the center beneath, walls papery, more or less transparent, diameter $\frac{1}{5}$ inch, aphid, summer.....................*Phylloxera caryæfoliæ* Fitch
Gall similar to *P. caryæseptem*, opening on upper surface, smaller, more flattened but slightly convex above and beneath, opening round or oval, surrounded by short, recurved, pubescent bracts, a minute, closed nipple beneath, diameter $\frac{1}{8}$ to $\frac{1}{4}$ inch, height $\frac{1}{12}$ to $\frac{1}{8}$ inch, aphid, summer................................*Phylloxera picta* Perg.
Galls smaller though similar to *P. picta*, opening on upper surface, more convex and often with a slight depression above, no opening above before maturity, a minute, closed nipple beneath, diameter $\frac{1}{8}$ to $\frac{1}{4}$ inch, height $\frac{1}{12}$ to $\frac{1}{8}$ inch, aphid, summer *Phylloxera intermedia* Perg.
Gall convex, opening on the under surface, the walls papery, more elevated above than beneath, with a reddish or crimson fovea or dimple above, varying in depth; the orifice beneath small and surrounded by a fringe of short, flaring bracts, diameter $\frac{1}{8}$ to $\frac{1}{5}$ inch, height $\frac{1}{25}$ to $\frac{1}{8}$ inch, aphid, summer.......Hickory button gall, *Phylloxera foveola* Perg.
The gall concave above, with orifice on under surface; the walls papery, convex beneath, the nipple formed of rather long, slender filaments, the depression above as well as the surface beneath, including the filaments, with long, white hairs, diameter $\frac{1}{8}$ to $\frac{1}{4}$ inch, height $\frac{1}{12}$ to $\frac{1}{8}$ inch, aphid, summer ....*Phylloxera pilosula* Perg.
Galls small, the walls papery, slightly convex above, more prominent beneath, usually with a small shallow depression toward one side, above, nipple short, without bracts, the orifice beneath, more or less oval and fringed with short pubescence, diameter nearly $\frac{1}{25}$ inch, aphid, summer.............................*Phylloxera deplanata* Perg.
Gall medium, the walls papery, slightly convex above and beneath with a short nipple, having a rounded orifice surrounded by a burlike fringe of many filaments, diameter $\frac{1}{6}$ to $\frac{1}{4}$ inch, height $\frac{1}{8}$ inch, aphid, summer.............................*Phylloxera depressa* Shim.

Gall medium, opening on the under surface, walls papery, quite flat, above with a dimpled depression, the opening beneath round and with a downy orifice, diameter nearly $\frac{1}{12}$ inch, height $\frac{1}{8}$ inch, aphid, summer . . . .*Phylloxera foveata* Shim.

Gall medium, walls papery, convex and considerably elevated above and more prominent beneath, rather hard, smooth and shining, the orifice beneath round and closed; resembles the gall of *P. caryæsemen,* diameter $\frac{1}{50}$ to $\frac{1}{12}$ inch, aphid, summer . . . . .*Phylloxera minima* Shim.

Gall minute, walls papery, red, more convex and more prominent above than beneath, with a dimpled depression, the nipple short and the orifice beneath surrounded by short, hairy bracts, diameter $\frac{1}{12}$ inch, height up to $\frac{1}{5}$ inch, aphid, summer. Pl. 14 (8) . . . .
. . . . .Hickory seed gall, *Phylloxera caryæsemen* Walsh

Gall medium, walls papery, conical above and much more prominent than the convex under surface, the nipple short with the oval orifice beneath, fringed with short hairs, diameter nearly $\frac{1}{25}$ inch, aphid, summer. Pl. 14 (5) . . . .*Phylloxera caryæfallax* Riley

Gall large, fleshy, convex on both surfaces, more prominent on the lower, the circumference above buttonlike, with a more or less sharply defined edge above or sunken beneath the surface of the leaf, nipple short, surrounded by short bracts, the orifice beneath round, diameter $\frac{1}{8}$ to $\frac{1}{2}$ inch, height $\frac{1}{12}$ to $\frac{1}{6}$ inch, aphid, summer. Pl. 14 (7) . . . .
. . . .*Phylloxera rimosalis* Perg.

Gall subglobose, walls fleshy, about equally prominent above and beneath, without a nipple, the orifice beneath a transverse slit, diameter $\frac{1}{3}$ to $\frac{1}{2}$ inch, height $\frac{1}{12}$ to $\frac{1}{6}$ inch, aphid, summer . . . .
. . . .*Phylloxera caryæscissa* Riley

Gall subglobose, walls fleshy, somewhat more prominent above than beneath, without a nipple, the orifice beneath an elongate slit, size $\frac{1}{2}$ to $\frac{1}{3}$ inch, the extreme diameter aphid, summer. Pl. 14 (6). Fig. 46 . . . . .Globular hickory gall, *Phylloxera caryæglobuli* Walsh

Gall subglobose, walls fleshy, about equally prominent on both leaf surfaces, conical beneath, ending in a short nipple and splitting into several stout bracts, diameter $\frac{1}{8}$ to $\frac{1}{4}$ inch, height $\frac{1}{12}$ to $\frac{1}{5}$ inch, aphid, summer . . . .*Phylloxera conica* Shim.

Gall flat above, walls fleshy, either flush with or sunken below the leaf surface, globular or pyriform beneath and more or less constricted at the base, with or without a distinct nipple which, when present, splits

PLATE 6—MIDGE GALLS ON HICKORY. 1, Gall on hickory, of *Caryomyia antennata* Felt. (*After Thompson*). 2, Hickory seed gall, *Caryomyia caryæcola* O.S. 3, Hickory seed gall, *Caryomyia "caryæcola* O.S." Another type. (*After Stebbins*). 4, Hickory onion gall, *Caryomyia holotricha* O.S. (*After Thompson*). 5, Gall on hickory, of *Caryomyia sp.* 6, Gall on hickory, of *Caryomyia sp.* (*After Thompson*). 7, Hickory leaf gall, *Caryomyia caryæ* O.S. 8, Gall on hickory, of *Caryomyia thompson* Felt. (*After Thompson*). 9, Gall on hickory, of *Caryomyia consobrina* Felt. (*After Clarke*).

PLATE 6

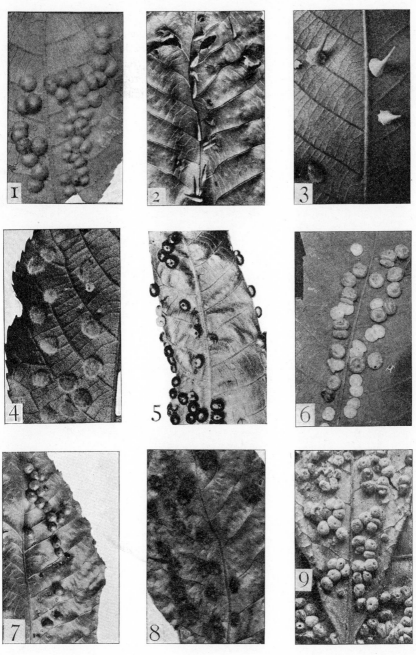

Courtesy N. Y. State Museum

into several bracts, diameter and height ⅕ to ½ inch, aphid, summer. Pl. 14 (4).....................*Phylloxera caryæ-avellana* Riley
Gall medium, walls fleshy, quite flat above, usually with a more or less distinct median depression, prominent and conical beneath, not constricted at the base, the nipple distinct, surrounded by short bracts, diameter nearly ⅛ inch, height ⅛ to ⅙ inch, aphid, summer....
.................................*Phylloxera symmetrica* Perg.

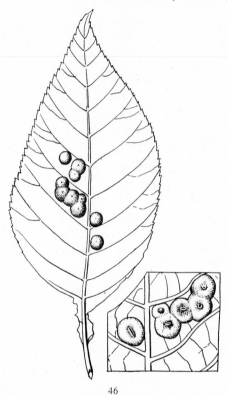

46

(Courtesy New York State Museum)

Fig. 46.—Globular hickory leaf gall, *Phylloxera caryaeglobuli,* a group of galls with a smaller group enlarged and showing the orifice on the under surface of the leaf.

Gall large, walls fleshy, more or less irregular, convex above, more prominent and conical beneath, splitting at maturity into several very long bracts, diameter ⅕ to nearly ½ inch, height ⅛ to ⅓ inch, aphid, summer.................................*Phylloxera notabilis* Perg.
Gall large, walls fleshy, globular, projecting about equally on both leaf surfaces, nipple short, with four or five short, stout, pubescent bracts surrounding the orifice, curving outwards when old, size variable, aphid, summer.......................*Phylloxera globosa* Shim.

Gall large, walls fleshy, pedunculate and more or less elongated, suspended from the under surface by a slender petiole, quite sticky when fresh, splitting at the apex into several long filaments, aphid, summer
.............................*Phylloxera caryægummosa* Riley

Globose leaf galls with no orifice, smooth or nearly so

Globular, smooth, yellowish-green leaf gall, diameter $\frac{1}{12}$ inch, midge, summer. Pl. 6 (7).........Hickory leaf gall, *Caryomyia caryæ*, O.S.
Globular, smooth, thin-walled, depressed, yellowish or brownish, diameter $\frac{1}{12}$ inch, midge, summer. Pl. 6 (9).......*Caryomyia consobrina* Felt
Caryomyia arcuaria Felt
Globular, smooth, thin-walled without a nipple, yellowish pubescent, diameter $\frac{1}{6}$ inch, midge, summer.............*Caryomyia similis* Felt
Globular, smooth, thick-walled, yellowish green or purplish, diameter $\frac{1}{6}$ inch, midge, summer. Pl. 6 (1)..........*Caryomyia antennata* Felt
Globular, smooth, thin-walled, with an empty chamber at the apex, diameter $\frac{1}{10}$ inch, midge, summer................*Caryomyia inanis* Felt

Globose leaf galls with no orifice, hairy

Globular, hairy, brown, thick-walled leaf gall, diameter $\frac{1}{4}$ inch, midge, summer..............Hickory peach gall, *Caryomyia persicoides* Felt
Globular, hairy, reddish, thin-walled gall, diameter $\frac{1}{6}$ inch, midge, summer. Pl. 6 (4)......Hickory onion gall, *Caryomyia holotricha* O.S.
Globular, hairy, thin-walled, melon-shaped gall, diameter $\frac{1}{10}$ inch, midge, summer. Pl. 6 (8)....................*Caryomyia thompsoni* Felt

Midrib or vein swellings

Rounded yellowish vein swelling, $\frac{1}{2}$ inch long, midge, summer......
.....................................*Caryomyia cynipsea* O.S.
Yellowish-green or purplish vein swelling, length $\frac{1}{4}$ to $\frac{1}{2}$ inch, aphid, early summer.........................*Phylloxera caryæ-venæ* Fitch
Globular nippled twig or leaf vein gall, diameter $\frac{1}{10}$ to $\frac{1}{3}$ inch, aphid, early summer...........................*Phylloxera perniciosa* Perg.
Reniform petiole or midrib gall, diameter $\frac{1}{10}$ to $\frac{1}{2}$ inch, aphid, early summer................................*Phylloxera caryæren* Riley

Leaf stem or twig gall

Globose, conical, spiny or smooth petiole or twig gall, diameter $\frac{1}{4}$ to 1 inch, very common, aphid, early summer........................
.................Hickory gall aphid, *Phylloxera caryæcaulis* Fitch
Globular with numerous long fleshy filaments, diameter $\frac{1}{4}$ to $\frac{1}{2}$ inch, aphid, early summer......................*Phylloxera spinuloides* Perg.
Clustered galls, apparently deformed flower and leaf buds, splitting when mature into 4 or more broad bracts, diameter $\frac{1}{8}$ to $\frac{1}{2}$ inch, aphid, early summer......................*Phylloxera devastatrix* Perg.

Similar to the preceding, usually with a short, stout nipple-like projection on one side, diameter about ¼ inch, aphid, early summer......
......................................*Phylloxera georgiana* Perg.
Oval, smooth, petiole gall, nearly an inch long and with a slight central depression, aphid, early summer.......*Phylloxera subelliptica* Shim.
Globular, nippled, twig, petiole or vein gall, diameter ¹⁄₁₀ to ⅓ inch..
......................................*Phylloxera perniciosa* Perg.

Swellings in husks

Irregular swellings in the husks of the nut, midge, summer........
..................Hickory husk midge, *Caryomyia nucicola* O.S.

Birch Family *(Betulaceæ)*

Birch and the related hazelnut and alder are hosts for a number of gall insects. The birch and the hazelnut are both attacked by related gall-making beetles and also afford attractive conditions for several gall midges, the former, in addition, being a host to an alternate generation of the spiny witch-hazel gall aphid. Much the same conditions obtain in alder except that the *Coleopterous* borer belongs in an entirely different group. The three principal genera have buds or catkins attacked by gall midges.

Hazelnut *(Corylus)*

Globose constricted twig swelling, diameter ¾ inch, beetle........
....*Agrilus politus* Say
Deformed catkins, swollen basally, midge, spring. Pl. 7 (3)........
..................Hazel catkin gall, *Cecidomyia squamicula* Steb.
Aborted terminal or lateral buds, diameter ½ inch, mite, spring.....
......................................*Eriophyes avellanæ* Jaru.
Slightly swollen aborted buds, length ⅙ inch, midge, spring. Fig. 47.
..............................Hazel bud gall, *Cecidomyia sp.*
Buds, swollen, aborted before or slightly after opening, mite, spring.
....*Eriophyes sp.*
Red-haired leaf fold, midge, summer...........................
..........................Red plush gall, *Lasiopteryx coryli* Felt
Thickened midribs and veins, mite..............*Eriophyes coryli* Steb.

Hop hornbeam *(Ostrya)*

Terminal folded leaves, midge........................*Cecidomyia sp.*
Globose, red-tinted pocket gall, diameter ¹⁄₂₅-¹⁄₁₂ inch, mite..*Eriophyes sp.*

Hornbeam, Ironwood *(Carpinus)*

Reddish vein folds, midge, summer............................
..................Hornbeam leaf fold, *Cecidomyia pudibunda* O.S.

Birch *(Betula)*

Irregular crowded bud deformations, incipient "witch's broom," mite. Pl. 15 (2)..............................*Eriophyes betulæ* Steb.

Irregular twig and branch annulations, beetle..................

......................Bronze birch borer, *Agrilus anxius* Gory

Swollen infertile seeds, midge, spring...........................

..................Birch seed midge, *Oligotrophus betulæ* Winn.

Leaves corrugated by approximate, lobulate, interveinal swellings, aphid, early summer..

.........Spiny witch hazel gall aphid, *Hamamelistes spinosus* Shim.

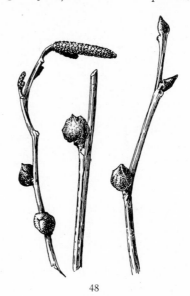

47   48

(Courtesy New York State Museum)

FIG. 47.—Hazel bud gall, *Cecidomyia sp.*
FIG. 48.—Alder bud gall, *Dasyneura serrulatæ.*

A nodula pocket gall, whitish-pink, reddish or brownish pile or *Erineum* on leaves, produced by undescribed mites.............*Eriophyes sp.*

Alder *(Alnus)*

Irregular oval stem swelling, length 2½ inches, beetle.............

........................Alder stem borer, *Saperda obliqua* Say

Bud gall, diameter ¼ to ½ inch, midge, spring. Fig. 48............

......................Alder bud gall, *Dasyneura serrulatæ* O.S.

Small pocket galls and whitish or reddish pile or Erinea are produced on the leaves by undescribed forms, mite. Pl. 15 (1)......*Eriophyes sp.*

Irregular stem swelling, beetle.............*Eupristocerus cogitans* Web.

Beech and Oak Family *(Fagaceæ)*

Beech and Chestnut Galls

The buds and leaves of the common chestnut are infested by several gall midges and the western chinquapin is host for a gall wasp, an exceptional record aside from the oaks and roses. The beech in this country appears to have no gall midge fauna, although two midges produce leaf galls on the European beech. A species of gall mite is somewhat common in this country.

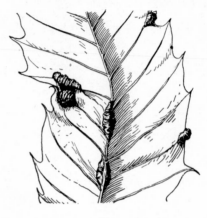

49

50

(Courtesy New York State Museum)

Fig. 49.—Chestnut bud gall, *Rhopalomyia castaneæ.*
Fig. 50.—Chestnut vein gall, *Cecidomyia sp.*

Beech *(Fagus)*

White, yellowish or brownish pile or Erinea on the leaf, mite, summer. Pl. 15 (7) . . . .*Eriophyes sp.*

Chestnut *(Castanea)*

Bud or petiole gall, midge, spring. Fig. 50 . . . .
. . . . .Chestnut bud gall, *Rhopalomyia castaneæ* Felt
Ribbed, green or brown vein swelling, length ½ inch, midge . . . .
. . . .*Cecidomyia castaneæ* Steb.
Blister leaf gall, diameter ⅛ inch, gall wasp . . . .*Cynipid*

PLATE 7—MIDGE GALLS. 1, Balsam gall midge, *Cecidomyia balsamicola* Lintn. *(After Thompson)*. 2, Gall of *Cecidomyia sp.*, on balm of Gilead. 3, Hazel catkin gall, *Cecidomyia squamulicola* Stebb. 4, Touch-me-not gall, *Cecidomyia impatientis* O.S. *(After Thompson)*. 5, Gall on cherry racemes produced by *Cecidomyia racemi* Stebb. *(After Stebbins)*. 6, Wild cherry bud gall, *Cecidomyia serotinæ* O.S. *(After Clarke)*. 7, Smilax blister, *Camptoneuromyia rubifolia* Felt. 8, gall of sexual generation of the gouty oak gall, *Plagiotrochus punctatus* Bass. 9, Linden wart gall, *Cecidomyia verrucicola* O.S., young galls. *(After Thompson)*.

PLATE 7

Courtesy N. Y. State Museum

Hemispherical capsule gall, diameter ⅛ inch, mite................
.....................................*Eriophyes dentatæ* Steb.
Galls encircling young twigs, caterpillar......*Ectoedemia castaneæ* Busck
Irregular burr swelling, midge...........*Cecidomyia chinquapin* Beutm.
Irregular petiole swelling, length ½ inch on *C. pumila,* midge........
....*Cecidomyia sp.*

Western Chinquapin *(Castanopsis)*

Brown thin-shelled blossom gall, diameter ½ to 1 inch, gall wasp, spring
...........Chinquapin blossom gall, *Andricus castanopsidis* Beutm.
Vein swelling or leaf roll, length ⅙ inch, midge...........*Cecidomyia sp.*

Oak Galls *(Quercus)*

The oaks are numerous in species, long-lived and widely distributed, all characteristics favoring the existence of insects with local habits and complex life histories. There is no natural group of trees or plants possessing a larger or more interesting gall insect fauna than the oaks. The gall wasps are limited to a great degree to the oaks. This restriction is offset to a considerable extent by the great number of species and the astonishing abundance of individuals on favored trees. The exhaustive studies of Dr. A. C. Kinsey and Dr. L. H. Weld have done much to establish the relationships and define the species in this complex group. The abbreviation "Mex." follows species recorded from Mexico and was added for the convenience of the student.

No part of the host tree escapes. The finer roots, the bark of the larger roots, the bark of the trunk and larger branches, if it be not too old and thick, the twigs, the leaves, the buds, the flowers, both staminate and pistillate, the latter resulting in galls in the acorns or fruit, all are susceptible to attack by gall wasps and to a much less extent by other gall-making insects.

There is far more to the study of oak galls than the discovery of new galls or the rearing of producers which have not been recognized heretofore. Studies of gall wasps in Europe and to a less extent in this country have shown that many species have an alternate generation, the two developing sometimes in similar, though mostly in entirely different galls, and presenting such marked structural differences in a number of species that up to within recent years they have been referred by entomologists to different genera. The working out of these relationships involves extensive rearings and may eventually give valuable clues as to methods of controlling certain species which in one generation are injurious to highly prized trees.

Names of Oaks

Popular names have been used in preference to scientific names for many of the better known oaks. The following list of common and scientific names is for the convenience of those especially interested in the terminology adopted, aside from those designated by their scientific names.

Basket oak, *prinus*

Black oak, *velutina*

Black jack oak, *marilandica*

Blue jack oak, *cinerea*

Burr oak, *macrocarpa*

California black oak, *kelloggii*

Canyon live oak, *chrysolepis*

Chestnut oak, *montana*

Chinquapin oak, *prinoides*

Coast live oak, *agrifolia*

Cork oak, *suber*

English oak, *robur*

Interior live oak, *wislizeni*

Live oak, *virginiana*

Laurel-leaved oak, *laurifolia*

Oregon oak, *garryana*

Overcup oak, *lyrata*

Pin oak, *palustris*

Post oak, *stellata*

Pubescent oak, *lanuginosa*

Red oak, *maxima*

Scarlet oak, *coccinea*

Scrub oak, *ilicifolia*

Shingle oak, *imbricaria*

Spanish oak, *rubra*

Swamp white oak, *bicolor*

Turkey oak, *catesbaei*

Valley oak, *lobata*

Utah oak, *utahensis*

Water oak, *nigra*

White oak, *alba*

Willow oak, *phellos*

Yellow chestnut oak, *muhlenbergii*

agrifolia, coast live oak

alba, white oak

bicolor, swamp white oak

catesbaei, turkey oak

chrysolepis, canyon live oak

cinerea, blue jack oak

coccinea, scarlet oak

garryana, Oregon oak

ilicifolia, scrub oak

imbricaria, shingle oak

kelloggii, California black oak

lanuginosa, pubescent oak

laurifolia, laurel-leaved oak

lobata, valley oak

lyrata, overcup oak

macrocarpa, burr oak

marilandica, black jack oak

maxima, red oak

montana, chestnut oak

muhlenbergii, yellow chestnut oak

nigra, water oak

palustris, pin oak

phellos, willow oak

prinoides, chinquapin oak

prinus, basket oak

robur, English oak

rubra, Spanish oak

stellata, post oak

suber, cork oak

utahensis, Utah oak

velutina, black oak

virginiana, live oak

wislizeni, interior live oak

Oak Galls, Skeleton Key

1. Root galls or subterranean galls, p. 87
   a. Galls on true roots, p. 87
      1. On small fibrous roots, p. 87
      2. On roots ¼ to ½ inch in diameter, p. 88
   b. Galls at the crown, frequently subterranean, p. 89
      1. Subterranean stem swellings, woody, many-celled, the bark not greatly thickened, p. 89
      2. Cells in thickened bark at crown of tree, p. 89
         a. Numerous galls forming swollen areas on the bark, p. 89

    b. Galls usually forming groups of less than a dozen, sometimes single, p. 89

    c. Detachable galls at crown, either on the main stem, at the base of sprouts from stumps or on the "runner oak" sprouts, p. 90

    d. Single or scattered in small numbers, many-celled, p. 90

    e. Clustered when fresh, fleshy, pure white or rosy red at apex, fig-shaped growing quickly in spring and after insects emerge, either, rotting or shriveling into a hard but not woody mass, p. 90

    f. Tissues not so spongy as in above, at least part of gall alternately becoming brittle or woody and persisting, p. 92

    g. Individual galls averaging more than $\frac{1}{4}$ of an inch in diameter, p. 92

    h. Bullet galls of harder texture and no separable inner cell, p. 93

2. Galls of branches and twigs, the deformations not separable from the plant. (Compare with b-d, e, f, g-h), p. 94-96, 98, 104-105

    a. No visible gall or only a slight swelling

    b. Twig dwarfed but not especially modified, p. 95

    c. Twig shortened, distorted and forms a short, many-celled, ovoid mass, p. 96

    d. Twig swollen, dwarfed or distorted into more or less club-shaped, many-celled, rarely one-celled gall, p. 96

    e. A swelling surrounding the twig, especially at the base of the lateral shoots, often large, abrupt and woody; potato galls, p. 98

        1. Woody or a little woody fiber surrounding the larval cell, p. 98

        2. Woody fiber abundant, without horn-like projections, p. 99

        3. Larval cells each surrounded by a tube of cellular tissue different from the general substance of the gall; tubes may project from the surface in the mature gall, p. 102

            a. Tubes never project, p. 102

            b. Tubes project like horns or spines, p. 104

    f. Many-celled, woody swellings at the base of twig, eccentric on twig. (Grade to last group), p. 104

    g. Pustular elevations of the bark, often enlarging the twig, p. 104

    h. One-celled terminal enlargements of club galls on twigs, p. 105

3. Galls attached to branches and twigs and more or less separated from the normal plant tissues. (Compare with 2, p. 94 and also oak apples 10, p. 173. See also b and c on p. 120 and d on p. 124), p. 106

    a. Bullet galls, that is, woody galls attached to the twigs and in small clusters or solitary, p. 106

1. Many-celled, p. 106
2. Small, one-celled, without a distinct central cell, p. 110
   a. Situated in fissures in the twigs, p. 110
   b. Not inserted in fissures in the twigs, p. 110
3. Bullet and similar galls of a pithy or other substance, with a central cell containing a larva. The cell may be closely attached to the substance of the gall or fill a larger or smaller cavity within the gall, p. 111
   a. Globular or subglobular in shape, p. 111
   b. Form more ovoid, with a point at the apex, p. 117
   c. Form more or less conical, p. 119
   d. Not globular or conical, p. 120
4. Woody, a central kernel and the outer substance of the gall chambered, clustered, p. 120
   a. Interior of galls more or less corky, p. 120
   b. Galls distinctly woody, with the structure of typical bullet galls and clustered in compact, characteristic masses about a supporting twig, p. 120
   c. Galls in compact clusters around the twig, but bladder-like and not woody, p. 124
   d. Galls on twigs consisting of fibrous material which conceals one or more cells, p. 124
      1. Cells large, solitary or clustered, p. 124
      2. Cells small, numerous, massed in a cluster beneath the fibers, p. 126

4. Bud galls consisting of one or more larval cells or capsules in a leaf bud, p. 128.
   a. Hard cell or cells surrounded by a number of modified leaves. See also b, c, p. 131, 132.
      1. Cells surrounded by a few thread-like bodies, p. 128.
      2. Cells surrounded by a rosette of linear leaves, p. 128.
      3. Several cells surrounded by a rosette of aborted leaves, p. 129.
      4. Galls in blasted buds with no circle of aborted leaves, p. 130
         a. A hard cell in the bud, p. 130
         b. A soft capsule in the bud, p. 131
         c. Capsules in the bud, blasting it completely or so that only a few deformed and imperfect leaves appear, p. 132

5. Galls of the leaves (in some cases the leaf itself is aborted and the gall issues from the twig or bud) p. 137
   a. Galls on the leaf stems or petioles, p. 137
   b. A thickening of the mid-vein, sometimes of the petiole or lateral veins, p. 140. See also (13) p. 198 and (15), a, b, p. 209, 210
      1. Swellings abrupt, p. 140
         a. Midrib thickenings, not detachable, p. 140

b. Detachable galls on midribs only, p. 142
2. Swellings less abrupt and localized enlargements of mid-veins (more rarely of lateral veins and the petioles), p. 144
3. A whole leaf is swollen to form a fleshy, elongated gall, p. 148
c. Galls involving or attached to the blade or lamina of the leaves, p. 148
    1. Little or no thickening of the leaf tissues
       See also below (2-3), (4-5), (6), (7-8), (9-10), (11), (12), (13), (14), (15-16), (17), (18) respectively, on p. 148
       a. Small blister-like or pustular swellings of the leaf blades, p. 148
       b. Superabundant leaf hairs (erineum) or more or less distinct dimples, p. 152
    2. Blister above blade or lamina, woolly gall beneath, p. 153
    3. Rounded gall with several cells imbedded in the blade or lamina of the leaf, p. 154
    4. Galls making a sort of a thickened and elevated area in the blade or lamina, p. 154
       a. The platform consists of crowded, one-celled galls, p. 154
       b. The platform is a single, many-celled gall, p. 155
    5. Roly-poly galls, hollow, spherical or semi-spherical or conical, usually succulent; the gall enclosing a chamber in which the larval cell lies free. Some of these galls are loosely attached to the leaf, though most often they are imbedded in the blade, p. 158
       a. Gall globular, p. 159
       b. Gall hemispherical or conical, attached to the underside of the leaf, p. 160
    6. Gall solid, spherical, succulent, usually firmly attached to the leaf blade, p. 161
    7. Gall small, solid, fleshy and loosely attached to the leaf, p. 161
    8. Galls moderate-sized, hard, loosely attached to the vein below and with a faceted or spiny surface, p. 164
       a. Surface faceted, p. 149
       b. Facets on the surface pointed or spine-tipped, p. 166
       c. Spines of the facets long, p. 167
    9. Gall solid, attached to the leaf and with a central hard kernel or larval cell. These approach the oak apple in structure, p. 170

PLATE 8—MIDGE GALLS. 1, Oak spangles, *Cecidomyia poculum* O.S. (*After Thompson*). 2, Probably the same as figure 1. (*After Weld*). 3, Vein pocket gall, *Parallelodiplosis florida* Felt, on oak. (*After Clarke*). 4, Oak gall of *Cecidomyia,* adult unknown. Resembling much that of *Neuroterus niger* Gill. (*After Clarke*). 5, Marginal fold gall of *Itonida foliora* Rssl. & Hkr., on oak. (*After Clarke*). 6, Oak leaves with lobes folded by *Cecidomyia sp.,* adult unknown. (*After Clarke*). 7, Oak blister midge, *Cincticornia pustulata* Felt. (*After Clarke*). 8, Oak leaf showing galls of *Cincticornia sp.,* possibly *C. simpla* Felt. 9, Purple oak vein gall, *Cincticornia podagræ* Felt.

PLATE 8

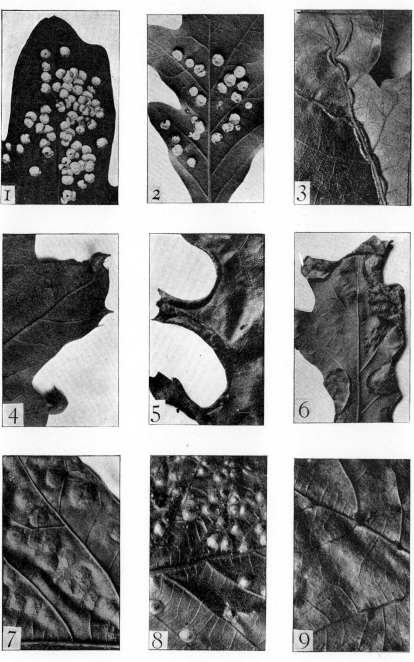

Courtesy N. Y. State Museum

10. Oak apples, i.e., galls with a central hard kernel or larval cell, a firm (often hard) outer shell and a spongy or fibrous intervening substance, p. 173
   a. Intervening substance is spongy, p. 173
      1. Gall large, diameter ¾ inch or more, p. 173
      2. Gall small, about ¼ inch in diameter, p. 176
   b. The substance lying between the rind or outer shell and the kernel is fibrous and often very scanty, p. 176
      1. Gall large, kernel central, leaf usually aborted, p. 176
      2. Gall small, leaf aborted, p. 186
      3. Gall small, leaf present and gall usually on the underside and solitary, p. 190
11. Galls small, the leaf present, they tend to cluster, p. 194
   a. Cells central in the gall, p. 194
   b. Cell basal, against the leaf, p. 194
12. Galls small, thin-walled, globose or fusiform, usually marginal on the leaf and piercing the leaf blade, p. 195
13. Galls small, with peculiar or varied shapes and attached to the leaf blade, p. 198
14. Galls composed apparently of crystalline matter and attached to the leaves, p. 206
   a. Gall solitary, globular, p. 206
   b. Galls clustered, tubular, p. 207
15. Small, fleshy galls clustered on the leaves, p. 209
   a. Galls split mid-vein in their growth, p. 209
   b. Galls do not split mid-vein in growing, p. 210
16. Woolly galls attached to the leaves and covered with woolly fibers, p. 212
   a. Galls composed of small cells, each with a separate crown of wool, p. 212
   b. Galls composed of seed-like cells in groups and covered with wool, p. 213
   c. Galls with large cells, not seed-like, but clustered under wool as before, p. 214
   d. Galls with small cells and bonded together by a hard substance, p. 218
   e. Galls many-celled and under wool, p. 218
17. Galls with a stem or petiole or an extension of a vein above or beyond the leaf surface and attached to the leaves, p. 219
18. Marginal folds of leaves or leaf lobes, p. 220
19. Presumably leaf gall, the gall unknown, p. 220

6. Galls of the aments, catkins or peduncles, p. 221

   a. Irregular woolly or hairy flower galls on the stems or peduncles of the pistillate flowers, p. 221

b. Axis or stem of staminate flowers enlarged and containing or bearing the cells or galls, large galls, diameter at least half an inch, p. 221

c. Axis or stem of staminate flowers normal in size although often shortened, bearing numbers of individual galls which are modified anthers or filaments, the individual galls rarely over ¼ inch in diameter, often clustered into masses, p. 222

d. Galls clasping the stem or peduncle, 2-20 in number, p. 224

7. Acorn galls, p. 224

a. Galls of the acorn cup (cupule) and not involving the acorn itself, p. 224

   1. Large globose, thick-walled, hard, mottled, brownish or reddish galls on the side of the acorn cup, easily detached and dropping to the ground in the fall, always on red oaks, p. 224

   2. Smaller galls, more or less imbedded in the tissue of the cup, often falling to the ground in the fall when mature, p. 225

   3. Galls known as "pip galls" produced between the acorn and the cup, p. 227

   4. Galls beside immature acorns of red oak, p. 227

b. Galls inside the acorn, p. 226

   1. Cells in the cluster, confluent or protruding, a stony mass more or less filling the interior and which may be lifted out intact, often can be detected only by cutting acorns open, p. 226

   2. Cells single, not confluent or separable from the wall of the acorn, p. 226

Root or Subterranean Galls

Presumably many of these galls have escaped observation and it is quite within possibilities that systematic search for them would result in a number of interesting finds. There are comparatively few galls, 36, known on true roots, probably in part because they are less accessible to gall insects. Some occur on small fibrous roots usually not much below the surface of the soil and others on roots with an appreciable diameter. Most of the galls in this division occur at the crown, at or just below the surface of the ground, the difference between these and stem galls being due mostly to their location. The relations of these galls to both roots and subterranean portions of the stem are quite similar to those of the more numerous and varied galls of branches and twigs, which are treated in greater detail on a following page.

1. Root or Subterranean Galls

  a. Galls on true roots:

    (1) On small fibrous roots:

      Single or small brown clusters, diameter ¼ inch, just below surface, on swamp white oak, gall wasp, Pl. 33 (2) . . . .
      . . . . *Callirhytis ellipsoida* Weld

Abrupt, ellipsoidal, one-celled, brown, thin-walled swellings, on white oak, gall wasp..............*Callirhytis elliptica* Weld

(2) On roots ¼ to ½ inch in diameter:

Single, globose galls or irregular, lobed masses 4 inches in diameter, on post oak, gall wasp, Pl. 20 (1)...................
...........................*Odontocynips nebulosa* Kieff.

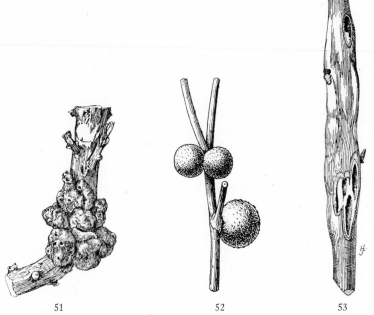

51   52   53

(Courtesy New York State Museum)

Fig. 51.—Oak fig root gall, *Belenocnema treatæ.* (*After Beutm.*)
Fig. 52.—Oak bullet gall, *Disholcaspis globulus.*
Fig. 53.—Gall of oak twig midge, *Lasioptera querciperda.*

Probably the same gall, on live oak and overcup oak.

Fleshy, fig-shaped, white, clustered, drying to dark brown, on live oak and *Q. geminata*, gall wasp. Fig. 51.................
...............Oak fig root gall, *Belenocnema treatæ* Mayr

Detachable galls at crown of live oak, may be the work of the same species.

Many-celled, abrupt, woody swellings, 3 to 5 inches long, larval cells oval, on California black oak and interior live oak, spring, gall wasp. Pl. 19 (7)............*Callirhytis humicola* Kins.

Larval cells in scurfy bark of roots and base of trunk. Presumably on white, swamp white, chinquapin, basket and post oaks, gall wasp, agamic generation..........*Callirhytis futilis* O.S.

b. Galls at the crown, frequently subterranean:

(1) Subterranean stem swellings, woody, many-celled, the bark not not greatly thickened:

Abrupt, irregularly rounded, brown, diameter ½ to 1½ inches, on scarlet, Spanish, black jack, blue jack, and black oaks and *Q. myrtifolia,* and *Q. texana,* gall wasp.................. ....*Eumayria floridana* Ashm.

A similar gall occurs on *Q. emoryi.*

Slightly one-sided enlargements, diameter ½ inch or less, cells thin-walled, nested under bark, on *Q. fendleri,* gall wasp, adults in September. Pl. 20 (7).......*Compsodryoxenus tenuis* Weld

Similar galls on larger stems, on *Q. fendleri, Q. gambelii,* and *Q. undulata,* adults in spring, gall wasp...*Bassettia tenuana* Weld

Slightly spindle-shaped enlargements at base of current year's shoots in fall, cells not twice as long as broad, not nested but. scattered, on post oak and *Q. chapmani,* gall wasp........... ....*Compsodryoxenus humilis* Weld

Gradual, many-celled swellings nearly one inch long on live oak, gall wasp................*Compsodryoxenus pattersoni* Kins.

Similar in external appearance but the cells are at least twice as long as broad, placed lengthwise, on *Q. chapmani,* gall wasp. Pl. 30 (2).....................*Bassettia floridana* Ashm.

(2) Cells in thickened bark at crown of tree:

(a) Numerous galls forming swollen areas in the bark:

On main roots of white and basket oaks, gall wasp, agamic generation.....................*Callirhytis futilis* O.S.

On main roots or where bending limbs touch the ground, on canyon live oak, gall wasp...*Callirhytis hartmani* Weld

At base of sprouts or saplings, swollen areas possibly 15 inches long, on burr oak, gall wasp.................. ....*Compsodryoxenus illinoisensis* Weld

Small cells in swollen and distorted bases of young sprouts, on *Q. breviloba,* gall wasp. Pl. 30 (1)............... ....*Neuroterus contortus* Weld

(b) Galls usually forming groups of less than a dozen, sometimes single:

Ellipsoidal, one-celled, brown cells protruding from the bark in rows or groups or single, detachable, sometimes confluent, on turkey oak and *Q. myrtifolia, Q. shumardii, Q. texana,* gall wasp. Pl. 33 (4)..........*Andricus ovatus* Weld

Similar gall on *Q. shumardii*......*Andricus melanicus* Kins.

Similar in color and structure to oak fig gall, p. 142, but not so large, clusters roughly globular, diameter ¾ inch, on young shoots of *Q. subturbinella* and under debris, gall wasp......................*Xanthoteras mediocre* Weld

Smooth, abrupt, local swellings with an area of ½ to 2½ square inches, in the thick bark, the number of cells evident externally, on scarlet and Spanish oaks................ ....*Callirhytis rubida* Weld

Similar swellings, the number of cells not so apparent, on scarlet oak ....*Callirhytis Marginata* Weld

Irregular, globose, fleshy, many-celled stem swelling, sometimes under debris, diameter 2 inches, on *Q. diversicolor,* gall wasp. Pl. 20 (4).......*Callirhytis rhizoxenus* Ashm.

(c) Detachable galls at crown, either on the main stem, at the base of sprouts from stumps or on the "runner oak" sprouts:

Single or scattered in small numbers, one-celled or monothalamous:

Button-shaped, irregularly ridged, diameter ½ inch, leaving a radiating scar when detached, woody when mature, on white, swamp white, burr, basket and post oaks and *Q. chapmani,* gall wasp. Pl. 33 (3).......*Holocynips badia* Bass.
(*corallusa* Weld)

Globular or pointed, thin-walled, gray with dense, short pubescence, single, sessile, diameter ¼ to ½ inch, on *Q. chapmani, Q. margaretta,* gall wasp.................. ....*Biorhiza ocala* Weld

(d) Single or scattered in small numbers, many celled:

Large, rounded, brown masses, up to 3½ inches in diameter, like rotten wood inside when mature and with many thin-walled brittle cells, on white, swamp white, burr, chestnut and probably post oaks, gall wasp................ ....*Holocynips maxima* Weld

(e) Clustered, when fresh, fleshy, pure white or rosy red at apex, fig-shaped, growing quickly in spring and after insects emerge either rotting or shriveling into a hard but not woody mass:

Globose or fig-shaped, in clusters of 12 or less, on white and

PLATE 9—MIDGE GALLS. 1, Subglobose vein gall on oak, produced by *Cecidomyia sp.,* adult unknown. 2, Gall on oak, of *Cincticornia majalis* O.S. (*After Thompson*). 3, Oak pill gall, *Cincticornia pilula?* Walsh. (*After Thompson*). 4, Clematis bud gall, *Contarinia clematidis* Felt. (*After Thompson*). 5, Grape blister gall, *Cecidomyia sp.* (*After Weld*). 6, Chokecherry midge, *Contarinia virginianiæ* Felt. (*After Thompson*). 7, Arrow-wood blister midge, *Cystiphora viburnifolia* Felt. (*After Clarke*). 8, Honey locust pod gall, *Dasyneura gleditschiæ* O.S. (*After Clarke*). 9, Loosestrife bud gall, *Dasyneura lysimachiæ* Beutm. (*After Clarke*).

PLATE 9

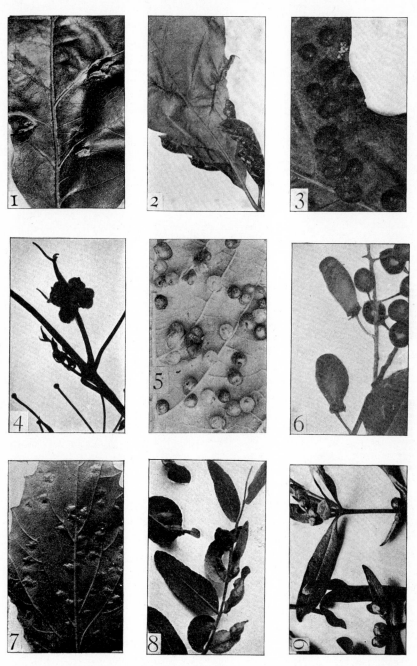

Courtesy N. Y. State Museum

post oaks and *Q. chapmani,* gall wasp. Pl. 36 (5).......
.............Fig root gall, *Trigonaspis radicola*[1] Ashm.
Similar to preceding, but with longer and more slender
pedicel, on valley oak and *Q. douglasii,* spring, gall wasp. .
........................*Trigonaspis obconica* Weld
White, fleshy, fig-shaped, many-celled, on *Q. gambeli, Q.
diversicola,* gall wasp..........*Trigonaspis fumosa* Weld
Same on roots of unknown oak in Utah and Colorado, gall
wasp.................*Trigonaspis pumiliventris* Bass.

(f) Tissues not so spongy as in above, at least part of gall ulti-
mately becoming brittle or woody and persisting:
Individual galls less than ¼ inch in diameter, fig-shaped
with a slender stalk, surface ribbed, walls brittle, dimensions ¼ by ⅙ inch, in clusters of 30 to 100, on Spanish
and turkey oak and *Q. myrtifolia, Q. texana,* gall wasp. Pl.
33 (1).....................*Callirhytis enigma* Weld
Elongate, angular, wedge-shaped cells with rounded ends,
cluster resembles ears of corn or honeycomb, maximum
diameter 3 inches, white when fresh, becoming tan and brittle, on red, black jack, blue jack, water, laurel-leaved and
turkey oaks and *Q. myrtifolia* and *Q. texana,* gall wasp.
Pl. 36 (9)......................................
.........Honeycomb twig gall, *Dryocosmus favus* Beutm.
Onion-shaped, pointed, longitudinally striate, white or rosy
when fresh, later tan and brittle, at base of sprouts, on red,
Spanish, turkey, blue jack, black jack, black oaks, laurel-
leaved oak and *Q. myrtifolia* and *Q. texana,* gall wasp. Pl.
29 (9).................*Biorhiza cœpuliformis* Beutm.

(g) Individual galls averaging more than ¼ of an inch in diameter:
Hemispherical clusters up to 4 inches in diameter, of 1 to
35 galls, each 1 to 1½ inches in diameter, white, fleshy,
later tan color and rough, one-celled, on coast and upland
live oaks and California black oak, gall wasp...........
..........................*Callirhytis apicalis* Ashm.
Hemispherical clusters of a few galls, with a maximum diameter of 1½ inches, tissue dense, tawny yellowish inside,
a few cells at base, on California live oak, gall wasp......
.........................*Callirhytis fulva* Weld
Bullet galls on base of shoots resembling those of *Dishol-*

---

[1] Brodie was the first to suggest a connection between the fig gall and a root gall in
1896; Weld presented some circumstantial evidence in 1921; later Kinsey suggested this
was the alternate generation of *Xanthoteras forticorne* Walsh.

caspis globulus, inner cell distinct, often free, diameter $\frac{1}{3}$ to $\frac{1}{2}$ inch, on white and possibly chestnut oaks, gall wasp. Pl. 18 (1)...Globular root gall, *Disholcaspis globosa* Weld

Globose, reddish bullet gall, major diameter $\frac{3}{4}$ inch, on post oak and *Q. margaretta,* gall wasp. Pl. 18 (4)..........

........................*Disholcaspis terrestris* Weld

Similar to preceding, on *Q. breviloba,* gall wasp..........

........................*Disholcaspis brevinota* Weld

Globular, yellowish, tinged with rose, fleshy, diameter $\frac{1}{2}$ to $\frac{4}{5}$ inch, on *Q. gambeli,* gall wasp. Pl. 18 (9).........

.........................*Disholcaspis lacuna* Weld

(h) Bullet galls of harder texture and no separable inner cell:

Blunt, sometimes pointed, brownish-red, diameter $\frac{1}{4}$ to $\frac{1}{3}$ inch, on *Q. gambeli,* gall wasp. Pl. 20 (2)..............

........................*Disholcaspis acetabula* Weld

Similar and probably identical with preceding, on *Q. grisea, Q. diversicolor, Q. toumeyi,* gall wasp.................

........................? *Disholcaspis acetabula* Weld

Galls of Branches and Twigs

The numerous deformations (165 are listed) produced by gall wasps upon the trunk and the larger branches are found usually upon relatively young wood. Distinct gradations may be traced from gall wasp cells, occurring under the bark without appreciable swelling of the twig and the decided enlargements better known because they are more conspicuous.

The method of development is more clearly seen in the case of galls upon the smaller branches or twigs. The exceedingly variable growths which range from slight enlargements of tender bark to irregular swellings which may more than double the normal size of the twig, clearly develop from the tender inner bark and softer outer wood, the active growing part of the branch. Most of these galls are compound or many-celled, that is, they contain a number of cells, frequently irregularly placed, and as a rule the enlargement is proportional to the degree of infestation.

The gouty oak gall, a knotty oval enlargement which frequently doubles the normal diameter of an infested twig, sometimes forms almost continuous masses for several inches or a foot or more along the twig and greatly affects the circulation of the sap. Large trees may be seriously injured and parts killed by the work of this or allied species. The horned oak gall is a similar deformation and noteworthy because of the characteristic, horn-like projections, really tubular extensions from the cells of the gall makers. The alternate generations of these two species develop in inconspicuous blister galls in the leaves. Four years may be required to complete the life cycle of these species.

Some twig galls split the bark as they push out from the lower tissues and certain of these may be nearly as abundant as the gouty oak gall or the horned oak gall mentioned above. Galls in this group have a rather definite form and structure. A portion of the normal inner bark, as a result of stimulation by the gall producer, develops into a bud-like or seed-like structure, as pointed out elsewhere in this work, the gall maggot occupying the place of the seed and being nourished by the more nutritious inner layers of the gall. The seed-like character of these galls is suggested further by their dropping from the branches when mature. A number of these twig galls secrete a sweetish liquid attractive to bees and others insects and under favorable conditions an infested tree may be literally "roaring" because of the many insects attracted by the sweets.

The bullet galls are in a class by themselves, since they are one-celled or monothalamous. That is, each contains but one larva. The popular name is in a large degree descriptive. These galls are solid, save for the central cell inhabited by a stout, whitish grub. They occur singly or in clusters, are firmly attached to the twigs and are conspicuous objects in winter. Like those mentioned in the preceding paragraph, they have bud-like or seed-like characteristics.

The gall of the wool-sower is one of the most beautiful of the twig galls. It is globular and composed of numerous closely placed, stemmed, hairy cells, the outer portion simulating a group of close-set, creamy-white flowers, each with a central delicate pink spot. The whole has a freshness which contrasts strongly with its surroundings. It excites the admiration of all on account of its delicacy and beauty. It may be ranked as one of the finest of natural objects. This gall occurs upon white oak twigs in June, the entire mass having a diameter of 1 to 2 inches. It is really a bud gall and is produced by a female wasp depositing eggs in a series of buds around the stem. The wool-sower gall wasps are easily reared in late June or early July, if the nearly matured galls are put in a suitable container.

2. Galls of branches and twigs, the deformations not separable from the plant. (Compare with p. 106):

   a. No visible gall or only a slight swelling. See also b, d, e, f-g, h, on pages: 95-96, 98, 104, 105

   Minute cell under leaf scar, on swamp white oak, gall wasp, spring. Pl. 34 (9)......................... *Neuroterus escharensis* Weld

   Cell under leaf scar, length $\frac{1}{16}$ inch, on valley oak, gall wasp, spring .... *Neuroterus evolutus* Weld

   Swollen twigs containing large numbers of cells, hidden under bark, diameter $\frac{1}{8}$ inch, on black jack, blue jack, Spanish and turkey oaks, gall wasp. Pl. 33(8).................... *Callirhytis crypta* Ashm.

   Slight, very inconspicuous enlargements at base of new shoots, on scarlet and black oaks, gall wasp...... *Bassettia ceropteroides* Bass.

   Slight swellings in vigorous shoots an inch in diameter or less, cells $\frac{1}{8}$ by $\frac{1}{25}$ inch, just under bark, on California black oak, spring, gall wasp. Pl. 17 (6).......................*Eumayria herberti* Weld

Slightly swollen twigs of the preceding summer's growth, on *Q. gambeli*, gall wasp.......................*Neuroterus virgens* Gill.

Slight, hardly visible, wavy swellings at base of tender new shoots, on turkey oak, gall wasp................*Andricus catesbœi* Ashm.

Apparently normal twigs with elongate oval cells, each with a shell-like lining, on valley oak and *Q. dumosa, Q. durata, Q. douglasii*, gall wasp. Pl. 17 (4) ....*Bassettia ligni* Kins.

Scattered, elongated, thin-walled, in wood of previous season, on old trees, scarcely visible externally, on English oak, gall wasp........ ....*Loxaulus ashmeadi* Kieff.

Slightly swollen twigs, on white oak, gall midge, summer. Fig. 53... ....Oak twig midge, *Lasioptera querciperda* Felt

None or a slight stem swelling, larval cells in the wood, on valley oak, gall wasp.......................*Compsodryoxenus atrior* Kins.

54

(Courtesy New York State Museum)

FIG. 54.—Gall of *Neuroterus tectus*. (*After Beutm.*)

Reared from apparently normal oak twigs, gall midge, summer..... ....*Lasioptera quercirami* Felt

Elongate oval twig gall, possibly an unmodified twig, gall midge.... ....*Lasioptera howardi* Felt

Slender twigs, swollen to possibly twice the normal size, cells $\frac{1}{10}$ inch long, just under the bark, spring, on European cork oak, California. Pl. 17 (5).....................*Plagiotrochus suberi* Weld

b. Twig dwarfed but not especially modified:

Irregular, many-celled swellings of new growth, bent, ½ inch long, bearing distorted leaves, May, on swamp white oak. Pl. 21 (3) ....*Neuroterus distortus* Bass.

Irregular enlargements of small twigs, the stems of flower clusters and leaves, on chinquapin oak, gall wasp. Fig. 54............... ....*Neuroterus tectus* Bass.

Inconspicuous enlargements of the upper portion of very young tender shoots, on post oak, gall wasp......*Dryophanta longicornis* Bass.

Irregularly rounded or ovate, woody, many-celled swellings with aborted leaves, on post oak, gall wasp. Fig. 85.................
....*Neuroterus obtusilobæ* Karsch.

c. Twig shortened, distorted and forms a short, many-celled ovoid mass:
Woody, apical swellings, ¾ to 1½ inches long, ½ inch in diameter, on scarlet, shingle, Spanish and black oaks, spring, gall wasp. Pl. 27 (8)..............................*Plagiotrochus scitula* Bass.

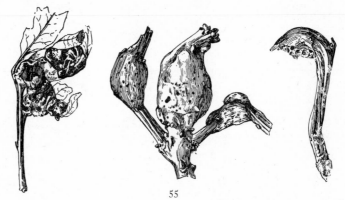

55

(Courtesy New York State Museum)

Fig. 55.—Oak potato gall, *Neuroterus batatus*. (*After Beutm.*)

Woody, many-celled twig gall, length ¾ inch, diameter ¼ inch, resembles gall of *Plagiotrochus scitula,* on scrub and shingle oaks, gall wasp...............................*Callirhytis tuberosa* Bass.

d. Twig swollen, dwarfed or distorted into a more or less club-shaped many-celled, rarely one-celled gall:
Irregular, potato-shaped, many-celled, woody twig galls, green in summer, with pale blue bloom on surface, brown in winter, diameter to 1¼ inches, on white oak, spring, gall wasp, agamic generation. Pl. 33 (1) Fig. 55..........Oak potato gall, *Neuroterus batatus* Fitch

Irregular, length ¼ to 4 inches, diameter ¼ to 1 inch, similar to *N. batatus* but on the twigs (winter form) or the midrib and petiole of

PLATE 10—MIDGE GALLS. 1, Rose leaf midge, *Dasyneura ? rosarum* Hardy. (*After Thompson*). 2, Willow pod midge, *Dasyneura salicifolia* Felt. (*After Clarke*). 3, Elm buds blasted by *Dasyneura ulmea* Felt. (*After Houser*). 4, Galls of Chrysanthemum midge, *Diarthronomyia hypogœa* H. Lw. 5, Sunflower bullet gall, *Trishormomyia bulla* Felt. (*After Weld*). 6, Willow lipped gall, *Trishormomyia verruca* Walsh. (*After Clarke*). 7, Tulip spot gall, *Thecodiplosis liriodendri* O.S. (*After Thompson*). 8, Gall on Impatiens. of *Lasioptera impatientifolia* Felt. (*After Thompson*). 9, Thorn vein gall, *Lobopteromyia venœ* Felt. (*After Thompson*).

PLATE 10

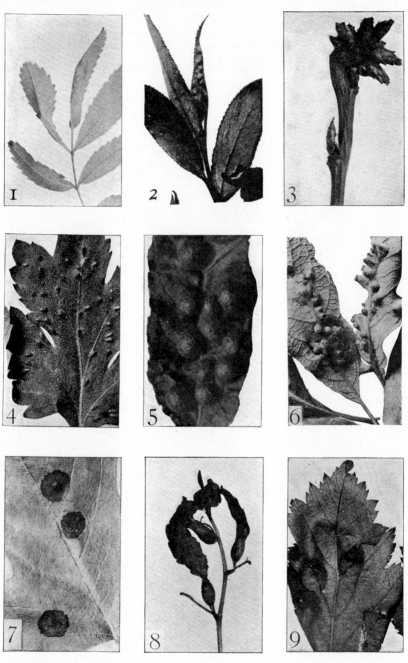

Courtesy N. Y. State Museum

the leaves (spring form), the blade of the leaf dwarfed, curled and shriveled, on swamp white and basket oaks, gall wasp, agamic generation. Pl. 29 (5) Fig. 56.....................................

....................Noxious oak gall, *Neuroterus noxiosus* Bass.

Irregular, many-celled, woody twig gall, length 5 inches, diameter 1¼ inches, twigs not more than ¼ inch in diameter, on coast live oak, gall wasp...............................*Andricus sp.*

Subglobose, lateral, grayish-red or fulvous twig gall, the surface smooth, shining and irregularly warty, diameter ⅓ inch, gall wasp..

....*Cynips sp.*

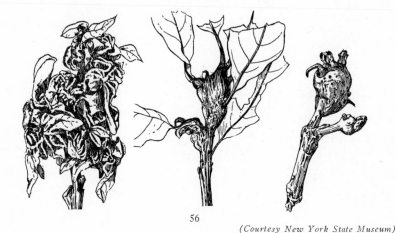

56

(Courtesy New York State Museum)

FIG. 56.—Noxious oak gall, *Neuroterus noxiosus.* (*After Beutm.*)

Egg-shaped, sessile, one-sided stem swelling, bearing many small leaves, ½ by ⅖ inch, one-celled, on *Q. toumeyi*, fall, gall wasp. Pl. 20 (6)..............................*Andricus toumeyi* Weld

    e. A swelling surrounding the twig, especially at the base of the lateral shoots, often large, abrupt and woody; potato galls:

      (1) Woody or a little woody fiber surrounding the larval cells:

          Hemispherical, woody, many-celled knots at the base of young shoots, diameter ½ to ¾ inch, larval cells thin-walled, on white oak, gall wasp....................*Loxaulus mammula* Bass.

          Globose hard knots, the surface rough, blackened, deeply and irregularly fissured, diameter about 1 inch, apical on twig, on *Q. grisea*, gall wasp. Pl. 20 (5)..........*Andricus ruginosus* Bass.

          Hard, woody knots sometimes terminal, on shoots of oak sprouts, more often enlargements at base of small lateral branches; terminal galls, diameter 1¼ inches, strawberry-shaped, on pin and red oaks, gall wasp. Pl. 18 (7)......*Callirhytis seminosa* Bass.

(2) Woody fiber abundant, without horn-like projections:

Irregular, potato-shaped, many-celled, woody, green with a whitish bloom, diameter 1 inch, on white oak, gall wasp, sexual generation, spring. Fig. 55...............................
................Oak potato gall, *Neuroterus batatus* Fitch
Similar gall on swamp white oak, brown, gall wasp, agamic generation, winter. Pl. 29 (5), Fig. 56.......................
..............................*Neuroterus noxiosus* Bass.

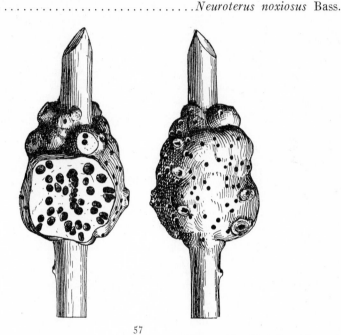

57

(Courtesy New York State Museum)

FIG. 57.—Gouty oak gall, *Plagiotrochus punctatus*.

Irregular, globose, frequently confluent, length 5 inches, diameter 1½ inches, on scarlet, scrub, water, Spanish, black and red oaks, flies in June, gall wasp, sexual generation. Pl. 2 (6) Fig. 57........Gouty oak gall, *Plagiotrochus punctatus* Bass.
Abrupt, irregular, potato-like twig or branch swelling, length ½ to 1 inch, diameter ⅓ inch, on live oak, gall wasp. Pl. 19 (5)......Live oak potato gall, *Plagiotrochus batatoides* Ashm.
Irregular branch or stem swelling close to the ground, ½ to 3 inches long and ½ inch in diameter, resembles preceding or that of *Callirhytis medullæ* or *Neuroterus rileyi*, on *Q. chapmani*, gall wasp.......................................*Andricus sp.*
Hard, smooth, knot-like twig swellings, diameter ¾ inch or more,

on *Q. emoryi,* fall, gall wasp.........*Plagiotrochus coxii* Bass.

Gall similar to preceding, more regularly cylindrical, elongate, diameter ⅗ inch, length 2½ inches, on *Q. hypoleuca.*........ ....*Plagiotrochus translatus* Kins.

Slightly globoid, one or many-celled twig swellings, 2 or 3 times the normal stem diameter, maximum dimensions ⅓ by 3 inches, on *Q. breviloba,* gall wasp.......*Plagiotrochus elongatus* Kins.

A more irregular, many-celled gall, diameter ⅓ inch, on post oak, gall wasp.....................*Plagiotrochus stellatœ* Kins.

A short, globoid stem swelling, diameter ⅓ inch, one to four cells, on *Q. breviloba,* gall wasp..*Plagiotrochus rufopleurœ* Kins.

Elongate, many-celled, oval or spindle-shaped, dimensions 1 by 2 inches, on California live oak, gall wasp. Pl. 17 ((3)........ ....*Andricus spectabilis* Kins.

Gall character similar to preceding......*Andricus incisus* Kins.
Andricus ukiahensis Kins.

A gradual stem enlargement, often symmetric, containing compact clusters of larval cells, maximum dimensions 1¼ by ¾ inches, on canyon live oak, gall wasp. Pl. 17 (2)............ ....*Plagiotrochus asymmetricus* Kins.

Gall differs from *A. asymmetricus* in having almost the entire swelling compactly filled with larval cells, swelling more symmetrical, length ⅛ inch, on California live oak, gall wasp..... ....*Plagiotrochus annectans* Kins.

Gall practically identical with preceding................... ....*Plagiotrochus compactus* Kins.

Short, blunt, irregular, many-celled, very rough swellings, diameter ¼ to ½ inch, length ¼ to 1¼ inches, on valley oak, gall wasp..........................*Neuroterus varians* Kins.

Rather regular, spherical to ovoid, many-celled, grayish brown swellings on small twigs, maximum dimensions 2 by 3 inches, gall wasp.......................*Andricus furnaceus* Kins.

Dark brown, woody, many-celled, surrounding twigs and composed of very many distinct, thoroughly fused masses, the surface rough and cracked, gall wasp. Mex................... ....*Andricus peredurus* Kins.

Irregularly rounded or elongate, woody, many-celled swelling much like that of *A. coxii,* on "live oak," Arizona, gall wasp... ....*Compsodryoxenus maculipennis* Ashm.

Very hard, ovate or elongate, woody, many-celled, twig swelling, on canyon live oak, gall wasp........................... ....*Compsodryoxenus brunneus* Ashm.

Irregular, dense, corky, many-celled swelling, maximum dimensions ⅔ by 2 inches, internally woody, soft, spongy, larval cells
closely imbedded, somewhat separable, on *Q. gambeli, Q. undulata,* gall wasp. Pl. 17 (7)........*Plagiotrochus frequens* Gill.

Identical appearing gall, gall wasp........................
........................*Plagiotrochus piceoderma* Kins.

A gradual twig or branch swelling, 1½ to 3 inches long, ½ to 1
inch in diameter, on blue jack oak, gall wasp...............
..............................*Callirhytis medullæ* Ashm.

58   59

(Courtesy New York State Museum)

FIG. 58.—Gall of *Neuroterus longipennis*. *(After Beutm.)*
FIG. 59.—Gall of *Neuroterus rileyi*. *(After Beutm.)*

Irregular twig enlargement, maximum dimensions 1 by 3½
inches, usually much smaller, larval cells distinct, more or less
imbedded, usually not completely surrounded, never separable,
on *Q. dumosa,* gall wasp. Pl. 17 (1)........................
....................*Plagiotrochus chrysolepidicola* Ashm.

Galls similar to the preceding:

On valley oak..................*Plagiotrochus pugnus* Kins.
Plagiotrochus pugnoides Kins.

On oregon oak ....*Plagiotrochus garryana* Kins.
On *Q. douglasii*. Pl. 19 (9)......*Plagiotrochus kelloggi* Kins.
On *Q. dumosa* ....*Plagiotrochus diminuens* Kins.
          Plagiotrochus alutaceus Kins.
On *Q. douglasii*..............*Plagiotrochus atricinctus* Kins.
          Plagiotrochus compositus Kins.

Irregular twig swelling, ½ to ¾ inch in diameter, with many thin-walled cells, on *Q. dumosa.* gall wasp.................
..........................*Cynips rufescens* McC. & Egb.

Elongated twig swelling, length 1⅕ inch, diameter ⅘ inch, on *Q. douglasii*, gall wasp................*Cynips kelloggi* Full.

Oblong, irregular, woody swellings on leaf petioles or at the base of the new shoots, length ⅓ inch, diameter ⅙ inch, on laurel-leaved oak, gall wasp. Fig. 58.."*Neuroterus*" *longipennis* Ashm.

Irregularly rounded or elongate, somewhat potato-shaped, many-celled, length ¾ to 1¼ inches, diameter ½ to ¾ inch, on *Q. arizonica, Q. oblongifolia,* and *Q. grisea,* gall wasp. Pl. 20 (8)
..............................*Andricus wheeleri* Beutm.

Fusiform twig gall, length 1¼ inches, diameter ¼ inch, on post oak, gall wasp................................*Cynips sp.*

Broadly clavate or ovate, apical twig swelling, length ½ to 1 inch, on post oak, gall wasp....................*Cynips sp.*

Irregularly globose, lobulated, apical twig swelling, diameter ¾ to 1 inch, mite............................*Eriophyes sp.*

(3) Larval cells, each surmounted by a tube of cellular tissue different from the general substance of the galls; tubes may project from the surface in the mature gall:

 (a) Tubes never project:

  Globose or elongate, very abrupt twig swellings, length ½ to 2½ inches, wood hard, curled, the bark smooth and within concealed, rounded, sub-compressed tubes, on coast live oak, gall wasp. Pl. 30 (8).......................
  ....*Plagiotrochus suttoni* Bass.

  A more robust gall, diameter 2¼ inches, length 3¼ inches, on coast live oak, gall wasp..*Plagiotrochus polythyra* Kieff.

PLATE 11—MIDGE GALLS. 1, White snake root flower buds from which was reared *Lestodiplosis eupatorii* Felt, a predator. 2, Gall of Cratægus leaf from which was reared *Lestodiplosis cratægifolia* Felt. This midge is probably predacious. (*After Thompson*). 3, Gall on Cratægus leaf from which was reared *Lestodiplosis cratægifolia* Felt. (*After Thompson*). 4, Cherry leaf from which was reared *Mycodiplosis cerasifolia* Felt. (*After Thompson*). 5, Beaked willow gall, *Phytophaga rigidæ* O.S. 6, Elm leaves deformed by *Phytophaga ulmi* Beutm. (*After Thompson*). 7, Willow cabbage gall, *Rhabdophaga brassicoides* Walsh. 8, Willow twig showing deformation provisionally referred to *Rhabdophaga globosa* Felt. 9, Nodule willow gall, *Rhabdophaga nodula* Walsh.

PLATE 11

Courtesy N. Y. State Museum

Similar gall but elongate, cylindrical, diameter 1⅛ inches, length 5 inches, on interior live oak, gall wasp.........
.........................*Plagiotrochus lustrior* Kins.

(b) Tubes project like horns or spines:

Globose twig gall, irregular, woody, variable in size, with many horn-like projections, on scrub, water, pin, Spanish and shingle oaks, and *Q. digitata,* spring, gall wasp. Pl. 1 (9).......Horned oak gall, *Plagiotrochus cornigerus* O.S.

Abrupt, irregular, woody, tuber-like gall, at first smooth, later rough, with deep fissures and spiny succulent tubes, diameter ½ to 1¼ inches, on laurel-leaved oak, gall wasp, sexual generation. Pl. 2 (5).....*Andricus clavigerus* Ashm.

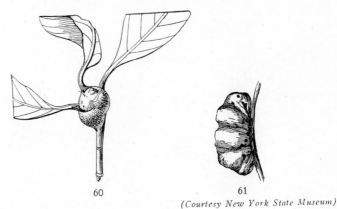

60

61

(Courtesy New York State Museum)

Fig. 60.—Gall of *Callirhytis clavula.*
Fig. 61.—Gall of *Disholcaspis truckeensis. (After Beutm.)*

f. Many-celled woody swellings at the base of twig, eccentric on twig (grade to last group):

A hard, knotty swelling at the base of small twigs and branches, length ⅓ to ¾ inch, diameter about ½ inch, on water oak, gall wasp
.................................*Callirhytis aquaticæ* Ashm.

g. Pustular elevations of the bark, often enlarging the twig:

Abrupt, irregular twig swellings, varying from round, pustule-like bodies, ⅙ inch in diameter to confluent, many-celled masses, 1 inch long and ½ inch in diameter, on chinquapin oak, gall wasp.........
.................................*Neuroterus mutatus* Kins.

Similar gall on basket oak, gall wasp....*Neuroterus atripleuræ* Kins.

Similar gall on yellow chestnut oak, gall wasp...............
.................................*Neuroterus mutatus* Kins.

Pustulate, oval bark swellings, about ⅛ inch in diameter, many

galls, usually confluent around and along the twigs for a length of an inch to 6 inches, on chinquapin oak, gall wasp..................
..............................*Neuroterus thompsoni* Kins.

h. One-celled, terminal enlargements of club galls on twigs:

Globose, apical, woody twig galls, length ½ to 1 inch, on white and? post oaks, gall wasp. Pl. 27 (2) Fig. 60........................
....................White oak club gall, *Callirhytis clavula* O.S.

Ovate, globose, or club-shaped apical gall, leafy, diameter ⅓ inch,

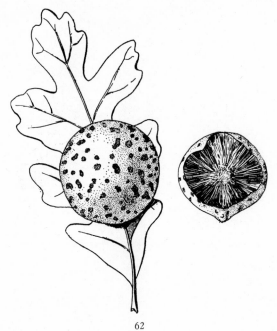

62

(*Courtesy New York State Museum*)

Fig. 62.—Gall of *Cynips mirabilis.* (*After Beutm.*)

on willow oak, June, gall wasp.............*Callirhytis phellos* O.S.

Club-shaped, woody, apical galls on small limbs, the apex blunt and generally turned to one side, on scrub, blue jack, shingle and Spanish oaks and *Q. myrtifolia, Q. texana,* gall wasp. Pl. 2 (9)......
....................Scrub oak club gall, *Callirhytis similis* Bass.

Irregular, subglobose, apparently one-celled swelling of terminal twigs, diameter ½ inch, on valley oak, gall wasp..............
......................................*Callirhytis nigra* Full.

Irregular, one-celled, green twig gall, length ¾ inch, diameter ¼ inch, bearing many small leaves, on *Q. grisea, Q. undulata,* fall, gall wasp. Pl. 30 (9).....................*Andricus howertoni* Bass.

3. Galls attached to branches and twigs and more or less separated from the normal plant tissues, (Compare with (2), on p. 82, and also oak apples, (10), p. 173. See also (b) on p. 120 and (c) and (d) on p. 124.

a. Bullet galls, that is, woody galls attached to the twigs and in small clusters or solitary:

(1) Many-celled or polythalamous:

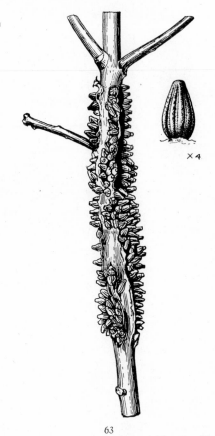

× 4

63

(Courtesy New York State Museum)

FIG. 63.—Ridged bunch gall, *Callirhytis gemmaria.*

Subglobular, many-celled, sessile twig gall, diameter 1 to 4 inches on valley oak and *Q. douglasii*, gall wasp. Pl. 24 (7)........ ....*Andricus californicus* Bass.

Gall like preceding on *Q. dumosa*, gall wasp............... ....*Andricus intermedius* Kins.

Globose, clustered, many-celled, buff colored, diameter 1½ to

2¾ inches, on Oregon oak, gall wasp...*Andricus spongiolus* Gill.
Globose, many-celled, sessile twig galls resembling round apples, surface red or green turning to brown, smooth, dimensions 1¼ to 2½ inches, often with 50 or more radiately arranged larval cells, on evergreen oak, and interior live oak, gall wasp. Pl. 24 (8)....................*Callirhytis pomiformis* Bass.
(*C. rossi* Kieff. probably identical)

Similar to preceding, on coast live oak, gall wasp...........
..........................*Callirhytis maculipennis* Kieff.

Similar to preceding, on coast live oak, gall wasp...........
..........................*Callirhytis descansonis* Kins.

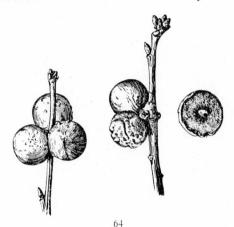

64

(Courtesy New York State Museum)

FIG. 64.—Oak bullet gall, *Disholcaspis globulus*. (*After Beutm.*)

Gall surface much roughened, densely covered with projections, each ending in a filament, a mossy appearance, on interior live oak, gall wasp...................*Callirhytis distincta* Kins.

Gall similar, surface smooth, on interior live oak, gall wasp....
..........................*Callirhytis provincialis* Kins.

Globose, slightly nippled, wrinkled, with many short, spine-like projections, light yellowish-brown, some of the spines tipped with pink, diameter ¾ inch, on interior live oak, gall wasp....
..........................*Callirhytis yosemite* Beutm.

Spherical, with a conical apex, yellowish-brown, surface roughened, with a whitish pile when on the twigs, slightly pubescent when on the leaf, interior spongy, the center very hard, many-celled, diameter 1⅓ inches, on interior or coast live oak, gall wasp
..........................*Callirhytis rossi* Kieff.

Globose, moderately thin-shelled, yellowish, almost smooth,

diameter ⅘ to 1½ inches, on *Q. emoryi* and *Q. hypoleuca,* gall wasp. Pl. 23 (1)...............*Amphibolips trizonata* Ashm.

Globose, yellowish-brown, twig gall with an uneven wrinkled surface, internally spongy, the larval cell rounded, diameter 1¾ to 3½ inches on oak, gall wasp. Mex. Fig. 128............
...........................*Amphibolips palmeri* Beutm.

65

(Courtesy New York State Museum)

FIG. 65.—Gall of *Disholcaspis omnivora.* (*After Beutm.*)

Globose, irregular, yellowish-brown to dark brown, mostly smooth and shiny, diameter ½ to ¾ inch, gall wasp........
...............................*Andricus maxwelli* Bass.

Globose, irregular, hard, pithy, brown, finely granulated and with a few short, blunt spines, interior hard, pithy, brown, many-celled, diameter ½ inch, on post oak, spring, gall wasp. Pl. 19 (8).....................*Andricus murtfeldtæ* Ashm.

Irregular, brown, somewhat smooth, arising from a slit and with transverse depressions indicating coalescence, length 1 inch, di-

PLATE 12—MIDGE GALLS. 1, Spiræa pod gall, *Rhabdophaga salicifolia* Felt. (*After Thompson*). 2, Basket willow gall, *Rhabdophaga salicis* Schr. 3, Willow tips showing blasted apical buds, the work of *Cecidomyia sp.,* adult unknown. 4, Wheat ear gall, *Rhabdophaga triticoides* Walsh, on willow. 5, Downy flower gall, *Rhopalomyia anthophila* O.S. (*After Weld*). 6, Beaked flower gall, *Rhopalomyia racemicola* O.S. (*After Weld*). 7, Solidago showing subterranean bud galls of *Rhopalomyia bulbula* Felt. (*After Thompson*). 8, Galls of gooseberry bud midge, *Rhopalomyia grossulariæ* Felt. (*After Houser*). 9, Root stalk midge, *Rhopalomyia hirtipes* O.S. (*After Stebbins*).

PLATE 12

Courtesy N. Y. State Museum

ameter ½ inch on canyon live oak, and *Q. vaccinifolia,* gall wasp. Pl. 21 (9), Fig. 61 . . . . *Disholcaspis truckeensis* Ashm.

Irregularly rounded, many-celled, becoming brown with age, rugose, fissured, length 2⅕ inches, diameter ⅙ inch, on unknown live oak, gall wasp, Mex. . . . *Andricus montezumus* Beutm.

(2) Small, one-celled, without a distinct central cell:

(a) Situated in fissures in the twigs:

Cylindrical, from cracks in bark, in vertical rows of 2-6, galls ⅛ inch long, diameter 1/12 inch, tan-colored, on *Q. undulata,* early summer, gall wasp. Pl. 36 (6) . . . . Tubular twig gall, *Andricus tubularius* Weld

Globose, densely rugose, gray, slightly flattened twig galls, the rugosities in 5 or 6 transverse rows, length and height 5/16 inch, the galls clustered in fissures or splits of the terminal twigs, on blue jack, willow, water and laurel-leaved oaks and *Q. myrtifolia,* fall, gall wasp. Pl. 35 (5) . . . . *Callirhytis difficilis* Ashm.

Usually smooth, brown, oval cells in rows filling longitudinal slits or fissures, in fall, on black, black jack, red, shingle, and Spanish oaks, gall wasp . . . . *Andricus excavatus* Ashm.

Globose, hard, brown or mottled light and dark green, twig galls, diameter ¼ to nearly ½ inch, occurring several together in fissures, on scarlet, black, black jack, blue jack, turkey, pin, willow, shingle, Spanish, laurel-leaved and scrub oaks and *Q. catesbæi,* and *Q. texana,* gall wasp . . . . Banded bullet gall, *Dryocosmus imbricariæ* Ashm. (*fasciatus* Bass.)

Terminal twig swellings ¼ to ½ inch in diameter and ¾ to 10 inches long, with ragged splits, and containing flattened seed-like, one-celled galls, on evergreen oak and *Q. kelloggii.* Pl. 19 (2) . . . . *Plagiotrochus perdens* Kins.

Identical gall with smooth bark, on interior live oak, gall wasp . . . . *Plagiotrochus destructor* Kins.

(b) Not inserted in fissures on the twigs:

Gall globose, more or less solid, largely naked, attached to twigs or leaves, diameter ⅖ inch, on valley oak and *Q. douglasii,* gall wasp. Pl. 17 (8) Fig. 62 . . . . *Cynips multipunctata* Beutm.

Numerous small, oblong, rugose, bud-like galls surrounding the twig, sometimes issuing from the sides of the larger branches, length ⅛ inch, on blue jack, red, scarlet, shingle, Spanish, turkey and scrub oaks and *Q. myrtifolia, Q. pumila* and *Q. texana,* gall wasp. Pl. 35 (6) Fig. 63 . . . .

........Ridged bunch gall, *Callirhytis gemmaria* Ashm.
Oblong, oval, longitudinally ribbed, brown galls without
a distinct cell, dehiscent, arising in clusters of 2 to 3 in bud
axils, on blue jack and Spanish oaks, gall wasp. Pl. 29,
(2)......Jumping ribbed gall, *Trisoleniella saltatus* Ashm.
Globular, covered with stellate hairs when fresh, later
smooth, one-celled, snuff-colored galls, diameter ¼ inch,
in small clusters on Oregon and valley oaks and *Q. douglasii, Q. dumosa, Q. durata*, summer, gall wasp. Pl. 18 (2)
.........................*Cynips washingtonensis* Gill.

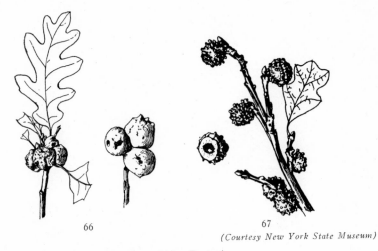

66   67

(Courtesy New York State Museum)

Fig. 66.—Gall of *Disholcaspis rubens*. (*After Beutm.*)
Fig. 67.—Gall of *Cynips corallina*. (*After Beutm.*)

Globose, many celled grayish stem gall, dimensions 3 to
4½ inches, on oak, gall wasp. Mex. ....
...........................*Andricus championi* Ashm.
Small, round, one-celled twig galls, smooth, when dry
wrinkled and resembling pepper corns, diameter 3/16 inch,
on white oak, gall wasp.......*Andricus indistinctus* Bass.
Subcylindrical, rounded apically, with a smooth, shin'ng,
light colored surface, dimensions ⅓ by ¼ inch, gall wasp
....*Cynips sp.*

(3) Typical bullet and similar galls of a pithy or other substance
with a central, thin and brittle-walled cell containing a larva.
The cell may be closely attached to the substance of the gall
or fill a larger or smaller cavity within the gall.

(a) Globular or subglobular in shape:

Globular, single or clustered, yellow, sometimes tinged with red, diameter ⅓ to ⅔ inch, on various white oaks, gall wasp, Fig. 64..................................
............Oak bullet gall, *Disholcaspis globulus* Fitch

Globular with a blunt point at the apex, harder and darker than *D. globulus,* the central cell not separating, length nearly ½ inch, gall wasp, Colorado...................
.........................*Disholcaspis colorado* Gill.

Globular, single or clustered, pale brown or yellowish, sometimes tinged with red, diameter ⅓ inch to nearly an

68   69
(Courtesy New York State Museum)

Fig. 68.—Gall of *Disholcaspis persimilis. (After Beutm.)*
Fig. 69.—Mealy oak gall, *Disholcaspis cinerosa. (After Beutm.)*

inch, on *Q. chapmani,* gall wasp. Fig. 65.............
......................*Disholcaspis omnivora* Ashm.

Globose, very hard, corky galls, diameter about ½ inch, on coast and upland live oaks and California black oak, gall wasp. Pl. 24 (9)..............................
.............Hard oak apple, *Callirhytis agrifoliæ* Bass.
(*clarimontis* Kieff.)

Globose, yellowish-brown or dark brown, sometimes mottled with purple or brown, the interior hard and with a small larval cell, diameter ⅛ to ⅙ inch, on interior live oak, gall wasp................*Andricus wislizeni* Ashm.

Globose, smooth or rough, light straw, usually red-tinted, diameter about ½ inch, on *Q. undulata,* gall wasp. Fig. 66
............................*Disholcaspis rubens* Gill.

Globose, reddish, buff-colored, irregularly and thickly studded with short, stout, blunt spurs, diameter ¼ to ½ inch, on *Q. douglasii,* gall wasp. Fig. 67...............
...............Studded oak gall, *Cynips corallina* Bass.
Globular, thick celled, slightly nippled, green, becoming brown, diameter ½ to ¾ inch, on black jack oak, gall wasp...................*Amphibolips globulus* Beutm.
Globose, yellow to reddish-brown, dimensions 1½ by 1 inch, on post oak, and *Q. breviloba, Q. laceyi,* fall, gall wasp, Pl. 21 (8)..
.......Prune-shaped gall, *Disholcaspis pruniformis* Kins.

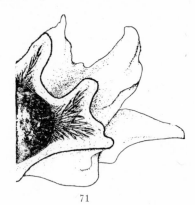

70   71

(Courtesy New York State Museum)

FIG. 70.—Gall of *Cynips ribes.* (*After Kinsey*)
FIG. 71.—Gall of *Cynips heldae.* (*After Kinsey*)

Globose, clustered, bluntly spurred, resembling small specimens of rough bullet gall, the surface more hoary, internally a larval cell attached but readily separated from the gall, diameter nearly ½ inch, on valley oak and *Q. douglasii,* gall wasp.........*Disholcaspis canescens* Bass.
Globular, thin-shelled, clustered twig gall, each with a fiber supported cell, a dense rusty brown pubescence, diameter ⅞ to 1⅗ inches, on *Q. reticulata,* gall wasp. Mex.......
..........................*Disholcaspis weldi* Beutm.
Nippled, mealy bullet gall, brown becoming dark gray or black, one celled, diameter ⅞ inch, on oak, gall wasp. Mex.
.........................*Disholcaspis unicolor* Kins.
Single or clustered, globose, nippled, covered with a dense mealy powder, within a pithy, free larval cell, diameter ½ to nearly 1 inch, on live oak, gall excretes honeydew, attrac-

tive to wasps, fall, gall wasp. Pl. 21 (2) Fig. 69.........
............Mealy oak gall, *Disholcaspis cinerosa* Bass.
Gall nearly as *D. cinerosa*, more often elongate, not strictly spherical and with a slender point basally, diameter ¾ inch, on *Q. oleoides*, gall wasp. Mex...*Disholcaspis pallens* Kins.
Irregular, somewhat rounded, the sides flattened, slightly oblique, ridged around the upper part of the sides the apex rounded, occurs singly or in rows, usually closely pressed

72   73

(Courtesy New York State Museum)

FIG. 72.—Rough bullet gall, *Disholcaspis mamma*. (*After Beutm.*)
FIG. 73.—Gall of *Disholcaspis sileri*. (*After Beutm.*)

together, diameter ¼ to nearly ½ inch, on Canyon live oak, gall wasp. Pl. 30 (4)...........................
...................*Disholcaspis chrysolepidis* Beutm.
Globose, densely woolly, peach-like gall, diameter 1 to 2 inches on *Q. emoryi* and *Q. hypoleuca*, gall wasp. Pl. 23 (7)
........................*Amphibolips nigra* Beutm.

PLATE 13—MIDGE GALLS. 1, White flowered aster buds deformed by *Rhopalomyia lateriflori* Felt. (*After Clarke*). 2, Goldenrod bunch gall, *Rhopalomyia solidaginis* Lw. 3, Flower bud galls of *Aster undulatus*, deformed by *Rhopalomyia sp.* (*After Clarke*). 4, Subterranean galls on Solidago inhabited by *Rhopalomyia thompsoni* Felt. (*After Thompson*). 5, Purple vein gall on arrow-wood leaves produced by *Sackenomyia viburnifolia* Felt. 6, Grape filbert gall, *Schizomyia coryloides* Walsh & Riley. (*After Weld*). 7, Gall of elder flower midge, *Youngomyia umbellicola* O.S. (*After Weld*). 8, Gall on oak leaves produced by *Cincticornia globosa* Felt. (*After Clarke*). 9, Dogwood spot gall, *Lasioptera corni* Felt. (*After Clarke*).

PLATE 13

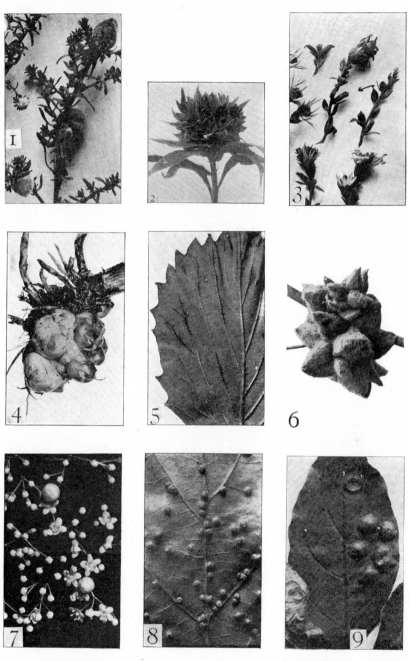

Courtesy N. Y. State Museum

Brownish yellow or russet peach, average diameter 1¼ inches, on *Q. emoryi, Q. hypoleuca,* gall wasp. Mex. .....
........................*Amphibolips gumia* Kins.

Brassy yellow and rosy russet, later greenish brown or darker, average diameter ⅞ inch, on *Q. fulva, Q. eduardi,* gall wasp. Mex..............*Amphibolips jubatus* Kins.

Yellow tan and rosy russet, later brown or black, diameter ¼ to ⅙ inch, on *Q. eduardi,* gall wasp. Mex............
........................*Amphibolips elatus* Kins.

Yellow tan and rosy russet, later dark brown to grayish black, average diameter 2 inches, on *Q. serrulata, Q. mexicana,* gall wasp. Mex........*Amphibolips maturus* Kins.

Yellow tan and rosy russet, later dark brown to grayish black, average diameter 2⅕ inches, on *Q. eduardi,* gall wasp. Mex........................*Amphibolips nebris* Kins.

Yellow tan and rosy russet, later darkens, average diameter 1 inch, on *Q. incarnata,* gall wasp. Mex. ....
........................*Amphibolips niger* Beutm.

Golden or reddish yellow and rosy russet, later dirty brown or grayish black, average diameter 1½ inches, on *Q. eduardi,* gall wasp. Mex..............*Amphibolips pistrix* Kins.

Oblate, pale brown, broadly attached, the flattened apex excretes honeydew in Sept., diameter ⅙ to ¼ inch, on valley and Oregon oaks and *Q. dumosa, Q. durata,* gall wasp. Pl. 36 (4)........*Disholcaspis eldoradensis* Beutm.

Globose, apical, somewhat pointed, crimson, scarlet, turning dark brown, one-celled, diameter ¼ to ⅓ inch, on *Q. fendleri, Q. gambelii, Q. undulata,* fall, gall wasp. Pl. 20 (3)....................*Disholcaspis perniciosa* Bass.
(*mellariæ* McCook, *monticola* Gill.)

Gall similar to that of *D. perniciosa,* globular, with drawn out, nipple-shaped tip, light tan yellow to rose and tan brown, diameter up to ⅓ inch, scattered on stems or in clusters of 3-5, on *Q. læta,* gall wasp. Mex............
........................*Disholcaspis lætæ* Kins.

Similar, ellipsoidal or compressed cushion-shaped, rich tan to ruddy brown, later blackish, diameter up to ⅓ inch, in clusters up to 20 on young stems, on *Q. potosina,* gall wasp. Mex......................*Disholcaspis potosina* Kins.

Pointed breast-shaped, with conical tip, tan brown or darker, diameter up to ⅓ inch, height somewhat greater, in elongate clusters up to 20 on young twigs, on *Q. breviloba,* gall wasp, Mex......................*Disholcaspis pulla* Kins.

Similar, tip bluntly conical, tan or rosey brown, diameter nearly to ½ inch, singly or in clusters of 2-4 on twigs, on *Q. reticulata* complex, gall wasp. Mex..................
.........................*Disholcaspis purlans* Kins.

Similar, ellipsoidal or swollen, less often cushion-shaped, usually without a nipple, yellow brown to tan or darker, diameter ⅓ inch, in dense elongate clusters up to 30 galls on stems, on *Q. repanda var.*, gall wasp. Mex..........
......................*Disholcaspis purpurea* Kins.

Similar galls, globose, often resembling grains of dent corn, rose purple, diameter ⅓ inch, height ½ inch, in dense clusters up to 15 galls on stems, on *Q. macrophylla*, gall wasp,
...........................*Disholaspis regina* Kins.

Globose, one-celled, mottled, smooth, with a blunt tip, diameter ⅓ inch, on unknown oak, Mexican, gall wasp. Pl. 39 (9).................*Andricus marmoreus* Kins.

Spherical, berry-like, very succulent, green and more or less translucent when fresh, bright red when very young, shriveling, drying, becoming blackened and rather obconical with age, diameter ⅙ to ¼ inch, on *Q. douglasii*, gall wasp. Fig. 70..........................*Cynips ribes* Kins.

Gall subglobular, green, one-celled, with blunt, warty elevations, apex slightly prolonged, diameter ¼ inch, probably an acorn gall, on willow oak, Pl. 19 (4)................
............Warty oak gall, *Callirhytis middletoni* Weld

Rounded, with a nipple, diameter about ½ inch, brick-red or yellowish-brown, becoming dark, surface very rough, probably solid when young, hollow when mature, on *Q. dumosa*, gall wasp...........*Disholcaspis simulata* Kins.

Gall mostly light buff, to yellowish brown, partly tinged with rose red, on Oregon oak, gall wasp...............
...................*Disholcaspis vancouverensis* Kins.

Globose, solitary, woody, thin-shelled, the tip frequently slightly pointed, the base somewhat excavated and partly surrounding the twig, pale yellow, with short gray hairs, internally a small basal cell, diameter ½ inch, on Oregon oak, gall wasp........................*Andricus sp.*

Globose, woody, solitary or clustered twig gall with a short stem, the dry galls of the same color as the twig, diameter ⅓ inch, Oregon, gall wasp.............*Callirhytis sp.*

Globose or cubical with many ridges or pointed projections, single or clustered, length ⅓ inch, diameter ⅕ inch, on valley oak, fall, gall wasp. Fig. 71.....*Cynips heldœ* Full.

(b) Form more ovoid, with a point at the apex:

Globose, obscurely pointed, green, bright red, turning to brown or dark red, diameter ¼ to ¾ inch, on swamp white and burr oaks and *Q. lyrata,* gall wasp. Pl. 21 (1) Fig. 72........Rough bullet gall, *Disholcaspis mamma* Walsh

Irregularly pyriform twig gall with a bent point apically, diameter ½ inch, on burr oak, gall wasp.............
........................*Andricus macrocarpæ* Karsch

Globose with pointed apex attached to twigs singly or in groups of two to three, the surface covered with a mealy, grayish powder, diameter ¾ to 1 inch, gall wasp, on live oak......................*Disholcaspis cinerosa* Bass.

 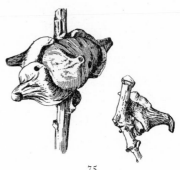

74   75

(Courtesy New York State Museum)

Fig. 74.—Gall of *Disholcaspis conalis.* (*After Weld*)
Fig. 75.—Gall of *Disholcaspis bassetti.* (*After Beutm.*)

Ovate, green, becoming brown, bud gall, usually with leaves growing upon the sides and internally a closely imbedded though separate larval cell, length ⅓ inch, on *Q. gambelii, Q. diversicolor* and *Q. undulata,* summer and fall, gall wasp. Pl. 38 (7) Fig. 73..............*Disholcaspis sileri* Bass.

Brown or yellowish-brown with a sharp projecting point, one-celled, diameter ⅓ inch, on *Q. dumosa,* gall wasp. Pl. 29 (7)....................*Disholcaspis plumbella* Kins.

Single or clustered, globose, diameter ⅓ to ⅔ inch, a short basal attachment and a very fine, short, apical point, surface smooth or slightly roughened, light to dark green, tinged with rose-red when fresh, browning with age, internally solid with a central cell, on canyon live oak, gall wasp
............................*Heteroecus malus* Kins.

Globose or fusiform, brownish-yellow, always tapering more or less moderately to a pointed apex, diameter ¼ to ½ inch, on canyon live oak and *Q. vaccinifolia*............
.........................*Heteroecus pacificus* Ashm.
(*bakeri* Kieff.)

Gall similar, much shorter and more robust, on canyon live oak, gall wasp............*Heteroecus subpacificus* Kins.

Gall similar, though averaging smaller, on canyon live oak, gall wasp...................*Heteroecus gracilis* Kins.

Conical, truncate and slightly convex above, tapering to point of attachment, as broad as high, ¼ inch, cell large, evidently once covered with wool, probably from a leaf in cluster, unknown oak, Missouri, gall wasp.............
..........................*Andricus perplexus* Ashm.

(c) Form more or less conical:

Conical, hard, black or brownish-black galls issuing from the bud axils on the larger branches, the apex sometimes

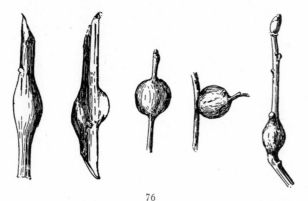

76

(Courtesy New York State Museum)

FIG. 76.—Gall of *Compsodryoxenus brunneus*. (*After Beutm.*)

curved, length ½ inch, on willow and laurel-leaved oaks, gall wasp...................*Callirhytis conifera* Ashm.

Conical clustered twig or branch gall, covered with dense short white pubescence when young, often deep red, becoming brown or black when dry, length ½ to ¾ inch, on shingle, Spanish and scrub oaks, June-July, gall wasp. Pl. 1 (8).............,.......*Callirhytis ventricosa* Bass.

Conical, with clasping base, ½ to ¾ inch high, basal diameter ⅓ to ½ inch, often lopsided, single or clustered, on small twigs in fall, greenish with whitish pubescence, brown in fall, on Oregon oak, gall wasp. Fig. 74........
....*Disholcaspis conalis* Weld

Globose, usually with a produced curving apex, single or clustered twig gall, green, turning to brown, on burr and swamp white oaks, fall, gall wasp. Fig. 75.............
..........................*Disholcaspis bassetti* Gill.

(d) Not globular or conical:

Ovate or bud-like, one-celled, green or fleshy, on trunks of young trees or stems of very young shoots, length ¼ inch, on scarlet, Spanish and black oaks, spring, gall wasp. Pl. 35 (7).........Rough bud gall, *Callirhytis rugulosa* Beutm.

Spindle-shaped, blunt at both ends, ½ inch long, diameter ⅕ inch, a bud gall, mottled with white, on pin oak, spring, gall wasp. Pl. 35 (9)...............................
......Ellipsoidal bud gall, *Amphibolips ellipsoidalis* Weld

Trumpet-shaped, fluted, with sessile or clasping base, diameter and length about ¼ inch, arising from a weak bud, yellowish white, on *Q. arizonica*, summer, gall wasp. Pl. 32 (7)............Oak trumpet gall, *Andricus tubalis* Weld

(4) Woody, a central kernel and the outer substance of the gall chambered, clustered.

(a) Interior of galls more or less corky:

Elongate, fusiform, one-celled, in cluster on twig, the interior corky, filamentatious, length ¾ to 1 inch, diameter ½ inch, on scarlet, black, black jack, ? laurel-leaved, Spanish and willow oaks, gall wasp. Pl. 3 (2).............
..........................*Andricus formosus* Bass.

Rounded or crown-shaped, clustered, 9-ridged, apex pointed, pale green, soft when fresh, becoming hard after drying, thick-walled, diameter ¼ to ½ inch, length ⅓ to ½ inch on pin, water and willow oaks, also on leaves, spring, gall wasp.........Oak crown gall, *Andricus coronus* Beutm.

Compound, cylindrical, distal portion with diameter twice the basal part, a little longer, and containing the cell; brown, yellowish, later blackening, dimensions ¾ by 1 inch, on canyon live oak, gall wasp. Pl. 32 (5)...............
.........Double oak gall, *Heteroecus sanctæ-claræ* Kins.

Similar gall on same oak.........*Heteroecus aliud* Kins.

Similar gall on same oak........*Heteroecus fuscior* Kins.

(b) Galls distinctly woody with the structure of typical bullet galls and clustered in compact and characteristic masses about the supporting twig:

PLATE 14—PLANT GALLS. 1, Long spruce cone gall, *Adelges cooleyi* Gill. 2, Hackberry nipple gall, *Pachypsylla mamma* Riley. (*After Thompson*). 3, Red pouch gall, *Melaphis rhois* Fitch. 4, Hickory leaf gall produced by *Phylloxera caryæ-avellana* Riley. (*After Thompson*). 5, Hickory leaf gall produced by *Phylloxera caryæfallax* Riley. (*After Thompson*). 6, Hickory leaf gall produced by *Phylloxera caryæglobuli* Walsh. (*After Thompson*). 7, Hickory leaf gall produced by *Phylloxera rimosalis* Perg. (*After Thompson*). 8, Hickory seed gall, *Phylloxera caryæsemen* Walsh. (*After Thompson*). 9, Axillary Spiræa bud galls, *Cecidomyia sp.* (*After Clarke*).

PLATE 14

Courtesy N. Y. State Museum

Clustered, compact, somewhat fig-shaped, yellowish-brown, covered with a felt-like substance, on live oak, gall wasp. Pl. 18 (6) Fig. 77............*Disholcaspis virens* Ashm.

(*ficigera* Ashm.)

Closely compressed clusters covered with a rust-colored velvety substance, spongy internally, reddish-brown, length of masses 2 to 4 inches, diameter 3/4 to 1 1/2 inches, on burr and post oaks and *Q. chapmani, Q. margaretta,* fall, gall wasp. Fig. 78............*Disholcaspis spongiosa* Karsch

(*ficula* Bass.)

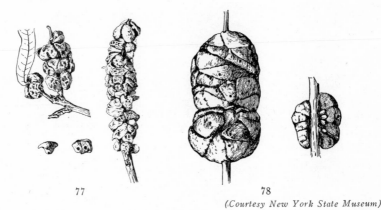

77   78

(*Courtesy New York State Museum*)

Fig. 77.—Woolly fig gall, *Disholcaspis virens*. (*After Beutm.*)
Fig. 78.—Gall of *Disholcaspis spongiosa*. (*After Beutm.*)

Dark reddish brown, resembling a nubbin of red dent corn, later darker to black, diameter 1/4 inch, length 1/3 inch, on *Q. grisea, Q. arizonica, Q. oblongifolia, Q. toumeyi,* gall wasp. Ariz. & Mex.............*Conobius spicatus* Bass.

(*Loxaulus spicatus* Bass.)

Dark reddish brown, later? darker, length 1/3 inch, diameter 1/4 inch, of whole cluster 1 inch, on *Q. undata,* gall wasp. Mex...........................*Conobius strues* Kins.

Globose enlargement, diameter 1 1/2 inch, composed of a series of brown, wedge-shaped, closely fitted cells, on burr, over-cup and swamp white oak, fall, gall wasp. Pl. 18 (3)............Pine cone oak gall, *Cynips strobilana* O.S.

Clustered, mushroom-shaped, arising from a broad, inverted, cone-shaped base, dimensions 1/8 by 1/2 inch, on live oak, gall wasp.'..............*Disholcaspis fungiformis* Kins.

Dense cluster of fungiform galls, differing from *fungiformis* by the slender, sharply pointed or broader tip some 1/4 inch long, light red yellow weathering to brown or black, diameter gall ¼ inch, of cluster up to 40 galls 3 inches, on *Q. læta,* gall wasp. Mex............*Disholcaspis insulana* Kins.

Globose or irregular, clustered, woody, clay-brown or reddish tinged, diameter of individual galls ⅓ to ¾ inch, of mass 1⅕ inch, gall wasp. Mex......................
......................*Disholcaspis mexicana* Beutm.

79

(Courtesy New York State Museum)

Fig. 79.—Gall of *Disholcaspis succinipes. (After Beutm.)*

Galls rosy to brownish tan, later dark brown, usually irregularly triangulate, much compressed in clusters, diameter 1 inch, of cluster, 3⅓ inches, on *Q. rhodophlebia,* gall wasp. Mex......................*Disholcaspis largior* Kins.

Globose, rugose, dark brown, diameter ⅓ inch, in clusters of 10 or 12, sometimes irregular, also on petioles, midribs and strong lateral veins, on valley oak, gall wasp........
...........................*Cynips conspicua* Kins.

Globose or bud-shaped in clusters of 5-20, yellowish-brown turning black, diameter ⅛ to ¼ inch, on live oak, gall wasp. Fig. 79.............*Disholcaspis succinipes* Ashm.

Bluntly conical, each gall distorted by pressure, a slight projection basally extending into the twig, dark purple when fresh, becoming rich brown, darker at the tips, dimensions ⅓ by ½ inch, on *Q. breviloba*, fall, gall wasp. Pl. 18 (4).....................*Disholcaspis pattersoni* Kins.

(c) Galls in compact clusters around the twig, but bladder-like and not woody as in the last group:

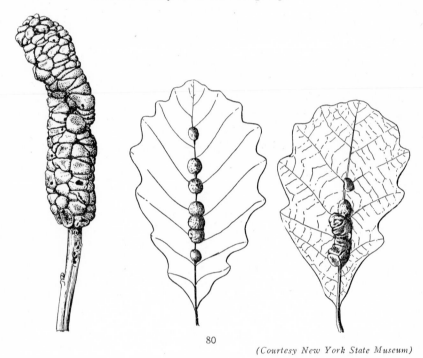

80

(Courtesy New York State Museum)

Fig. 80.—Oak fig gall, *Xanthoteras forticorne*. (*After Beutm.*)

Numerous, soft, thin-shelled, reddish, yellowish-brown or brown galls, frequently closely pressed together and somewhat resembling figs, on white, chinquapin and basket oaks, summer, fall, gall wasp. Fig. 80.....................
..............Oak fig gall, *Xanthoteras forticorne*[1] Walsh

(d) Galls on twigs, consisting of fibrous material which conceals one or more cells:

(1) Cells large, solitary or clustered:

Elongate or oblong, woody, tube-like, resembling a

[1] Kinsey suggests a possibility of *Trigonaspis radicola* and *T. ornata* being alternate generations of *Xanthoteras forticorne* Walsh.

date seed, sessile on the branch and covered with a
long brownish-yellow wool, length 1 inch, diameter ¼
inch, internally small, solid, the more porous tissue
with a cylindrical cavity extending from the base to
hardly more than half-way to the tip, on canyon live
oak, gall wasp.................................
......Woolly tube gall, *Heteroecus dasydactyli* Ashm.
Gall short, ovoid or spindle-shaped, tapering point
short, not usually curved, more or less smooth, singly
or in small clusters, on canyon live oak, gall wasp....
....................*Heteroecus eriophorus* Kins.
Gall similar to preceding, point strongly curved, singly
or in clusters up to ten, on canyon live oak, gall wasp
......................*Heteroecus pygmæus* Kins.
Elongate, scurfy, shaped like a date seed, cylindrical,
dimensions ¼ by ¾ inch, obtuse apically, slightly
tapering basally, covered with a dense, scurfy, rich
golden-brown pubescence, weathering to pale brown or
black, internally with a central cylindrical cavity extending from the base almost to the tip of the gall, on
canyon live oak, gall wasp.....................
..................*Heteroecus melanodermus* Kins.
Globose, in cracks of young twigs, diameter up to 2⅞
inches, average 2¼ inches, with a slender sharply
pointed pedicel at base, light pinkish to rose and light
russet brown, often finely spotted, sometimes whitish or
bluish, on *Q. oblongifolia, Q. arizonica, Q. sacame, Q.
diversicolor* (?), *Q. grisea, Q. toumeyi*, gall wasp.
Pl. 23 (8)...............*Cynips aggregata* Weld
Globose, in cracks of young twigs, diameter up to 2½
inches, average 1⅞ inches, globular, sharply pointed
pedicel, light rose or yellow, older galls light rosy tan,
sometimes browner, in dense clusters on *Q. hæmatophlebia, Q. rodophlebia*, gall wasp. Mex............
.........................*Cynips cucurbita* Kins.
Globose, in cracks of young twigs, diameter up to 2
inches, average 1½ inch, with slender sharply pointed
pedicel, l'ght yellow-tan to dark russet-brown, spotted
or irregularly striped with purple, often whitish or
bluish, single or in large clusters, on *Q. sacame*, gall
wasp. Mex..................*Cynips finitima* Kins.
Globose, in cracks of young twigs, diameter up to 2¾
inches, average 2¼ inches, with slender sharply pointed
pedicel, pinkish-rose to brownish-tan and darker

brown, obscurely mottled with purple, bluish, singly or in large clusters, on *Q. sacame, Q. chihuahuensis,* gall wasp. Mex.....................*Cynips sierræ* Kins.
Irregular, hard, many-celled, woody gall, broadly attached to the twig and covered with a compact mass of white woolly substance, sometimes tinged with red or brown, length about ¾ inch, diameter ½ to ¾ inch, on post, overcup oak and *Q. durandii,* fall, gall wasp. Pl. 18 (8).............*Andricus aciculatus* Beutm.

81

(Courtesy New York State Museum)

FIG. 81.—Gall of wool sower, *Callirhytis seminator.*

(2) Cells small, numerous, massed in a cluster beneath the fibers:

Globular, white, pinkish-marked, wooly growth with seed-like grains on twigs in June, diameter 1½ to 2 inches, on white, chestnut, and basket oaks, gall wasp. Fig. 81......Wool-sower, *Callirhytis seminator* Harr.

PLATE 15—PLANT MITE GALLS. 1, Leaf galls on *Alnus incana,* produced by a plant mite, *Eriophyes sp. (After Thompson).* 2, Bud galls on yellow birch produced by a plant mite, *Eriophyes sp.* 3, Foliage deformed by ash *Psyllid, Psyllopsis fraxinicola* Forst. 4, Hickory leaves with margins inrolled by *Eriophyes sp. (After Thompson).* 5, Hazel or Corylus buds deformed by *Eriophyes sp. (After Thompson).* 6, Bayberry leaves badly deformed by *Eriophyes sp. (After Thompson).* 7, Beech leaves affected by *Eriophyes sp. (After Thompson).* 8, Ash leaves showing numerous galls of *Eriophyes fraxini* Garm. *(After Thompson).* 9, Ash flower gall, *Eriophyes fraxinifloræ* Felt. *(After Thompson).*

PLATE 15

Courtesy N. Y. State Museum

Large twig gall composed of a woolly white or pinkish mass, having a diameter of 3 to 4 inches and encircling twigs ¼ inch in diameter, each mass with from few to many cells and covered with long white wool, on oak, gall wasp.................*Andricus furnessæ* Weld

Irregular, globose, brownish yellow twig gall, smooth above, hairy below, length 1¼ inch, diameter ½ inch, gall wasp. Mex...........*Andricus bonanseai* Mayr

Bud Galls

There are many galls which originate in buds and are placed in other divisions as a matter of convenience. The 43 listed below obviously develop in the bud and do not produce changes in the structure of the affected part to such an extent as to obscure the point of origin.

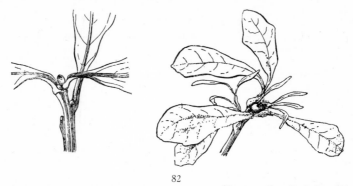

82

(Courtesy New York State Museum)

Fɪɢ. 82.—Threaded oak gall, *Cynips pallipes*. (*After Beutm.*)

4. Bud galls consisting of one or more larval cells or capsules in a leaf bud.
    a. Hard cell or cells surrounded by a number of modified bud scales or leaves. See also (b), (c), (d).
        (1) Cells surrounded by a few thread-like bodies:
            Oblong, oval thin-shelled, blackish-brown galls among thrifty young buds and surrounded by six or more long, brown, thread-like bodies, length ⅛ inch, on white oak, gall wasp. Fig. 82....
            ....Threaded oak gall, *Cynips pallipes* Bass.
        (2) Cells surrounded by a rosette of linear leaves:
            Conical, axillary leaf bud gall covered with a dense, rosette-like cluster of aborted leaves, cell oval, length ⅛ inch, on chinquapin oak, gall wasp. Pl. 3 (3) Fig. 84.........................
            ....Oak rosette gall, *Cynips frondosa* Bass.
        Dormant bud galls covered with short, fuzzy abortive leaflets and

occurring in masses on trunks of shingle, black jack, water, pin, willow and Spanish oaks and *Q. cinerea,* spring, gall wasp. Fig. 83...........Leafy bud gall, *Dryocosmus floridensis* Beutm.

(*Andricus peltatus* Wells & Metcalf)

Urn-shaped bud gall hidden within numerous stiff, tangled bracts, diameter ½ to ¾ inch, middle cell brownish, length ⅛ inch, on live oak and *Q. geminata,* fall, gall wasp. Pl. 27 (3)..............Leafy oak gall, *Andricus foliatus* Ashm.

Small, brown, acorn-shaped gall issuing from bud axil and surrounded by a dense mass of small, narrow, silky leaflets, cell diameter ⅛ inch, on post oak and *Q. chapmani,* gall wasp. Pl. 34 (1)...........................*Andricus stropus* Ashm.

83

(Courtesy New York State Museum)

FIG. 83.—Leafy bud gall, *Dryocosmus floridensis,* side and sectional view, at right two leafy bracts. *(After Wells and Metcalf)*

(3) Several cells surrounded by a rosette of aborted leaves:

Rosette cluster of dense narrow leaflets from a bud, inclosing 3-5 deciduous cells, length of cells ⅛ inch, on post oak, gall wasp.........................*Andricus topiarius* Ashm.

(?*Callirhytis turneri* Ashm.)

Conical, axillary leaf bud gall, with a dense rosette-like cluster of aborted leaves, length of cell ⅛ inch, on chinquapin oak, gall wasp. Pl. 3 (3) Fig. 84.............................. ....Oak rosette gall, *Cynips frondosa* Bass.

Many-celled bud gall surrounded by thick, compact leaf clusters, on valley oak and *Q. dumosa,* fall, gall wasp. Pl. 29 (1)...... ....*Andricus wiltzœ* Full.

Spindle-shaped bud gall with a densely compacted mass of golden-brown or purplish, short, narrow, flattened filaments, galls ¼ by ½ inch, on *Q. breviloba,* gall wasp................. ....*Trigonaspis ornata*[1] Kins.

Globose, one-celled, thin-shelled, green, turning brown or gray, dropping in summer, diameter ⅛ inch, on swamp white oak, gall wasp.......................*Callirhytis flavohirta* Beutm.

[1] Kinsey suggests this may be the bud gall from eggs of the March brood of *Xanthoteras forticorne* Walsh.

Bud gall in October with leaf rudiments, resembles somewhat gall of *A. cinnamoneus* Ashm., on Spanish oak and *Q. myrtifolia,* fall, gall wasp.....................*Callirhytis cryptica* Weld

(4) Galls in blasted buds with no circle of aborted leaves:

    (a) A hard cell developing from a bud:

Globose, milk-white or pale greenish white, or specked and marbled with green or lilac, fleshy when fresh becoming woody, dry and hollow, diameter ⅛ to ¼ inch on white, swamp white and post oaks, spring, gall wasp. Pl. 35 (4).......Marbled oak gall, *Andricus pisiformis* Beutm.

Rounded or oval, one-celled, blackish flower or leaf bud gall, length ⅛ inch, on chinquapin, white and probably

84   85

(Courtesy New York State Museum)

FIG. 84.—Oak rosette gall, *Cynips frondosa.*
FIG. 85.—Gall of *Neuroterus obtusilobæ.* (*After Beutm.*)

other oaks, gall wasp. Pl. 34 (5).....................
...............Hard oak bud gall, *Acraspis gemula* Bass.
Globose, nippled, half protruding from bud scales, smooth, truncate at base, green or brown, on white and probably post oaks, fall, gall wasp. Pl. 34 (6).................
......................*Callirhytis mamillaformis* Weld
Thin-shelled, fusiform bud gall, with longitudinal ridges ending in points before apex of gall, length ¼ to ⅙ inch, on twigs of valley oak, gall wasp..*Cynips lobata* McC. & Egb.
Oval, one-celled, with rather flattened ends, protruding from buds, diameter ⅛ inch, on interior live oak, gall wasp....
...........................*Andricus attractans* Kins.
Clustered, roundly conical or broadly fusiform, angular

basally, reddish-brown, puberulent, length ⅙ to ¼ inch,
on post oak, gall wasp.....................*Cynips sp.*

Gall elongate, slender, cone-like, loose cluster of fasciated
leaves, length about 1 inch, diameter ⅓ inch, on *Q. serrulata*
or a close relative, gall wasp. Mex...*Erythres hastata* Kins.

Gall a swollen, compact cone of fasciated leaves, length 1
inch, diameter ½ inch, on *Q. rossii*, gall wasp. Mex.......
...............................*Erythres jaculi* Kins.

(b) A soft capsule developing from a bud:

Smooth, reddish-brown vesicle in the bud surrounded by
bud scales, on swamp white and chinquapin oaks, gall wasp.
Pl. 34 (7) Fig. 86.................................
............Soft oak bud gall, *Neuroterus vesiculus* Bass.
(*affinis* Bass.)

86   87
(*Courtesy New York State Museum*)

FIG. 86.—Soft oak bud gall, *Neuroterus vesicula.* (*After Beutm.*)
FIG. 87.—Gall of *Dryophanta clarkei.* (*After Beutm.*)

A small thin-walled, globular bark gall, on post-oak and ?
Q. breviloba, gall wasp.........*Neuroterus cerinus* Kins.

Similar gall on post oak, gall wasp....................
.........................*Neuroterus ocularis* Kins.

Seed-like, thin-walled cell in winter buds, ⅛ inch long, com-
pletely hidden, on Oregon and valley oak, possibly also on
Q. douglasii, Q. dumosa, Q. durata, fall, gall wasp........
...............................*Cynips occultata* Weld

Similar to preceding, cell broadest at base and tapering
to a pointed apex, surface tan color, wall much thinner,
length ¹⁄₁₀ inch, diameter ¹⁄₂₀ inch, on valley oak, fall, gall
wasp............................*Cynips operta* Weld

Blister-like, thin-walled, white cells on the concave inner face of bud scales of overwintering strong buds, one or two on a scale, on white oak, early spring, sexual generation, gall wasp, adults in May. Pl. 34 (8).................

.........................*Acraspis erinacei* Beutm.

(*bicolens* Kins.)

Many-celled, brown, thin-walled, diameter ⅛ inch, on white and post oaks, resembles gall of *D. vesiculus,* gall wasp. Fig. 87...............*Dryophanta clarkei* Bass.

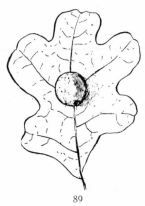

88   89

(*Courtesy New York State Museum*)

FIG. 88.—Gall of *Neuroterus sad'erensis. (After Weld)*
FIG. 89.—Gall of *Acraspis carolina. (After Beutm.)*

Small, thin, completely concealed capsules occurring singly on *Q. undulata,* gall wasp.......*Andricus cellularius* Gill.

A slight swelling of the bud, young leaf or petiole on swamp white oak and *Q. montana?,* spring, gall wasp. Pl. 21 (3).......................*Neuroterus distortus* Bass.

(c) Capsules hidden in the bud, blasting it completely or so that only a few deformed and imperfect leaves appear:

Bud brown, enlarged, bud scales intact inclosing a cavity

PLATE 16—PLANT MITE GALLS. 1, *Eriophyes sp.* on red maple, *Acer rubrum. (After Thompson).* 2, Wild cherry pouch gall, *Eriophyes ? padi* Nal. *(After Thompson).* 3, Base of poplar leaves deformed possibly by *Eriophyes populi* Nal. *(After Thompson).* 4, Leaf gall on *Pyrus arbutifolia,* produced by *Eriophyes sp. (After Thompson).* 5, Oak buds blasted by *Eriophyes sp. (After Thompson).* 6, Galls on poison ivy produced by *Eriophyes sp. (After Thompson).* 7, Terminal leaves of Rhus deformed by *Eriophyes rhoinus. (After Thompson).* 8, Willow leaf gall produced by *Eriophyes sp. (After Thompson).* 9, Maple bladder gall, *Phyllocoptes quadripes* Shim.

PLATE 16

Courtesy N. Y. State Museum

on one side of which is an eccentric cell, length ⅓ to ½ inch, on *Q. chapmani* in fall, gall wasp................ ....*Andricus cinnamoneus* Ashm. Smooth, thin-shelled, globular gall, diameter ⅛ inch, occasionally inclosed by bud scales, on laurel-leaved oak, gall wasp......................*Andricus calycicolus* Ashm. Many-celled, small, round, brown, thin-walled, diameter ⅛ inch on white and post oaks, resembles gall of *N. vesicula,* gall wasp. Fig. 87............*Dryophanta clarkei* Bass. Minute, round, thin-shelled gall in apparently normal young buds, on post oak, diameter ¹⁄₂₅ inch, gall wasp.......... ....*Dryophanta cressoni* Beutm.

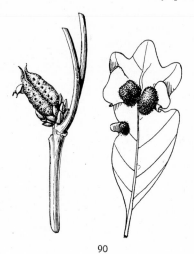

90

(Courtesy New York State Museum)

Fig. 90.—Gall of *Neuroterus minutus.*

Ellipsoidal, deciduous, lateral bud gall, attached to twig, diameter ⅙ inch, grayish with purplish streaks, on swamp white oak, fall, gall wasp. Pl. 24 (4)................... ....*Andricus deciduatus* Weld Globose, ⅙ to ⅓ inch long, succulent, green, bright red when young, the surface pebbled, with low, indefinite ridges terminating in soft, short spines, walls moderately thin, on small twigs of valley oak and *Q. douglasii,* April, gall wasp....................*Cynips lobata* McC. & Egb. Small, irregular, globular or ovate, slightly nippled, light brown bud gall, the surface with a fine scurfy pubescence, diameter ⅓ inch, on canyon live oak, gall wasp......... ....*Heteroecus chrysolepidis* Ashm.

Spindle-shaped, blunt-tipped, green, red-striped bud gall, length 1 inch, diameter $\frac{1}{10}$ inch, on red oak, spring, gall wasp. Pl. 23 (3)...........*Callirhytis gallæstriatæ* Weld

Kidney-shaped, $\frac{1}{5}$ to 1 inch long, many-celled, woody, yellowish green to brown, on *Q. vaccinifolia*, gall wasp.... ....*Andricus reniformis* McC. & Egb.

Oblong, oval, longitudinally ribbed, red-brown galls, without a distinct cell, occurring in groups of two or three and developing from buds, on blue jack and Spanish oaks, spring, gall wasp. Pl. 29 (2)............................... ....Jumping ribbed gall, *Trisoleniella saltatus* Ashm.

Clustered, globular, woolly bud capsules, apical or axillary clusters with a diameter of $\frac{1}{4}$ to $\frac{1}{3}$ inch, on *Q. ? gambelii*, gall wasp.................*Neuroterus congregatus* Gill.

Rounded, one-celled, yellowish, woolly bud gall, diameter $\frac{1}{2}$ inch, within a thin-shelled cell, diameter $\frac{1}{6}$ inch, on canyon live oak, gall wasp............................ ....*Heteroecus eriophorus* Kieff.

Globose, opaque, yellowish, sparsely brown-spotted, glabrous apically, one-celled, diameter $\frac{1}{3}$ inch, within spongy, a thick-shelled cell, diameter $\frac{1}{4}$ inch, on coast live, upland, live and California black oaks, gall wasp.................... ....*Callirhytis agrifoliæ* Bass.
(*clarimontis* Kieff.)

Oval, smooth, glabrous, woody, length $\frac{1}{2}$ inch, apically with a thin, longitudinally striate, thick and more or less bent point about $\frac{1}{3}$ inch long, on canyon live oak, gall wasp ....*Heteroecus pacificus* Ashm.

Globose, yellowish-brown, many-celled, with numerous irregular, longitudinal and transverse ridges or tuberosities, diameter $1\frac{1}{2}$ inches; apically a conical spur with a length of $\frac{1}{4}$ inch, within numerous oval cells, on interior live oak, gall wasp......................*Callirhytis rossi* Kieff.

Globular or elliptical, grayish-red, woody, the apex slightly pointed, length $\frac{1}{2}$ inch, California, gall wasp............ ....*Cynips sp.*

Subglobose, one-celled, yellowish, diameter about 1 inch, gall wasp...............................*Cynips sp.*

Ovate bud gall, the surface with numerous reddish scales, length $\frac{1}{2}$ inch, diameter $\frac{1}{3}$ inch, gall wasp............. ....*Andricus sp.*

Bud gall composed of a basal oblate part, with a height of $\frac{1}{8}$ inch and a conico-pyramidal portion, with a height

of ½ inch and a diameter of ⅓ to ½ inch, the larval cell in the basal portion, resembles *D. bassetti,* gall wasp.....
.........................*Heteroecus sanctæ-claræ* Full.

Subglobose, lateral bud gall, diameter ⅓-½ inch, gall midge.............................*Cecidomyia sp.*

Irregular, oval, bud gall, the leaflets hardly extending from the bud, mite.........................*Eriophyes sp.*

Irregular, swollen buds, mite. Pl. 16 (5)..............
....................................*Eriophyes sp.*

Gall narrowly cylindrical, silvery brown, diameter ¼ inch, length ⅓ inch, on *Q. undata,* gall wasp, Mex...........
.............................*Femuros geniale* Kins.

Similar gall, diameter ¼ inch, length ⅓ inch, on *Q. potosina, Q. chihuahuensis, Q. undata, Q. reticulata,* gall wasp, Mex.
.............................*Femuros integrum* Kins.

Gall cylindrical, tip widely flaring cup-shaped, silvery to yellow brown, diameter ½ inch, of top and length ¾ inch, on *Q. conglomerata,* gall wasp, Mex...*Femuros lusum* Kins.

Gall nearly globular or slightly elongated, cavity in upper half of gall nearly closed, silvery gray to purplish brown, on *Q. macrophylla,* gall wasp, Mex....................
.............................*Femuros perfectum* Kins.

Globular, diameter average over ½ inch, on *Q. repanda,* gall wasp, Mex.................*Femuros repandæ* Kins.

Globular, diameter average ⅝ inch, on *Q. texcocana, Q. conglomerata, Q. rhodophlebia,* gall wasp, Mex.........
.............................*Femuros ruidum* Kins.

Gall similar to two preceding, diameter ⅓ inch, on *Q. sacame, Q. hæmatophlebia, Q. rhodophlebia,* gall wasp, Mex.
.............................*Femuros ocri* Kins.

Leaf Galls

An extremely large series of oak leaf galls are known, probably because they are so readily detected. They are exceedingly variable in form and occur upon the leaf stem or petiole, at the base of the leaf itself, upon the midvein, upon the lateral veins or upon the leaf surface between the veins. There are two sets or groups of these galls. The spring or vernal which develop quickly while the leaves are increasing in size. These are of soft tissue which shrivels after the gall wasps escape in early summer. Such galls usually produce both sexes. The fall or autumnal galls appear in mid-summer on full grown leaves, they develop more slowly than the earlier spring forms and drop to the ground either before or with the leaves in the fall. These galls are composed of firmer tissue and develop a thick nutritive layer, the nourishment of the larva. The adults do not emerge until the following spring and they may remain in the galls for periods up to five years. These galls produce the female or asexual generation.

The position of the galls is somewhat characteristic, as well as the general type of gall and the method of production. Some originate in the deeper tissues and burst from cracks in the midrib. The vein galls may be little more than folds in the leaves or thickened, fleshy swellings of the veins and adjacent tissues, in which case they usually contain a number of cells. Even the normal leaf surface is thick enough so that a number of species are able to produce numerous galls without causing conspicuous swellings, some being mere blistered areas upon the leaf surface.

The shape of the leaf gall may vary from a slight, inconspicuous swelling to an oval or globose enlargement and in a number of species there may be very remarkable diversities. Some are disk-shaped, others top-shaped, angulate or even ornamented with well marked facets or strongly spined surfaces. The yellowish or reddish oak hedgehog gall is about half an inch in diameter and has a surface netted with fissures or cracks and is more or less densely covered with spines. The alternate generation of this species develops in small, almost imperceptible galls on the bud scales of strong terminal winter buds. These remarkable variations are greatly modified plant tissues, usually found upon the affected part or some other portion of the plant, or may be, as pointed out elsewhere, a blind though controlled response to irritation.

Leaf galls may occur singly, in groups or even in masses, may be smooth or more or less densely covered with woolly matter, really modified plant hairs. The same variation as to occurrence applies to the woolly as to the smooth or naked galls.

5. Galls of the leaves. (In some cases the leaf itself is aborted and the gall issues from the twig or bud.)

  a. Galls on the leaf stem or petiole:

Globose, hard, projecting equally above and beneath on petiole or midrib, at first smooth, reddish-brown, minutely pubescent, later turning black, within 5 longitudinal partitions, diameter ¼ inch, on chestnut, white, swamp white, post, burr and chinquapin oaks and Q. *michauxii*, gall wasp, Pl. 1 (1) Pl. 27 (5) Fig. 92 . . . .
. . . . .Oak petiole gall, *Andricus petiolicolus* Bass.
(*Andricus cicatriculus* Bass.)
(*Andricus quinqueseptum* Ashm.)
(*Andricus concolorans* Kins.)

Midrib, many-celled swellings mostly near the base of the leaf, some on the petiole, on black, and red oaks, summer, gall wasp. Pl. 27 (7) Fig. 97 . . . . .Midrib tumor gall, *Plagiotrochus tumificus* O.S.

Irregular basal swelling of outermost leaves in terminal cluster, producing a conspicuous rosette at end of twig, July, on Q. *sadleriana*, gall wasp. Fig. 88 . . . .*Neuroterus sadlerensis* Weld

Many-celled, irregular, clustered swellings of petiole and midrib, covered with pinkish pubescence, on white oak, spring, gall wasp. Pl. 35 (8); Fig. 90..................*Neuroterus minutus* Bass.

Irregular swellings containing thin-walled cells on the petiole, midrib or portions of the catkins dwarfing growth, on burr oak, spring, gall wasp. Fig. 91.........................*Neuroterus vernus* Gill.

Similar to above but on chinquapin oak, spring, gall wasp. Fig. 54. ....*Neuroterus tectus* Bass.

91   92

(Courtesy New York State Museum)

Fig. 91.—Gall of *Neuroterus vernus*. (*After Beutm.*)
Fig. 92.—Oak leaf stalk gall, *Andricus petiolicolus*.

Irregular, globose, petiole gall about the size and color of a large dry pea, on *Q. arizonica, Q. oblongifolia, Q. diversicolor*, fall, gall wasp. Pl. 23 (6).............................*Cynips sulcatus* Ashm.

Globular, below ochreous, not shining, internally brown, fibrous, with at least two cells, diameter ⅓ inch, on *Q. arizonica*..............
..................................*Disholcaspis arizonica* Ckll.

Globular, on petiole close to leaf, diameter ¼ to ⅓ inch, red, with

PLATE 17—CYNIPID GALLS. 1, Gall of *Andricus chrysolepidicola* Ashm., on *Q. dumosa*. 2, Gall of *Andricus asymmetricus* Kins., on canyon live oak. 3, Gall of *Andricus spectabilis* Kins., on canyon live oak. 4, Gall of *Bassettia ligni* Kins., from bottom to top on valley oak and *Q. durata, Q. dumosa, Q. douglasii*, 5, Gall of *Plagiotrochus suberi* Weld, on cork oak. 6, Gall of *Eumayria herberti* Weld on California black oak. 7, Gall of *Plagiotrochus frequens* Gill., on *Q. gambellii*. 8, Gall of *Cynips multipunctata* Beutm., on valley oak. 9, Gall of *Cynips douglasii* Ashm., on *Q. douglasii, Q. dumosa*. (*All after Weld*).

PLATE 17

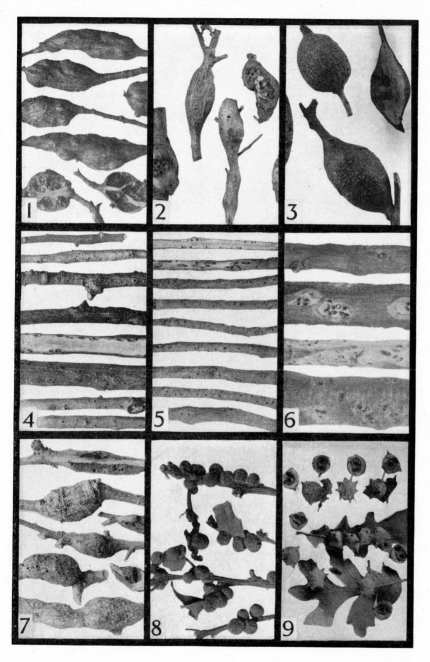

no separable larval cell, on *Q. texana,* fall, gall wasp. Pl. 26 (8)
...................................*Callirhytis attigua* Weld
Irregular, somewhat triangular, hard, finely rugose, blackish, seed-like gall, mostly covered with a whitish bloom, probably in clusters on petiole, gall wasp..............*Callirhytis crassicornis* Ashm.
Spindle-shaped, clustered, at base of petiole, galls ⅓ inch long, diameter ⅕ inch, brownish, covered with stellate hairs, on post oak, fall, gall wasp. Pl. 26 (5)...............*Andricus biconicus* Weld
A slight swelling of the petiole, young leaf or bud, on swamp white and ? chestnut oaks, gall wasp, bisexual generation. Pl. 21 (3).....
...................................*Neuroterus distortus* Bass.

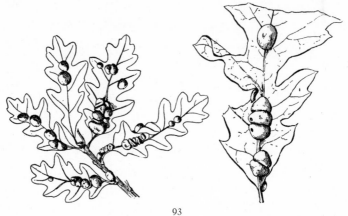

93

(Courtesy New York State Museum)

Fig. 93.—Gall of *Dryophanta eburnea.* *(After Beutm.)*

   b. A thickening of the midvein, sometimes of the petiole or lateral veins. (See also (13), p. 209, and (15), a, b, p. 209, 210)

     (1) Swellings abrupt

        (a) Midrib thickenings, not detachable:

Many-celled, abrupt, polished, hard swelling on underside of midrib 1 to 2½ inches long, ½ to ¾ inches in diameter, on *Q. wislizeni* and ? coast live oak, spring, gall wasp. Pl. 22 (3).....................*Callirhytis flora* Weld
Elongate, many-celled midrib swelling with the larval cells perpendicular to the surface of the leaf, length ¾ inch, diameter ⅓ inch, on *Q. gambelii,* gall wasp............
....................*Neuroterus quercicola* Dalle Torre
Similar gall, covered with bluish-gray, dense pubescense, on *Q. grisea,* gall wasp.........*Neuroterus pubescens* Kins.

Small, rounded, many-celled, midvein gall projecting equally
on both surfaces, diameter ⅛ inch, on *Q. chapmani*, gall
wasp....................*Callirhytis parvifoliæ* Ashm.

Globose, many-celled, midvein gall near the base of the
leaf, prominent on both surfaces, diameter ¼ inch, cells
radiating from a common center and not separable from
the woody fiber, on *Q. arizonica*, *Q. grisea*, *Q. oblongifolia*,
Q. toumeyi, gall wasp......*Plagiotrochus reticulatus* Bass.

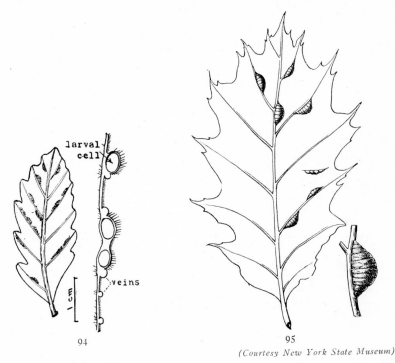

94   95

(Courtesy New York State Museum)

FIG. 94.—Gall of *Neuroterus fugiens*, showing leaf with galls and sections of galls
beside the veins. *(After Weld)*

FIG. 95.—Gall of *Cecidomyia sp.*, one enlarged.

Globose, greenish-brown, clustered leaf gall sometimes
slightly flattened basally, irregularly wrinkled and covered
with dense, short, woolly hairs, diameter ⅓ inch, on *Q.
douglasii*, gall wasp. Pl. 17 (8), Fig. 62...............
......................*Cynips multipunctata* Beutm.

Similar gall on *Q. douglasii*, gall wasp..*Cynips indicta* Kins.

Similar gall on valley oak, agamic form, gall wasp........
...........................*Cynips conspicua* Kins.

Irregular, many-celled, globose, occurring near the base of the leaf and projecting about equally above and below, diameter ⅙ to ¼ inch, on unknown oak, Ariz., gall wasp....
.........................*Andricus morrisoni* Ashm.

Irregular rounded, oval or elongate thickening of midrib and adjacent veins sometimes deforming the entire leaf, green, turning brown and becoming woody when old, length ½ to 1½ inches, thickness about ½ inch, on oregon oak, gall wasp...........*Neuroterus washingtonensis* Beutm.

Woolly midvein lemon yellow or orange brown, core many celled, diameter 1 to 1½ inches, on upper surface, on *Q. macrophylla,* gall wasp, Mex.....*Andricus mexicanus* Kins.

(b) Detachable galls on midribs only:

Midrib cluster on under side in fall, dropping when mature, each globular, tapering to a pedicel at base and pointed with a slight scar at apex, greenish, turning brown in winter, post oak, gall wasp.............*Andricus robustus* Weld

Globose, clustered, one-celled, with a more or less distinct nipple apically and a long stem basally, brown when old, probably green when fresh, diameter ⅙ to ¼ inch, stem ½ to 1¼ inches, resembles a huckleberry, on post oak, fall, gall wasp. Pl. 22 (5)...............................
........Huckleberry oak gall, *Callirhytis lustrans* Beutm.
(*impositus* Beutm., *verifactor* Kins.)

Soft, thin-shelled, red or brown vein galls, frequently closely pressed together and somewhat resembling figs, on white, basket and chinquapin oaks, (occasionally on twig) summer, fall, gall wasp. Fig. 80........................
.............Oak fig gall, *Xanthoteras forticorne* Walsh

Rounded, closely packed, lobed mass of cells on under side of midrib or lateral veins, ¼ to ⅓ inch in diameter, 20 or more rounded cells, pink, rose or tan color, on valley oak, gall wasp. Pl. 22 (6).....*Andricus confertus* McC. & Egb.

Rounded or elongate midrib swellings filled with oblong or elongate kernels, a few to 40; when young concealed in the tissues and bursting open in October, on red, black and scrub oaks, fall, gall wasp........................
..............Deciduous oak gall, or "black oak wheat"
Dryocosmus deciduus Beutm.

Globular, single or clustered leaf gall, covered with minute warty pubescent dots, one-celled, fleshy, on the upper surface, diameter ⅛ inch, on post oak, gall wasp. Fig. 105.
..............................*Biorhiza mellea* Ashm.

Globular, clusters of 2-12 along midrib and on underside, whitish or tan colored, sparsely pubescent, diameter ⅛ inch, on white oak, gall wasp, autumn. Pl. 25 (8)............
...........................*Cynips capillata* Weld
Globular, clusters of 2-4 along midrib, mostly on upper surface, with groups of stellate hairs, diameter ¼ inch, on

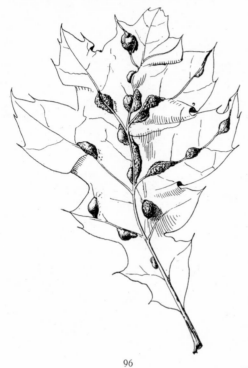

96

(Courtesy New York State Museum)

FIG. 96.—Gall of *Cecidomyia sp.* on black oak.

white and post oaks and ? *Q. breviloba, Q. chapmani,* gall wasp, midsummer. Pl. 32 (4); Fig. 86...............
.........................*Acraspis carolina* Ashm.
Midrib clusters, on under side of globose, bluntly tuberculate galls, dark red, diameter ¼ inch, with a scar at the apex and a short stalk, one-celled, on overcup oak, gall wasp. Pl. 30 (6)...............*Andricus rugatus* Weld
(c) Other galls associated with midribs:
Subglobular, straw-colored or brown, flattened next the leaf, within a larval cell with radiating fibers, diameter ⅙-¼

inch, on *Q. gambelii, Q. grisea, Q. undulata,* gall wasp.
Fig. 93....................*Dryophanta eburnea* Bass.
Globose, green, diameter $\frac{1}{12}$ inch, beside midrib of young
leaves, stunting them, the margin fimbriate, on valley oak,
and *Q. douglasii, Q. dumosa,* gall wasp. Pl. 30 (6).......
............................*Andricus fimbrialis* Weld

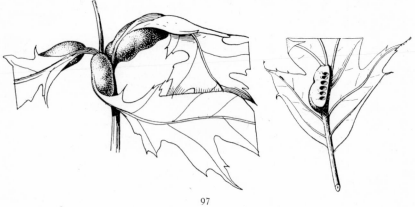

97

(Courtesy New York State Museum)

FIG. 97.—Midrib tumor gall, *Plagiotrochus tumificus,* three entire galls and one in
section.

Oval, the upper corners nodulate, thin-shelled, on under
side of midrib and lateral veins, greenish to tan, one-celled,
length $\frac{1}{10}$ inch, on evergreen oak, gall wasp............
....................*Callirhytis bicornus* McC. & Egb.
Tooth-shaped slightly spined, height $\frac{1}{2}$ inch, diameter $\frac{1}{4}$
inch, arising beside the midvein, a slit on the upper surface,
the greenish and crimson or purplish tinted gall below, on
Q. emoryi and *Q. wrightii,* scale insect...............
............................*Olliffiella cristicola* Ckll.
Fusiform, ribbed or carinate mid or lateral vein folds on
the under surface, length $\frac{1}{4}$ to $\frac{1}{3}$ inch, diameter $\frac{1}{8}$ inch,
gall midge. Pl. 9 (1); Fig. 95, 96........*Cecidomyia sp.*

(2) Swellings less abrupt and localized enlargements of midveins
(more rarely of lateral veins and the petioles):

PLATE 18—CYNIPID GALLS. 1, Globular root gall, *Disholcaspis globosa* Weld, on white
oak. 2, Gall of *Callirhytis washingtonensis* Gill, on Oregon oak. 3, Lobed oak gall,
Cynips strobilana O.S., on overcup oak. 4, Gall of *Disholcaspis pattersoni* Kins., on
Q. breviloba. 5, Gall of *Disholcaspis terrestris* Weld, on post oak. 6, Woolly fig gall,
Disholcaspis spongiosa Karsch, on post oak. 7, Gall of *Callirhytis seminosa* Bass., on
pin oak. 8, Gall of *Andricus aciculatus* Beutm., on post oak. 9, Gall of *Disholcaspis
lacuna* Weld, on *Q. gambellii.* (*All after Weld*).

PLATE 18

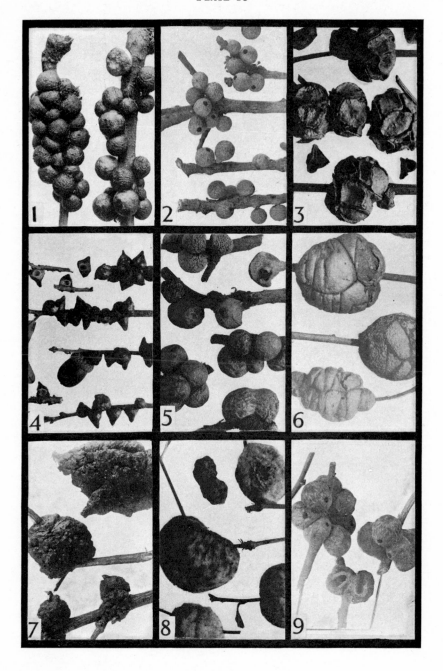

Hemispherical or irregular tufts $\frac{1}{2}$ inch long of rather long, whitish or reddish wool covering 2 to 6 irregular, brown, seed-like kernels on under side of midrib, diameter $\frac{1}{12}$ inch, on live oak, summer, gall wasp. Pl. 31 (7)......................
................Wool bearing gall, *Andricus lanigera* Ashm.
Midrib, fleshy, green, 1-6 larvae, with rosette of leaf-like rudiments on upper surface, on swamp white and burr oaks, June, gall wasp. Pl. 22 (7)................*Andricus foliosus* Weld

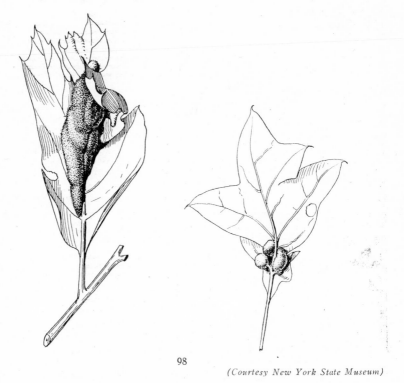

98

(Courtesy New York State Museum)

FIG. 98.—Woolly fold gall, *Cecidomyia niveipila,* badly and slightly deformed leaves and two galls in the early stages of development.   .

Irregular, elongate or globose enlargements of the midrib, on black jack oak, gall wasp. Pl. 22 (2).....*Callirhytis nigræ* O.S.
Irregular, many-celled, midrib swellings, often $1\frac{1}{4}$ inches long, $\frac{1}{2}$ inch in diameter, on red, scarlet, black jack oaks, fall, gall wasp. Pl. 22 (4)........Oak midrib gall, *Andricus piger* Bass.
Slight, fleshy swelling along the midrib, containing 2 or more small cells, diameter of latter $\frac{1}{10}$ inch, on laurel-leaved oak, gall wasp............................*Callirhytis cellæ* Ashm.
Hard, fusiform swelling of midvein or lateral vein, green, length

¾ inch, diameter ¼ inch, on burr oak, spring, gall wasp......
...............................*Callirhytis flavipes* Gill.

Irregular, pustule-like, many-celled petiole and midrib gall (usually in axis of staminate flowers), on post oak, gall wasp...
...............................*Neuroterus exiguus* Bass.

Pyriform or clavate reddish vein galls, the expanded portion of the lateral ridge with longitudinal striations, height ¼ inch, diameter ⅙ inch, on valley oak, gall wasp................
..............................*Andricus pistillaris* Trott.

Globose, one-celled, single or clustered mid or lateral vein galls, diameter ¼ to ⅓ inch, gall wasp.........*Cynips,* several *sp.*

Narrow, dark purplish, fusiform, thin-walled swelling on the underside of the mid or lateral veins; may contain 2 or more larvae, length ⅓ inch, gall midge. Pl. 8 (9)................
.............Purple oak vein gall, *Cincticornia podagræ* Felt

Large midrib fold with a conspicuous white pubescence, the leaf frequently deformed, gall midge. Fig. 98...................
................Woolly fold gall, *Cecidomyia niveipila* O.S.

Elongate, pocket-like swellings along the midrib of scrub oak, length ⅕ inch, gall midge. Pl. 8 (3).......................
..............Vein pocket gall, *Parallelodiplosis florida* Felt

Elongate fold gall close to the midrib on the under surface, length ½ inch, diameter $\frac{1}{25}$ inch, possibly identical with preceding, gall midge...................*Cecidomyia oruca* Walsh

Fusiform, thin-walled, striate, pale green vein swelling, length ⅕ inch, diameter ⅛ inch, on red oak, gall midge. Pl. 8 (1)
....*Cecidomyia sp.*

Hemispherical or subhemispherical, pale brown, minutely crackled vein gall, diameter ⅙ inch, height $\frac{1}{10}$ inch, gall wasp. Fig. 100.....................*Neuroterus cockerelli* Beutm.

A rounded blister-like swelling on the lateral veins, length ⅛ inch, diameter $\frac{1}{25}$ inch, on Spanish oak, gall midge.........
...............Oak vein blister, *Cincticornia americana* Felt

Possibly identical with above, gall midge. Pl. 9 (2)..........
...............................*Cincticornia majalis* O.S.

Subglobose or fusiform, pale green, yellow margined leaf fold, mostly on under surface, length ⅛ to ¼ inch, diameter ⅛ inch, gall midge............................*Cecidomyia sp.*

Oval, thin-walled, one-celled swellings on midrib and minor veins, covered with a dense brown pubescence, dwarfing leaf, on white oak, gall wasp.............*Neuroterus bassetti* D.T.

Oval midrib patches of long whitish or purplish plant hairs, on under surface, on *Q. englemanni*, mite..........*Eriophyes sp.*

(3) A whole leaf is swollen to form a fleshy, elongated gall:

Very irregular swollen mass originating from the midvein or petiole of the leaf and involving the whole structure, green and succulent, later shriveling and drying, size variable, on swamp white oak, gall wasp. Pl. 29 (5); Fig. 56.................
..............Noxious oak gall, *Neuroterus noxiosus* Bass.

Similar gall on chestnut oak, gall wasp...*Neuroterus prini* Kins.

c. Galls involving or attached to the blade or lamina of the leaves:

(1) Little or no thickening of the leaf tissues. See also nos. 2, 3, 4, 5,

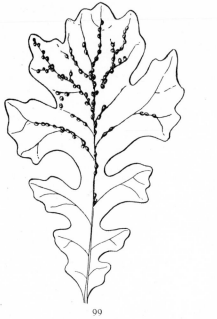
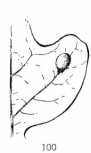

99   100

(Courtesy New York State Museum)

FIG. 99.—Gall of *Neuroterus niger*. (*After Beutm.*)
FIG. 100.—Gall of *Neuroterus cockerelli*. (*After Beutm.*)

6, 7, 8, 9, 10, 11, 12, 13, 14, 15, 16, 17 and 18 on pages 153, 154, 158, 161, 164, 170, 173, 194, 195, 198, 206, 209, 212, 219 and 220.

(a) Small blister-like or pustular swellings of the leaf blade:

Globose or blister-like, one-celled leaf vein swelling, more distinct on the upper side and with a minute nipple on the lower surface, diameter $\frac{1}{20}$ inch, on white and burr oaks, gall wasp. Fig. 99...............*Neuroterus niger* Gill.

Similar gall on white oak, gall wasp. Pl. 28 (6).........
.......................*Neuroterus perminimus* Bass.

Round blotches, thin-walled, one-celled, single or clustered, showing on both surfaces, exit holes below, diameter $\frac{1}{5}$ inch, on *Q. arizonica, Q. grisea, Q. oblongifolia, Q. toumeyi*, gall wasp. Fig. 101 . . . . *Neuroterus howertoni* Bass.

Clusters of green or brownish-yellow, egg-like cells on leaf blades, oval, length $\frac{1}{16}$ inch, on *Q. douglasii*, gall wasp. Pl. 29 (4) . . . . *Neuroterus decipiens* Kins.

Elongate, oval, blister-like leaf swelling without a nipple, on the under surface, length $\frac{1}{25}$ inch, on swamp white oak, gall wasp. Fig. 102 . . . .
. . . . Oak blister gall, *Neuroterus papillosus* Beutm.

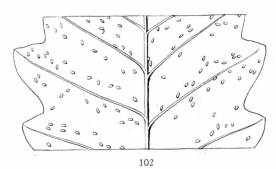

(Courtesy New York State Museum)

101   102

Fig. 101.—Gall of *Neuroterus howertoni.* (*After Beutm.*)
Fig. 102.—Oak blister gall, *Neuroterus papilosus.*

Slender, elongate, distinctly bounded on upper surface, no central point, often two cells fused, on live oak, gall wasp
. . . . *Neuroterus alimas* Kins.

Circular, slightly elongate, only a trace of a point on under surface, on *Q. arizonica*, gall wasp . . . .
. . . . *Neuroterus arizonicæ* Kins.

Circular, well defined boundaries, an indefinite central point on upper surface, on *Q. englemanni*, gall wasp . . . .
. . . . *Neuroterus englemanni* Kins.

More elongate than circular, not much thickening, on *Q. grisea*, gall wasp . . . . *Neuroterus griseæ* Kins.

Circular, slightly elongate, slightly larger than *pattersoni*, on post oak and *Q. breviloba*, gall wasp . . . .
. . . . *Neuroterus nigripes* Kins.

Circular, slightly smaller than *nigripes*, more defined boundaries, no central point on upper surface, on post oak, gall wasp . . . . *Neuroterus pattersoni* Kins.

Galls, minute, circular or ovoid pustules in leaf blade, naked, inconspicuous, on both surfaces, color same as leaf, old galls brownish, diameter $\frac{1}{25}$ inch, on *Q. macrophylla*, gall wasp, Mex. . . . . *Neuroterus reconditus* Kins.

Flattened, hemispherical gall, slightly pubescent, thick-walled, mostly on under surface, broadly attached, older galls dark brown, on post oak, gall wasp. . . . .
. . . .*Neuroterus pulvinus* Kins.

Blister-like, narrowly oval galls on or near the veins, length $\frac{1}{25}$ to $\frac{1}{12}$ inch, on Spanish oak, early summer, sexual generation, gall wasp. Pl. 2 (6). .*Plagiotrochus punctatus* Bass.

Ovoid, whitish galls, along midrib or larger veins, $\frac{1}{15}$ to $\frac{1}{10}$ inch long, on Spanish oak, pin and scrub oaks, early summer, sexual generation, gall wasp. . . . .
. . . .*Plagiotrochus cornigerus* O.S.

Narrowly oval, inconspicuous blister galls, along midvein on underside, length $\frac{1}{12}$ inch, on willow oak, early summer, sexual generation, gall wasp. Pl. 2 (5). . . . .
. . . .*Andricus clavigerus* O.S.

A lens-shaped thickening beside lateral veins, single or confluent, mostly on lower surface, on young leaves of burr and swamp white oaks, spring, gall wasp. Fig. 94. . . . .
. . . .*Neuroterus fugiens* Weld

Subelliptical, blister leaf gall, length $\frac{1}{10}$ inch, canyon live oak, Cal., gall wasp. . . . .*Neuroterus sp.*

Broadly yellow-margined, circular, blister gall, diameter $\frac{1}{8}$ inch, on scarlet oak, gall midge. . . . .
. . . . .Oak yellow-spot, *Cincticornia serrata* Felt

A variable brown, irregularly oval, pustulate leaf swelling, diameter $\frac{1}{5}$ inch, on black and Spanish oaks, gall midge, Pl. 8 (7). . . . .
. . . . .Oak blister midge, *Cincticornia pustulata* Felt

An irregularly oval, pustulate swelling showing equally on both leaf surfaces, no nipple, diameter $\frac{1}{5}$ inch, on black and Spanish oaks, gall midges. Pl. 8 (8). . . . .
. . . .*Cincticornia simpla* Felt
Cincticornia sobrina Felt

PLATE 19—CYNIPID GALLS. 1, Gall of *Callirhytis milleri* Weld, on coast live oak. 2, Gall of *Plagiotrochus perdens* Kins., on coast live oak. 3, Gall of *Callirhytis congregata* Ashm., on coast live oak. 4, Warty oak gall, *Callirhytis middletoni* Weld, ×3, on willow oak. 5, Live oak potato gall, *Plagiotrochus batatoides* Ashm., on live oak. 6, Gall of *Andricus virens* Ashm., on live oak. 7, Gall of *Callirhytis humicola* Kins., on interior live oak. 8, Gall of *Andricus murtfeldtæ* Ashm. ×3, on post oak. 9, Gall of *Andricus kelloggi* Full., on *Q. douglasii*. (*All after Weld*).

PLATE 19

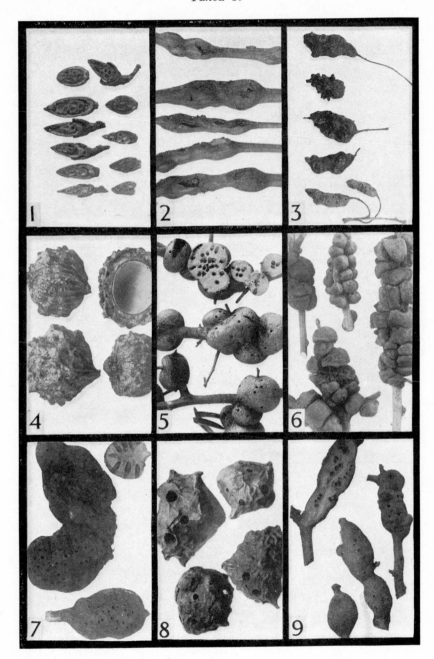

A slightly oval, blister-like swelling of the lateral veins, length ⅛ inch, gall midge.............................
...........Oak vein blister, *Cincticornia americana* Felt
Flat, inconspicuous, presumably blister gall, on Spanish oak, gall midge.................*Cincticornia quercifolia* Felt
Blister leaf gall, inconspicuous, greenish, circular, diameter ⅕ inch, on evergreen oak, gall midge....? *Cincticornia sp.*

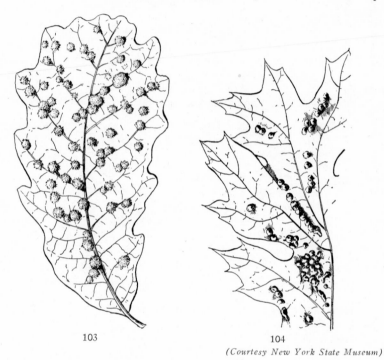

103   104

(Courtesy New York State Museum)

Fig. 103.—Oak flake gall, *Neuroterus floccosus. (After Beutm.)*
Fig. 104.—Gall of *Dryophanta modesta. (After Beutm.)*

(b) Superabundant leaf hairs (*Erineum*) or more or lest distinct dimples:
Yellowish-green dimples convex on the upper surface, lined with whitish or brownish hairs, on white oak, mite........
....................................*Eriophyes sp.*
Very small pocket galls crowded on the upper surface of the leaf, on swamp white oak, mite.........*Eriophyes sp.*
Galls on leaves of burr oak, mite...*Eriophyes querci* Garm.
Marginal deformation of leaves, on post oak, mite........
....................................? *Eriophyes sp.*

Large greenish-yellow dimples, slightly convex above, beneath filled with dense brown pubescence, on burr oak, mite ....*Eriophyes sp.*

Greenish or reddish elevations on the upper surface, the concavity below nearly filled with yellowish-brown hairs, on black jack oak, mite..................*Eriophyes sp.*

Brown erineum on undersurface of leaves, on Spanish oak, mite...............................*Eriophyes sp.*

Large patches of dense brown hairs on underside of leaf, on scarlet oak, mite.....................*Eriophyes sp.*

Velvety-red erineum on under side of leaf, the younger portion greenish, on black oak, mite........*Eriophyes sp.*

Snuff-brown erineum in large patches on under side of the leaf, on scrub oak, mite..................*Eriophyes sp.*

Ashen erineum in vein angles and spreading along veins, mostly on under side of leaves, on black and pin oaks, and *Q. texana*, mite........................*Eriophyes sp.*

(2) Blister above blade or lamina, woolly gall beneath:

Globose leaf gall, smooth above, thickly covered with white wool below, single or confluent, diameter $\frac{1}{16}$ to $\frac{1}{8}$ inch, on white oak, spring, gall wasp..........*Neuroterus exiguissimus* Bass.

Similar gall on white oak, gall wasp. Pl. 31 (2); Fig. 103...... ....Oak flake gall, *Neuroterus floccosus* Bass.

Wart-like above, hemispherical, white, dense woolly below, diameter $\frac{1}{10}$ inch, on post oak, gall wasp. Fig. 152.......... ....*Neuroterus verrucarum* O.S.

Similar gall on *Q. breviloba*, gall wasp..................... ....*Neuroterus inficiens* Kins.

Similar though smaller gall on post oak and *Q. breviloba*, gall wasp...........................*Neuroterus opacus* Kins.

Similar gall on burr oak, gall wasp....................... ....*Neuroterus macrocarpæ* Kins.

Similar, larger gall on swamp white oak, gall wasp............ ....*Neuroterus pernotus* Kins.

Similar, rather large gall, papilla on upper surface, on *Q. chapmani*, *Q. margaretta* (and ? *Q. geminata*), gall wasp.......... ....*Neuroterus restrictus* Kins.

Galls minute, elongate-oval, hard, thin-walled, elevated center on upper surface, surface minutely granulate, each gall broadly attached to under surface, sparsely hairy, cells $\frac{1}{100}$ by $\frac{1}{50}$ inch, on *Q. macrophylla*, gall wasp. Mex...*Neuroterus visibilis* Kins.

Similar gall, cells $\frac{1}{20}$ by $\frac{1}{25}$ inch, covered with a circular tangle

of brown hairs, under surface of leaf often densely covered with galls, on *Q. texcocana,* gall wasp. Mex....................
...............................*Neuroterus volutans* Kins.
Similar gall, cells $\frac{1}{35}$ inch long, densely covered and hidden by a whitish hair mass $\frac{1}{10}$ inch in diameter, on *Q. macrophylla,* gall wasp. Mex.................*Neuroterus vulpinus* Kins.

(3) Rounded gall with several cells imbedded in the blade or lamina of the leaf:

Small, slightly flattened, green leaf gall projecting from both surfaces, hollow, containing 2 or 3 oblong, filament suspended

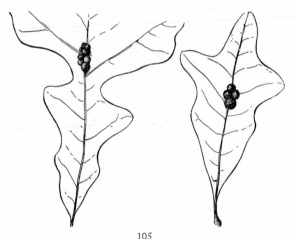

105

(Courtesy New York State Museum)

Fig. 105.—Gall of *Biorhiza mellea. (After Beutm.)*

cells, diameter $\frac{1}{8}$ inch, on white oak, gall wasp, agamic generation. Pl. 2 (6); Pl. 31 (3)..Oak wart gall, *Callirhytis futilis* O.S.
(*C. papillatus* O.S.)

Small, irregular, hard swelling on both sides of the leaf, concolorous, diameter $\frac{1}{6}$ inch, on Spanish and red oaks, spring, gall wasp. Pl. 28 (1), Fig. 104..........*Callirhytis modesta* O.S.
(*papula* Bass.)

Flattened, many-celled leaf galls projecting from both surfaces, diameter $\frac{1}{4}$ to 1 inch, the upper and lower surfaces resembling a honeycomb, on black oak, gall wasp.....................
...........Honey-comb leaf gall, *Plagiotrochus favosus* Bass.

(4) Galls making a sort of thickened and elevated area in the blade or lamina:

(a) The platform is formed of crowded, one-celled galls:

Pustulate, circular, one-celled swellings in leaf tissues, often several galls confluent, under surface of leaf somewhat distended, diameter $\frac{1}{20}$ inch, on *Q. engelmanni*, gall wasp . . . . *Neuroterus engelmanni* Kins.

Gall irregular, one or many celled in leaf blade, well developed on both surfaces, pubescence short and dense, galls separable or fused, on *Q. texcocana*, gall wasp, Mex. . . . . *Neuroterus junctor* Kins.

Spherical, one-celled, fleshy walled capsules imbedded in the leaf blade, diameter $\frac{1}{4}$ inch, walls thick, succulent, on coast, and upland live oaks and California black oak, gall wasp . . . . *Andricus perjoveatus* Kins.

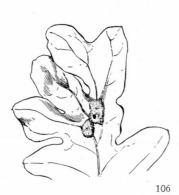

106

(Courtesy New York State Museum)

Fig. 106.—Gall of *Neuroterus irregularis*. (*After Beutm.*)

Subglobular, smooth, fleshy, white, pink or red, on undersurface, one-celled, diameter $\frac{1}{10}$ to $\frac{1}{6}$ inch, on scarlet oak, gall wasp . . . . "*Cynips sera*" Steb.

Subglobular, single or clustered, on both leaf surfaces, green or red tinged, diameter $\frac{1}{10}$ to $\frac{1}{5}$ inch, on canyon live oak and *Q. vaccinifolia*, gall wasp . . . . *Callirhytis flavens* McC. & Egb.

(b) The platform is made by a single, many-celled gall:

Irregular, somewhat flattened, many-celled, yellowish, pithy, leaf galls, on white and post oaks, gall wasp, Fig. 106. . . . . *Neuroterus irregularis* O.S.

Similar gall on white and post oaks, gall wasp. . . . . *Neuroterus variegatus* Kins.

Similar gall on *Q. breviloba*, gall wasp. . . . . *Neuroterus albipleuræ* Kins.

Flattened, often very irregular, green, succulent leaf galls, horizontal diameter $\frac{1}{4}$ to 1 inch, vertical diameter $\frac{1}{4}$ to

⅓ inch, on white oak, gall wasp. Pl. 27 (9); Fig. 167.....
.............................*Neuroterus majalis* Bass.

Pale yellowish-green, irregular, many-celled leaf galls, usually on the midrib, on *Q. dumosa,* gall wasp. Pl. 29 (3) Fig. 107.....................*Neuroterus fragilis* Bass.

Similar gall on *Q. douglasii,* gall wasp.................
.........................*Neuroterus pacificus* Kins.

107

(Courtesy New York State Museum)

FIG. 107.—Gall of *Neuroterus fragilis. (After Beutm.)*

Globose or subglobose, irregular, reddish, wrinkled leaf gall, diameter ⅛ inch, on red, pin and Spanish oaks, gall midge. Pl. 9 (3)...Oak pill gall, *Cincticornia pilulæ* Walsh

Similar to preceding, possibly identical, apparently southern, gall midge...........*Cincticornia symmetrica* O.S.

Gall similar to though much smaller than the oak pill gall, gall midge....................*Dasyneura florida* Felt

Roly-Poly Galls

The peculiar growths on oak we have termed roly-poly galls may represent an extreme development of the oak apple in that the central cell be-

PLATE 20—CYNIPID GALLS. 1, Gall of *Odontocynips nebulosa* Kieff., on post oak. 2, Gall of *Disholcaspis acetabula* Weld, on *Q. gambellii.* 3, Gall of *Disholcaspis perniciosa* Bass., on *Q. gambellii.* 4, Gall of *Callirhytis rhizoxenus* Ashm., on *Q. diversifolia.* 5, Gall of *Callirhytis ruginosus* Bass., on *Q. grisea.* 6, Gall of *Andricus toumeyi* Weld, ×3, on *Q. toumeyi.* 7, Gall of *Compsodryoxenus tenuis* Weld on *Q. fendleri.* 8, Gall of *Andricus wheeleri* Beutm., on *Q. arizonica.* 9, Gall of *Aulacidea nabali* Brodie on *Prenanthes alba.* (*All after Weld*).

PLATE 20

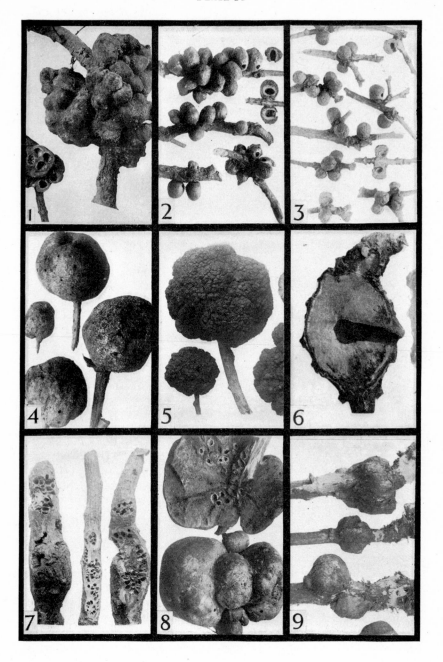

comes entirely free after a time and rolls about in the cavity bounded by the thick outer walls. These galls appear in early spring on the leaves of red oak and are at first solid, the larval cell being connected with the outer walls. Eventually definite layers are formed and the inner or cell walls retain nearly their original dimensions, while the outer walls thicken, increase in size and thus bring about the separation of the two and result in a free rolling cell, analogous to the free seeds in the seed capsules of certain lilies. The larva in this free cell probably secures nourishment by osmosis, from the thick nutritive inner layer of its cell, although in damp weather the outer shell of the galls contain more or less viscous fluid. The

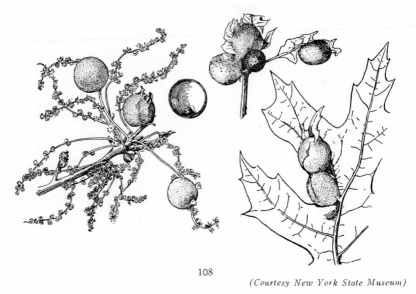

108

(Courtesy New York State Museum)

Fig. 103.—Succulent oak gall, *Andricus palustris*. (*After Beutm.*)

galls are usually not over half an inch in diameter and may be found here and there upon the leaves in summer.

One of the most common is the so-called succulent oak gall. The alternate generation of this species produces a small, globular, white or pinkish gall about one-eighth of an inch in diameter on the surface of oak leaves. When mature, the gall drops to the ground, increases in size, turns brown, becomes thin walled, the larva developing in the hollow gall. Here is a case where some believe there may be growth or development after the gall has separated from the plant of which it was once a part, though Dr. Weld questions it and suggests that any change in shape after the gall drops may be due to larval demands weakening the texture of the internal nutritive layer of the gall.

(5) Roly-poly galls, hollow, spherical, semi-spherical or conical,

usually succulent; the gall enclosing a chamber in which the
larval cell lies free. Some of these galls are loosely attached to
the leaf, though most often they are imbedded in the blade.

(a) Gall globular:

Globose, succulent, hollow leaf, bud and catkin gall containing a white, free globular kernel, green, sometimes red
tinged, diameter ¼ to ½ inch, on red oaks, gall wasp,
spring, Pl. 27 (1) Fig. 108.........................
..............Succulent oak gall, *Andricus palustris* O.S.

Globose, white or red-tinged, waxy, juicy, one-celled, diameter ⅛ inch, on under surface of leaves, on scarlet and red
oaks, fall, gall wasp.......*Zopheroteras compressum* Gill.

Globose or slightly ellipsoidal, not depressed, singly or 3 or
4 in a row, diameter ⅛ inch, greenish or yellowish green,
tinged with red, on both leaf surfaces of red oak, fall, gall
wasp....................*Zopheroteras sphærula* Weld

 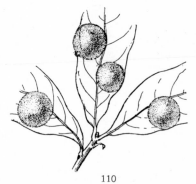

(Courtesy New York State Museum)

109   110

FIG. 109.—Gall of *Dryophanta aquaticæ*. (*After Beutm.*)
FIG. 110.—Gall of *Dryophanta laurifoliæ*. (*After Beutm.*)

Globose, hollow, plum-colored leaf gall similar to *Dryophanta palustris* and developing equally upon both leaf
surfaces, within a small free cell, on water oak, gall wasp,
Fig. 109................*Dryophanta aquaticæ* Ashm.

Gall similar to that of *D. palustris*, projecting about equally
on both surfaces of the leaf, length ⅕ inch, on willow and
laurel-leaved oaks, gall wasp. Fig. 110................
....................*Dryophanta laurifoliæ* Ashm.

Globose, succulent leaf gall similar to that of *Dryophanta
aquaticæ* but much smaller, on turkey oak, gall wasp......
....................*Dryophanta quercifoliæ* Ashm.

Globose, somewhat roughened, fuzzy, thick celled leaf galls closely resembling those of *D. palustris,* diameter ¼ to ⅓ inch, on scarlet and red oaks, gall wasp.................
......................*Dryophanta liberœcellulœ* Gill.

Globose, succulent, yellowish-green, containing a free cell and attached to the vein on the underside of the leaf of laurel-leaved oak, diameter ¹⁄₁₆ inch, height ¹⁄₁₀ inch, spring, gall wasp..................*Dryophanta confusa* Ashm.

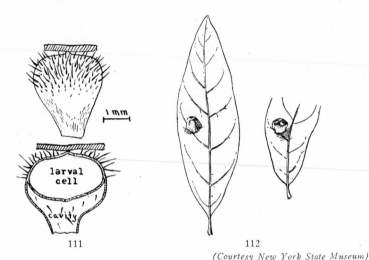

111   112
(Courtesy New York State Museum)

Fig. 111.—Gall of *Cynips cœpula.* (*After Weld*)
Fig. 112.—Gall of *Dryophanta cinereœ.* (*After Beutm.*)

(b) Gall hemispherical or conical, attached to the under surface of the leaf:

Subglobose, greenish-gray, somewhat longitudinally ribbed, rugose, sessile, within a loose kernel, diameter ⅙ inch, on red, Spanish, shingle, black, black jack, blue jack and willow oaks, gall wasp. Pl. 31, (4) Fig. 112.............
..........................*Dryophanta cinereœ* Ashm.
(*saccularia* Bass.)

Hemispherical leaf gall covered with a white, crystal-like pubescence, diameter ¹⁄₁₀ inch, on post oak, gall wasp. Fig. 152......................*Neuroterus verrucarum* O.S.

Single or clustered, conical, bluish-gray, one-celled leaf galls, height ⅛ inch, diameter ¹⁄₁₀ inch, on burr and overcup oaks, gall wasp. Pl. 28 (2), Fig. 114
..........................*Xystoteras volutellœ* Ashm.

(6) Gall solid, spherical, succulent, usually firmly attached to the leaf blade:

Globular or ovate, green, sometimes tinged with pink, translucent, diameter ¼ to ¾ inch, on red, scarlet, Spanish, scrub and black oaks, June, gall wasp. Fig. 115.....................
.........Translucent oak gall, *Amphibolips nubilipennis* Harr.

Globose, crisp, sour, succulent, green, turning brown, internally with a reddish larval cell, diameter ⅓ inch, on laurel-leaved shingle, water and willow oaks, spring, gall wasp. Fig. 116.....
........................*Amphibolips racemaria* Ashm.

Globose, white or rosy, juicy leaf gall on the upper surface, diameter ⅛ inch, on white and chestnut oaks, fall, gall wasp
...............................*Biorhiza rubina* Gill.

113

114

(Courtesy New York State Museum)

FIG. 113.—Gall of *Dryophanta cinereæ*. *(After Beutm.)*
FIG. 114.—Gall of *Xystoteras volutellæ*. *(After Beutm.)*

Subglobular, greenish-yellow, smooth, hard leaf galls, projecting on the under surface, internally hard, two-celled, fibrous, diameter ⅕ inch, vertical diameter ¹⁄₁₀ inch, on laurel-leaved, red, shingle and willow oaks, gall wasp. Pl. 28 (5).............
.............................*Callirhytis rugosa* Ashm.

Subhemispherical, brown, slightly nippled, one-celled, on the under surface of the leaf, diameter ¹⁄₁₅ inch, on black oak, gall midge. Pl. 13 (8).................*Cincticornia globosa* Felt

Globose gall, diameter ⅙ inch, on underside of running oak leaf, gall midge....................*Youngomyia quercina* Felt

(7) Gall small, solid, fleshy and loosely attached to the leaf:

Globular, thick walled, diameter about ¼ inch, whitish, pinkish, or purplish brown, with a stellate pubescence when young, agamic form, on *Q. grisea*, fall, gall wasp...*Acraspis arida* Kins.

Gall naked or with stellate pubescence, flesh colored to light brown, with considerable solid matter, rounded or flat basally, single on leaves, on *Q. oblongifolia, Q. breviloba,* gall wasp, Mex............................*Acraspis sagata* Kins.

Globular, single or clustered leaf galls covered with minute, warty, pubescent dots, one-celled, fleshy on the upper surface, diameter $\frac{1}{10}$ to $\frac{1}{8}$ inch, on post oak and ? *Q. chapmani* and *Q. margaretta,* gall wasp...............*Acraspis mellea* Ashm.

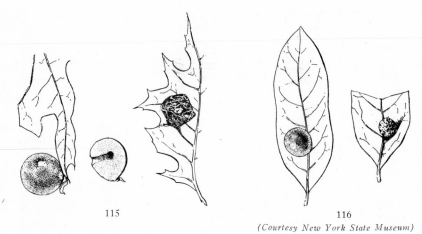

115   116

(Courtesy New York State Museum)

Fig. 115.—Translucent oak gall, *Amphibolips nubilipennis. (After Beutm.)*
Fig. 116.—Gall of *Amphibolips racemaria. (After Beutm.)*

Gall similar to *mellea,* white and naked when mature, on under surface of a vein, diameter $\frac{1}{3}$ inch, on post oak, fall, gall wasp ....*Acraspis unica* Weld

Gall similar to *mellea,* naked when mature, pinkish brown or darker, on post oak, gall wasp.........*Acraspis compta* Kins.

Gall similar to *mellea,* pubescent when young, finally naked, whitish to flesh-colored, rounded or flattened at base, single, on white and post oaks and *Q. breviloba, Q. chapmani,* and ? *Q. margaretta,* gall wasp................*Acraspis anceps* Kins.

Gall similar to *mellea,* quite small, rounded or flattened basally,

PLATE 21—CYNIPID GALLS. 1, Rough bullet gall, *Disholcaspis mamma* Walsh, on burr oak. 2, Mealy oak gall, *Disholcaspis cinerosa* Bass., on live oak. 3, Gall of *Neuroterus distortus* Bass., on swamp live oak. 4, Gall of *Andricus gigas* Weld, on overcup oak. 5, Gall of *Andricus biconicus* Weld, ✕4, on post oak. 6, Jewel oak gall, *Acraspis macrescens* Kins., ✕4, on burr oak. 7, Gall of *Amphibolips gainesi* Bass., on black jack oak. 8, Prune-shaped gall, *Disholcaspis pruniformis* Kins., on *Q. breviloba.* 9, Gall of *Disholcaspis truckeensis* Ashm., on canyon live oak. *(All after Weld).*

PLATE 21

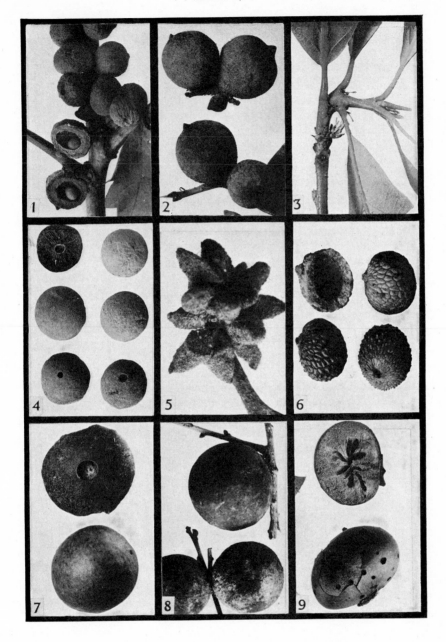

single, on post oak and *Q. floridana*, ? *Q. margaretta*, gall wasp
...............................*Acraspis bifurca* Kins.
Gall similar to *mellea*, rather large, single, on post oak and
Q. floridana or *Q. margaretta*, gall wasp. .*Acraspis litigans* Kins.
Gall similar to *mellea*, averaging large, naked when mature, light
pinkish brown, on *Q. minima*.........*Acraspis concolor* Kins.
Gall similar to *mellea*, scatteringly pubescent or more naked
when mature, light grayish brown, large with thin walls, usually
a conical base, clustered, on post and probably white oaks, gall
wasp............................*Acraspis crassior* Kins.
Gall similar to *mellea*, diameter ¼ inch, single, larger than related species, on white oak, gall wasp.....................
...............................*Acraspis albicolens* Kins.
Gall spherical with flat or slightly concave base, smooth, red
brown, white scurf, diameter ⅕ inch, on *Q. pringlei*, gall wasp,
Mex..........................*Acraspis conspecta* Kins.
Gall hemispherical with broadly flattened base, shrivelling considerably, light red or purple brown, diameter ¼ inch, on *Q.
intricata, Q. cordifolia*, gall wasp, Mex....*Acraspis rubella* Kins.

(8) Galls moderate-sized, hard, loosely attached to the vein below
and with a faceted or spiny surface:

(a) Surface faceted:

Spherical or ellipsoidal, naked and faceted to spiny, young
galls light green, rose-tinted, becoming yellow or brown,
spines when present purplish red, diameter ¼ inch, two-
celled, on veins of white oaks, gall wasp. Fig. 117........
..............Oak pea gall, *Acraspis pezomachoides* O.S.
Similar gall, probably on *Q. gambelii*, gall wasp.........
..........................*Acraspis cincturata* Kins.
Similar gall, both naked and spiny, on white oak.........
...............................*Acraspis ozark* Kins.
Similar gall, both naked and spiny, on white oak, gall wasp
...............................*Acraspis wheeleri* Kins.
Similar gall, always naked, two-celled, diameter ⅖ inches,
on white oak, gall wasp.........*Acraspis derivatus* Kins.
Spherical, spiny or naked, usually with 2 cells, spiny galls
with noticeably short and fine spines, indistinguishable from
C. derivatus, on white oak, gall wasp.................
...............................*Acraspis hibrida* Kins.
Spiny, elongate, many celled, often 1¼ inches long, on
white oak, gall wasp.............*Acraspis inflata* Kins.

Similar, smaller gall, irregularly spherical, short, bristly, not spiny, on white oak, gall wasp...*Acraspis advena* Kins.

Similar gall, known only in spiny form on swamp white oak, gall wasp....Yellow sea urchin, *Acraspis echinoides* Kins.

Oval or rounded, one-celled, pale green or yellowish leaf vein gall, the surface fissured, each facet with a short, hard point, diameter $\frac{1}{10}$ to $\frac{1}{6}$ inch, on burr oak, gall wasp. Pl. 21 (6)......Jewel oak gall, *Acraspis macrescens* Kins.

(*macrocarpæ* Bass.)

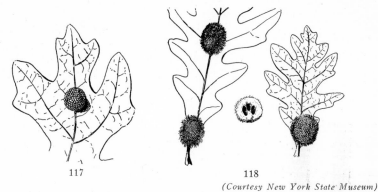

117   118

(Courtesy New York State Museum)

Fig. 117.—Oak pea gall, *Acraspis pezomachoides*. (*After Beutm.*)
Fig. 118.—Oak hedgehog gall, *Acraspis erinacei*. (*After Beutm.*)

Spheroidal, one-celled, green, light yellow, purplish-pink when young, straw yellow or brown when old, surface faceted, without spines, diameter $\frac{1}{4}$ to $\frac{1}{6}$ inch, on chestnut, basket and chinquapin oaks and *Q. michauxii,* gall wasp
.................................*Acraspis hirta* Bass.

Similar gall, moderate size, diameter $\frac{1}{5}$ inch, faceted surface fairly smooth, on *Q. gambelii,* gall wasp...............
.............................*Acraspis undulata* Gill.

Similar gall, elongate, spheroidal, diameter $\frac{1}{6}$ inch, faceted surface smooth, on burr oak, gall wasp................
.............................*Acraspis scelesta* Kins.

Similar gall, diameter $\frac{1}{4}$ inch, faceted surface with short, cone-like projections, on Utah oak, gall wasp...........
.............................*Acraspis packorum* Kins.

Similar gall, ellipsoidal, diameter $\frac{1}{5}$ inch, faceted surface smooth, on burr oak, gall wasp...*Acraspis obtrectans* Kins.

Similar gall, spheroidal, ellipsoidal, diameter $\frac{1}{7}$ inch, on burr oak, gall wasp...............*Acraspis opima* Kins.

Nearly spheroidal, diameter up to $\frac{1}{5}$ inch, surface some-
what rough and spiny, on *Q. gambelii*, gall wasp..........
............................*Acraspis bandero* Kins.
Spheroidal, diameter up to $\frac{1}{6}$ inch, surface rather rough
and spiny, on *Q. gambelii* complex, gall wasp...........
............................*Acraspis ulterior* Kins.

(b) Facets on the surface pointed or spine-tipped:
Globose leaf gall with the surface shiny, netted or fissured
like a strawberry and covered with short, spiny prickles,
yellowish, containing 1 to 4 cells, diameter $\frac{1}{5}$ to $\frac{1}{4}$ inch,
on swamp white oak, gall wasp. Pl. 25 (7). Fig. 119......
............Yellow sea urchin, *Acraspis echinoides* Kins.

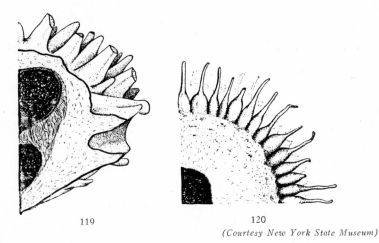

119

120

(Courtesy New York State Museum)

Fig. 119.—Red sea urchin, *Acraspis echinus,* enlarged. *(After Kinsey)*
Fig. 120.—Spiny oak gall, *Acraspis prinoides.* *(After Kinsey)*

Globular, woody, one-celled, midrib leaf gall with numerous
cone-like projections, green or yellowish, usually red-tinged,
diameter $\frac{1}{4}$ to $\frac{1}{2}$ inch, on chinquapin, yellow chestnut oaks,
and *Q. michauxii*, gall wasp. Figs. 120, 121............
..............Spiny oak gall, *Acraspis prinoides* Beutm.
Similar gall, one-celled, on *Q. michauxii* and probably other
chestnut oaks, gall wasp........*Acraspis suspecta* Kins.
Similar gall, one, two, or three-celled, diameter to $\frac{3}{4}$ inch,
on basket oak and chestnut oak, gall wasp.............
............................*Acraspis cruenta* Kins.
Similar gall, one-celled, diameter $\frac{1}{3}$ to $\frac{1}{2}$ inch, on yellow
chestnut oak and *Q. michauxii*, gall wasp..............
............................*Acraspis fuscata* Kins.

Similar gall, diameter ¼ inch, the faceted surface with short cone-like projections, on Utah oak, gall wasp.......
..............................*Acraspis hirtior* Kins.

Similar gall, yellow-brown, diameter up to ⅓ inch, average ⅕ inch, spines short, on *Q. repanda var.*, gall wasp, Mex.
..............................*Acraspis erutor* Kins.

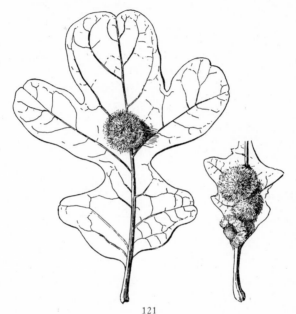

121

(*Courtesy New York State Museum*)

FIG. 121.—Hairy oak gall, *Acraspis villosa*. (*After Beutm.*)

Similar gall, yellow-brown, diameter up to ½ inch, average ⅓ inch, spines slender, flexuous, base up to ⅙ inch, the gall appearing as a tangled mass of coarse hairs on *Q. oblongifolia* complex, gall wasp, Mex......*Acraspis expletor* Kins.

Hemispherical, diameter ⅛ inch, height 1/10 inch, with short blunt crystalline spines and at base a circle of 12-15 star-like rays, yellowish white often red-tinged, on under side, on Oregon oak, fall, gall wasp. Fig. 122............
..................Star oak gall, *Andricus stellaris* Weld

(c) Spines of the facets long:

Globular, fissured, midrib leaf gall somewhat like that of *A. erinacei* but densely covered with long bristly-like hairs, pale yellow, one-celled, hairs ⅛ inch long, diameter ⅓ to ½ inch, on burr oak. Pl. 26 (7). Fig. 121.............
..................Hairy oak gall, *Acraspis villosa* Gill.

Globose or elongate, many-celled leaf gall netted with fissures or cracks, more or less densely covered with spines, yellow, sometimes shaded with red, length ½ to ¾ inch, diameter ¼ to ½ inch, on white oak, gall wasp, agamic generation. Pl. 31 (9); Pl. 34 (8). Fig. 123, 124.......
.............Oak hedgehog gall, *Acraspis prinoides* Beutm.

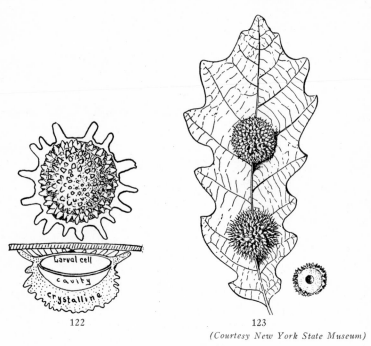

(Courtesy New York State Museum)

Fig. 122.—Star oak gall, *Andricus stellaris*. (*After Weld*)
Fig. 123.—Oak hedgehog gall, *Acraspis prinoides*. (*After Beutm.*)

Similar gall, rosy red to rosy brown, spines long, yellow, diameter ¼ to ½ inch, single, on under surface of *Q. arizonica, Q. grisea, Q. toumeyi* and *Q. undulata*, gall wasp.
......Reddish sea urchin gall *Acraspis acraspiformis* Weld
Similar, on *Q. arizonica* and *Q. grisea*, gall wasp........
.............................*Acraspis apache* Kins.

PLATE 22—CYNIPID GALLS. 1, Small oak spindle gall, *Andricus chinquapin* Fitch, on swamp live oak. 2, Gall of *Callirhytis nigræ* O.S., on black jack oak. 3, Gall of *Callirhytis flora* Weld, on coast live oak. 4, Oak midrib gall, *Andricus pigra* Bass., on black oak. 5, Huckleberry oak gall, *Callirhytis lustrans* Beau., on post oak ×4. 6, Gall of *Andricus confertus* McC. & Egb., ×4, on valley oak. 7, Gall of *Andricus foliosus* Weld, on swamp white oak. 8, Clustered midrib gall, *Cynips dimorphus* Beut., on burr oak. 9, Gall of *Cynips nigricens* Gill., on swamp white oak. (*All after Weld*).

PLATE 22

Similar gall, yellow brown, diameter ¼ to ⅓ inch, spines ⅙ inch, flexuous, slender, on *Q. arizonica,* and *Q. grisea,* gall wasp. Fig. 126..............*Acraspis expositor* Kins.

Similar gall, straw yellow, diameter to nearly ½ inch, spines ¹⁄₁₀ inch, flexuous, slender, on *Q. gambelii,* and *Q. submollis,* gall wasp......................*Acraspis alaria* Weld

Similar gall, straw yellow, diameter to nearly ⅗ inch, spines, ¹⁄₁₀ inch, flexuous, slender, on Utah oak, gall wasp........ ....*Acraspis calvescens* Kins.

Similar gall, straw yellow, staining brown, diameter ½ inch, spines nearly ¹⁄₁₀ inch, flexuous, slender, on burr oak, gall wasp.....................*Acraspis consocians* Kins.

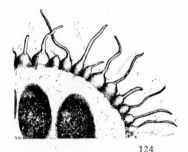

124

(Courtesy New York State Museum)

FIG. 124.—Oak hedgehog gall, *Acraspis erinacei,* showing spiny and nearly smooth types enlarged. (*After Kinsey*)

Subglobular, many-celled, yellowish-white, hairy vein gall, diameter ¼ to ½ inch, on canyon live oak, gall wasp...... ....*Andricus lasius* Ashm.

(9) Galls solid attached to the leaf and with a central hard kernel or larval cell. These approach the oak apple in structure.

Globular, grayish, pubescent, one-celled, thin-shelled gall, pithy internally, diameter ⅓ inch, on under surface, on swamp white oak, gall wasp...................*Cynips lanœglobuli* Ashm.

Globular, below brownish, the size of a pea or slightly larger, 2 to 10 on the underside of the leaf, within a dense, yellowish-brown, spongy mass, diameter ⅛ to ¼ inch, on live oak, gall wasp. Pl. 19 (6).......:........*Belenocnema fossoria* Weld

Similar gall, live oak, Texas, gall wasp..................... ....*Belenocnema kinseyi* Weld

Globular, thin-walled, brownish, diameter ½ inch, attached to midvein, larval cell in spongy tissue, on *Q. arizonica* and *Q. oblongifolia,* fall, gall wasp. Pl. 25 (3)...*Cynips plumbea* Weld

Gall spherical, rarely flattened at base, dull, slight shrivelling, a moderately heavy stellate pubescence, surface light tan to dark purplish brown, on *Q. rhodophlebia, Q. texcocana.* Mex.......
.................................*Cynips torosa* Kins.
Nearly spherical, occasionally with a short blunt point flattened, only on a limited base, dull, slightly shrivelled, lead-gray scurf, older gall reddish-tan to dark red-brown, up to ⅔ inch diameter, on *Q. intricata, Q. pringlei,* gall wasp. Mex.................
.................................*Cynips claripennis* Kins.
Spherical, slightly flattened at base, shrivelling slightly, conspicuous scurf, old gall bluish-gray, denuded dark purplish-tan,

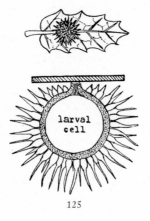

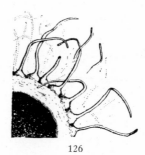

125   126

(Courtesy New York State Museum)

FIG. 125.—Reddish sea urchin gall, *Acraspis acraspiformis* (*After Weld*)
FIG. 126.—Section of a part of the gall of *Acraspis expositor,* enlarged. (*After Kinsey*)

diameter up to ¾ inch, on a relative of *Q. chihauhuensis* or *Q. microphylla,* gall wasp. Mex.............*Cynips fucosa* Kins.
Spherical, rarely flattened, with a conical point basally, shrivelling slightly, heavy scurf, old galls often bluish gray, denuded surface light tan to dark purplish brown, diameter up to 1 inch, average ¾ inch, on *Q. nudinervis, Q. conglomerata, Q. texcocana, Q. rhodophlebia, Q. convallata,* gall wasp. Mex..............
.................................*Cynips fuscipennis* Kins.
Subspherical, broadly flattened or concave at base, shrivelling shallow, a lead-gray scurf, older gall dark brown or reddish-brown, diameter up to ¾ inch, on *Q. undata, Q. chihuahuensis, Q. sacame, Q. reticulata,* and (?) *Q. depressipes,* gall wasp. Mex.
.................................*Cynips glabrescens* Kins.
Spherical, dull, shrivelled slightly, scurf limited, denuded surface

yellow to rosy-tan, diameter up to ¾ inch, average ⁹⁄₁₆ inch, on *Q. repanda,* gall wasp. Mex.............*Cynips hirsuta* Kins.

Globose, either with a flattened base or when in clusters with a conical tip, dull, marked shrivelling, bluish-gray, a persistent scurf, older gall rose or purplish-brown, diameter up to ⅔ inch, average about ¼ inch, on *Q. macrophylla, Q. hæmatophlebia, Q. undata, Q. sacame,* gall wasp. Mex......*Cynips jalisco* Kins.

Single gall with a flattened base, clustered gall with a conical tip, dull, marked shrivelling, bluish-gray, persistent scurf, older gall rose or purplish-brown, diameter up to ⅔ inch, average about ¼ inch, on *Q. potosina, Q. jaralensis,* gall wasp. Mex.........
...................................*Cynips munda* Kins.

Subspherical, with a conical tip or truncate base, dull, slight shrivelling, light-gray scurf, denuded surface rosy-tan or salmon or rose-brown, diameter up to ¾ inch, on *Q. macrophylla, Q. nudinervis,* gall wasp. Mex..............*Cynips scutata* Kins.

Large, spherical, with a conical or truncate base, slight shrivelling, light gray scurf, denuded surface rosy-tan or salmon or rosy-brown to dark brown, diameter up to 1 inch average ¾ inch, on *Q. macrophylla, Q. nudinervis,* gall wasp. Mex...........
...................................*Cynips subcostalis* Kins.

Hemispherical with broadly flattened base, surface smooth, shining, bluish-gray scurf, denuded surface tan-brown, diameter up to 1 inch, on *Q. sacame,* gall wasp. Mex...*Cynips subfusca* Kins.

Spherical, rarely flattened or more often pointed at base, dull, slight shrivelling, a heavy scurf, old gall bluish-gray, denuded surface light tan or dark purplish-brown, diameter up to over ¾ inch, average ⅔ inch, on *Q. texcocana, Q. conglomerata, Q. rhodophlebia, Q. repanda,* gall wasp. Mex..................
...............................*Cynips texcocana* Kins.

Oak Apples

These are rather common on individual trees and occasionally are so numerous as to suggest a fair crop of fruit on an apple tree. They appear to grow direct from the bud, whereas a more careful examination shows that each oak apple is a deformed leaf, hanging by the leaf stem or petiole, or is produced on a normal leaf. It is not difficult to find some oak apples with a small portion of the leaf attached, indicating the nature of the affected part. The attack by this gall wasp begins in the bud and the insect sometimes appropriates the entire leaf for its own purposes, literally compelling growth in this extraordinary manner. It will be seen upon cutting one of the larger oak apples in two, that there is a central cell with definite, firm walls and the space between it and the outer wall is more or less filled with corky matter which, in the case of the empty oak apple, lacks substance to such an extent that nothing remains but a series of radiating filaments supporting the central cell, the home of the grub or young gall wasp and the essential part of the deformity. A further step in this direction is seen in the free rolling globular or oval cells of the roly poly galls, see page 156.

Typical oak apples are globular and the larger ones an inch or two in diameter. There are a number of similar galls, so far as structures and development go, though of quite different form, such as the nearly empty, spindle-shaped galls with their central filament-supported cells.

(10) Oak apples, i.e., galls with a central hard kernel or larval cell, a firm (often hard) outer shell and a spongy or fibrous intervening substance.

(a) Intervening substance is spongy:

(1) Gall large, diameter ¾ inch or more:

Globular, smooth, shining or opaque leaf gall, in-

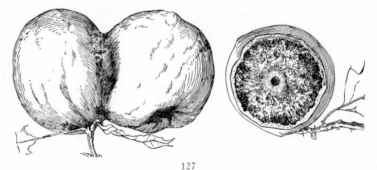

127

(Courtesy New York State Museum)

FIG. 127.—Large oak apple, *Amphibolips confluens*. (*After Beutm.*)

ternally a juicy, white, spongy substance and a large central, larval cell, green, turning with age to light brown, diameter 1¼ to 2 inches, usually on a vein or petiole, on scarlet, Spanish and black oaks, in May and June, spring, gall wasp. Pl. 24 (6), Fig. 127.....
....Spongy oak apple, *Amphibolips confluens* Harr.
Globular leaf gall, resembling that of the large oak apple and *A. cinerea*, but the surface is more closely reticulate and less glossy and the larval cell much darker in color, diameter 1¼ inches, on midrib near the base of leaf, on unkown oak, gall wasp........
................*Amphibolips carolinensis* Bass.
Globose, one-celled, very thin-shelled leaf and twig gall, internally soft, light, spongy, not unlike the large oak apple, diameter 1½ inches, gall wasp.........
................*Amphibolips longicornis* Bass.

Globular or gourd-shaped, reddish-brown, unspotted, wall thin, diameter nearly 1 inch, fall, on *Q. breviloba, Q. laceyi,* gall wasp, autmn. Pl. 24 (2)...........
.............................*Cynips cava* Weld
Subglobular, thin-shelled, brownish yellow or russet, diameter 1 to1⅓ inches, on larger veins, under side, on Oregon oak, gall wasp. Pl. 23 (9)...............
........................*Cynips mirabilis* Kins.
(*C. leachii* Kins.)

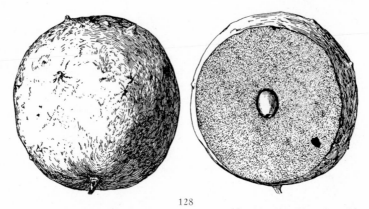

128

(Courtesy New York State Museum)

Fig. 128.—Palmer's oak apple, *Amphibolips palmeri.* (*After Beutm.*)

Fusiform, tapering, the apex usually somewhat curved, yellowish-brown twig gall, internally spongy, with a hard larval cell, length 1½ to 2¼ inches, diameter ¾ to 1½ inches, on Spanish and blue jack oaks, in May and June, gall wasp. Pl. 26 (2), Fig. 129.........
Acuminate oak apple, *Amphibolips acuminatus* Ashm.
Ellipsoidal, woody, greenish oak apple, the base rounded, apically a short, obtuse point, length ¾ inch, on canyon live oak, gall wasp.......*Amphibolips sp.*
Spongy oak apple, similar to *A. confluens,* diameter up to 2 inches, on *Q. ocoteæfolia,* gall wasp. Mex...
......................*Amphibolips dampfi* Kins.

PLATE 23—CYNIPID GALLS. 1, Gall of *Amphibolips trizonata* Ashm., on *Q. emoryi.* 2, Gall of *Andricus unica* Weld, ×3, on post oak. 3, Gall of *Callirhytis gallæstriatæ* Weld, ×3, on Spanish oak. 4, Gall of *Andricus aggregata* Weld, on *Q. oblongifolia.* 5, Gall of *Trichoteras coquilletti* Ashm., on canyon live oak. 6, Gall of *Cynips sulcata* Ashm., on *Q. oblongifolia.* 7, Gall of *Amphibolips nigra* Beutm., on *Q. emoryi.* 8, Gall of *Cynips maculosa* Weld, ×1¾, on *Q. dumosa.* 9, Gall of *Cynips mirabilis* Kins., on Oregon oak. (*All after Weld*).

PLATE 23

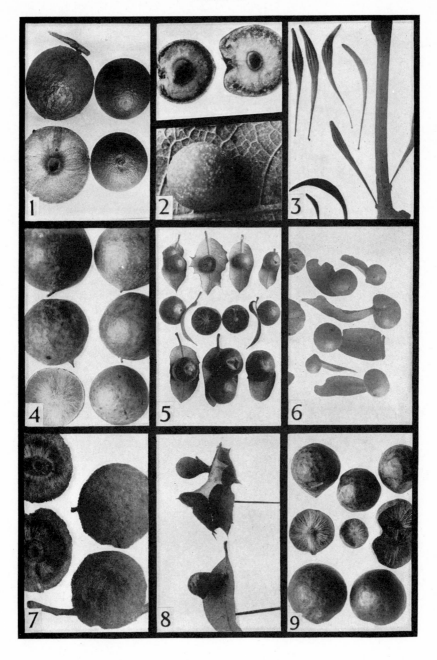

Globose or spindle-shaped, average diameter 1¼ inches, smooth except for minute black specks and blotches, on *Q. eduardi*, gall wasp. Mex.........
.....................*Amphibolips fusus* Kins.
Globose, slightly spindle-shaped, average diameter 1 inch, smooth except for minute black specks and blotches, on *Q. serrulata, Q. mexicana*, gall wasp. Mex.
.....................*Amphibolips nassa* Kins.

(2) Size small, about ¼ inch:

Globose, one-celled, light reddish leaf gall filled with spongy tissue, except for the large cell, diameter ¼ inch, on under side of midrib, on *Q. rydbergiana*, gall wasp................*Acraspis rydbergiana* Ckll.

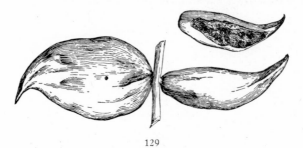

129

(Courtesy New York State Museum)

Fig. 129.—Spongy oak apple, *Amphibolips acuminata*. (*After Beutm.*)

Lemon-shaped, curved, with short, blunt spines, brown, thick-shelled leaf gall, internally slightly spongy, diameter ¼ inch, on willow and laurel-leaved oaks, gall wasp. Pl. 24 (5).....................
.......Spiny oak apple, *Amphibolips spinosa* Ashm.
Globose, thin-shelled, yellowish, pink or red shaded leaf gall, a fiber-supported cell, diameter ¼ to ¾ inch, on *Q. hypoleuca*, gall wasp. Mex.................
.....................*Dryophanta dugesi* Mayr

(b) The substance lying between the rind and the kernel is fibrous and often very scanty:

(1) Gall large, diameter 1 inch or more, kernel central, leaf usually aborted:

Globose, bright green with red spots, becoming yellowish-brown, slightly nippled, thin-shelled, glossy, the central larval cell supported by radiating fibers, diameter 1 to 1½ inches, on scarlet and Spanish oaks

in May and June, gall wasp. Pl. 26 (6). Fig. 130..
..Larger empty oak apple, *Amphibolips inanis* O.S.

Balloon-shaped leaf gall, green, outer wall thick, turning yellow when old, with central cell supported by
coarse, radiating fibers, length ¾ to 1⅛ inches, fall,
Texas, on black jack oak, gall wasp...............
..............................*Amphibolips sp.*

Globose, white, yellowish or brownish, velvety, thin-
walled, diameter 1½ to 2 inches, within a thick-walled
fiber supported cell with a diameter of ½ inch, galls

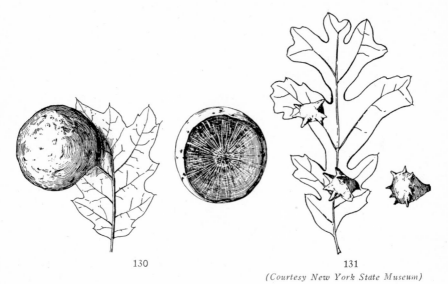

130   131
(Courtesy New York State Museum)

FIG. 130.—Larger empty oak apple, *Amphibolips inanis*. (*After Beutm.*)
FIG. 131.—Gall of *Cynips douglasii*. (*After Beutm.*)

usually in groups of 2 or 3 on the under side and near
the base of the leaf, gall wasp. Pl. 27 (6).........
......................*Disholcaspis lapiei* Kieff.
(*weldi* Beutm.)

Globose, thin-shelled with a central filament supported kernel, diameter ½ to 1½ inches, resembles
the larger empty oak apple, but averages smaller and
the color is darker, on *Q. vaccinifolia*, fall, gall wasp
...................*Callirhytis vacciniifoliæ* Ashm.

Globose or ovate, slightly nippled, dark crimson with
lighter mottlings and becoming brown, a thick-shelled
twig gall with filament-supported larval cell, length

1¼ to 1¾ inches, diameter 1 to 1½ inches, becomes wrinkled in drying, on blue jack oak, gall wasp. Pl. 25 (6). Fig. 134........*Amphibolips cinerea* Ashm.

Fusiform to subglobular, sharp pointed, yellowish, thin-shelled twig gall with a filament-supported cell, length ¼ to 1 inch, diameter ¼ to ½ inch, on willow oak, gall wasp. Fig. 138........................

Small pointed oak gall, *Amphibolips citriformis* Ashm.

Elongate, fusiform, dark green leaf gall, usually aris-

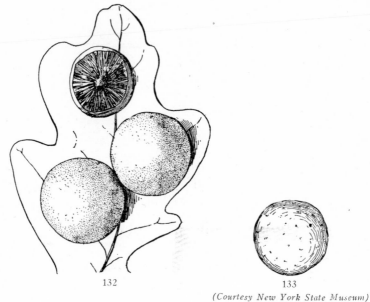

132

133

(Courtesy New York State Museum)

Fig. 132.—Spotted oak apple, *Cynips centricola. (After Beutm.)*
Fig. 133.—Gall of *Cynips rubræ. (After Beutm.)*

ing from the blade or petiole, internally with an ovate, filament-supported cell, length 1 to 2¼ inches, diameter 1¾ inches, on upper leaf surface, on scrub oak, summer, gall wasp. Pl. 26 (5), Fig. 139............

........Scrub oak gall, *Amphibolips ilicifoliæ* Bass.

Globose, one-celled, thin-shelled, often near the leaf margin and mostly on the rib with a filament-supported cell, brown or pinkish brown when dry, with a fine pubescence and nearly smooth, though not polished, diameter 1¼ to 2¼ inches, on *Q. arizonica, Q. chihuahuensis, Q. diversicolor, Q. grisea, Q. gam-*

*belii, Q. oblongifolia, Q. sacame, Q. toumeyi, Q. un-
dulate, Q. wrightii,* and probably related oaks, gall
wasp. Pl. 25 (2), Fig. 136......*Cynips bella* Bass.
(*maculipennis* Gill.)

Mature gall, globose, rosy tan, not mottled, diameter
up to 2 inches, average diameter 1½ inches, on *Q.
grisea,* gall wasp............*Cynips congesta* Kins.

Mature gall, globose, rosy or brownish-tan, not

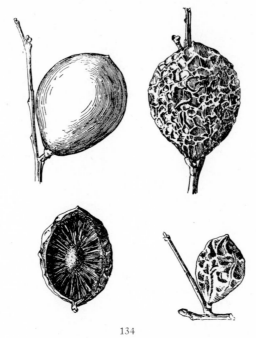

134

(Courtesy New York State Museum)

FIG. 134.—Gall of *Amphibolips cinerea.* (*After Beutm.*)

mottled, diameter up to 2⅛ inches, average 1⅞
inches, on *Q. subturbinella,* gall wasp..............
......................*Cynips vanescens* Kins.

Globose, rosy or more often light yellowish tan, conspicuously mottled with purplish brown, diameter up
to 1½ inches, average about 1 inch, on *Q. undata, Q.
chihuahuensis, Q. sacame,* gall wasp. Mex.........
.........................*Cynips aspera* Kins.

Mature gall, globose, rosy or light yellow-tan, conspicuously mottled with purplish brown, diameter up

to 1⅞ inches, average 1⅛ inches, on *Q. chihauhuensis, Q. undata,* gall wasp. Mex.....*Cynips pomifera* Kins.

Similar gall, on *Q. undulata, Q. grisea, Q. oblongifolia, Q. arizonica and Q. gambelii,* gall wasp...........
.......................*Cynips simulatrix* Kins.

Similar gall, rosy tan, obscurely freckled or unspotted, diameter up to 2 inches, average 1½ inches, on *Q. grisea, Q. intricata* (?), gall wasp...............
........................*Cynips pupoides* Kins.

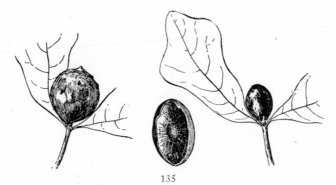

135

(Courtesy New York State Museum)

FIG. 135.—Gall of *Amphibolips melanocera.* (*After Beutm.*)

Similar gall, rosy or brownish-tan, unspotted or obscurely mottled, shining, diameter up to 2 inches, average 1¾ inches, on *Q. grisea,* gall wasp.........
........................*Cynips subnigra* Kins.

Mature galls light rosy tan, unspotted, often shining, average diameter 1¼ inches, maximum 1½ inch, on *Q. gambelii, Q. fendleri, Q. grisea,* gall wasp........
......................*Cynips brevipennata* Gill.
(*pellucidus* Kins.)

Similar gall, somewhat flattened basally, average diameter ⅚ inch, maximum 1½ inch, smooth, shining, brownish-yellow, striped with purplish, on *Q. subturbinella,* gall wasp.........*Cynips capronæ* Weld

PLATE 24—CYNIPID GALLS. 1, Gall of *Heterœcus pacificus* Ashm., on canyon live oak. 2, Gall of *Andricus cava* Weld, on *Q. breviloba.* 3, Spotted oak apple, *Cynips centricola* O.S., on post oak. 4, Gall of *Andricus deciduatus* Weld, ×3, on swamp white oak. 5, Spiny oak apple, *Amphibolips spinosa* Ashm., ×3, on willow oak. 6, Large oak apple, *Amphibolips confluens* Harris, on black oak. 7, Gall of *Andricus californicus* Bass., on valley oak. 8, Gall of *Callirhytis pomiformis* Bass., on coast live oak. 9, Hard oak apple, *Callirhytis agrifoliæ* Bass., ×3, on coast live oak. (*All after Weld*).

PLATE 24

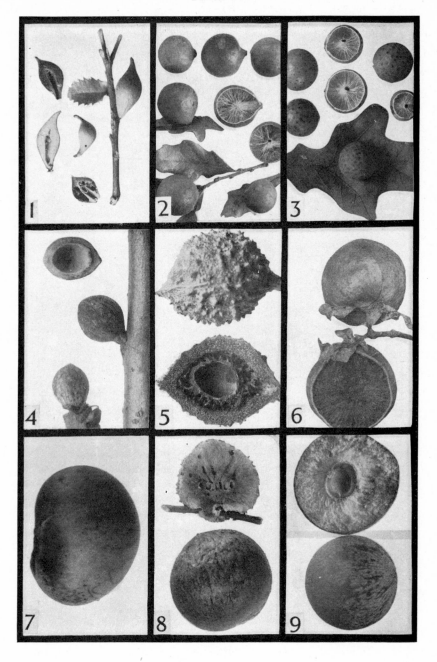

Similar gall, yellow-tan to rosy-tan, when mature touched with dark purple, peppered with fine purplish, average diameter 1¼ inch, maximum 1½ inch, on *Q. grisea*, gall wasp..........*Cynips catena* Kins.

Similar gall, light yellow, partly rosy or rosy-brown, many purplish spots, diameter up to 1½ inch, average 1 inch, on *Q. nudinervis*, gall wasp. Mex........

........................*Cynips conexa* Kins.

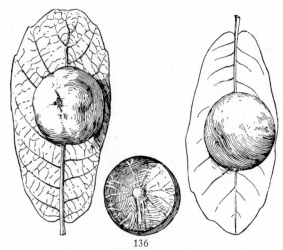

136

(Courtesy New York State Museum)

FIG. 136.—Gall of *Cynips bella*. (*After Beutm.*)

Similar gall, light rosy-tan, unspotted, up to 1⅞ inch, average diameter 1¼ inch, on *Q. gambelii*, gall wasp ....*Cynips cubitalis* Kins.

Similar gall, mature rosy or brownish-tan, dull, minutely roughened, diameter up to 1⅞ inches, average 1½ inches, on *Q. undata, Q. chihuahuensis*, gall wasp. Mex................*Cynips deceptrix* Kins.

Similar gall, mature galls rosy-tan, unspotted, diameter up to 1⅞ inch, average 1½ inch, on *Q. macrophylla, Q. jaralensis*, gall wasp, Mex. Fig. 137......

..........................*Cynips dugesi* Mayr

Similar gall, mature rosy or brownish-tan, unspotted, diameter up to 1⅞ inches, average 1½ inch, on *Q. undata, Q. chihuahuensis, Q. sacame, Q. gambelii*, gall wasp. Mex................*Cynips emergens* Kins.

Similar gall, mature, light olive tan, sometimes rosy,

unspotted, slightly tuberculate, diameter up to $1\frac{1}{2}$ inch, average $1\frac{1}{4}$ inch, on *Q. rhodophlebia,* gall wasp. Mex..........................*Cynips longa* Kins.

Similar gall, mature, light yellow to rosy-tan, flushed rose when younger, diameter up to $2\frac{1}{4}$ inch, average $1\frac{1}{4}$ inch, on *Q. pilicaulis,* gall wasp. Mex.........
..........................*Cynips lucaris* Kins.

137

(Courtesy New York State Museum)

FIG. 137.—Gall of *Cynips dugesi.* (*After Beutm.*)

Similar gall, light rose to bright rose, dirty brown when old, unspotted or obscurely mottled with purplish, diameter up to $2\frac{3}{4}$ inches, average $1\frac{3}{4}$ inches, on *Q. decipiens,* gall wasp. Mex..................
..........................*Cynips luminata* Kins.

Similar gall, yellowish or bright rosy-tan, rosy when younger, unspotted, smooth, thin-walled, up to 2 inches, average diameter 1¾ inches, on *Q. depressipes, Q. potosina,* gall wasp. Mex.....*Cynips occidua* Kins.

Similar gall, rosy-tan or bright rose, up to 1¾ inches, average diameter 1¼ inch, on *Q. potosina, Q. jaralensis, Q. intricata, Q. pringlei, Q. cordifolia,* gall wasp. Mex........................*Cynips oriens* Kins.

Similar gall, rich reddish or brownish-tan, mostly spotted, diameter up to 1½ inches, average 1 inch, on *Q. cordifolia, Q. pringlei,* gall wasp. Mex...........
.............................*Cynips pictor* Kins.

Similar gall, light yellow-tan, diameter up to 1¼ inches, average 1 inch, on *Q. macrophylla, Q. potosina,* gall wasp. Mex. ....*Cynips pulex* Kins.

138

(Courtesy New York State Museum)

Fig. 138.—Small pointed oak apple, *Amphibolips citriformis.* (*After Beutm.*)

Similar gall, light rosy-tan, smooth, shining, diameter up to 2 inches, average 1½ inches, on *Q. repanda,* gall wasp. Mex...................*Cynips pumilio* Kins.

Similar gall, rosy or brownish-tan, dull to shining, diameter up to 2¼ inches, average 1¾ inches, on *Q. undulata, Q. grisea, Q. oblongifolia, Q. arizonica, Q. gambelii,* gall wasp. Mex.....*Cynips simulatrix* Kins.

Similar gall, yellow to light rosy-tan, usually shining, sometimes powdered, diameter up to 2¾ inches, average 1⅞ inches, on *Q. macrophylla,* gall wasp. Mex.
.............................*Cynips spadix* Kins.

Similar gall, rosy-brown or darker, bluish, faintly, sometimes conspicuously spotted, mottled or striped with purplish, smooth, diameter up to 2 inches, average 1⅞ inches, on *Q. texcocana, Q. conglomerata, Q. decipiens,* gall wasp. Mex.......*Cynips spiculi* Kins.

Similar gall, light olive tan, less often rosy, smooth, shining, bluish, diameter up to 1¼ inch, average 1

inch, on *Q. texcocana*, gall wasp. Mex............
.......................*Cynips spinalis* Kins.
Similar gall, light yellowish-tan, part rich rosy or
purplish-brown, usually purple spots or streaks and
trace of bluish bloom, diameter up to 1½ inches, average 1¼ inches, on *Q. purpusi*, gall wasp. Mex.......
.......................*Cynips spinescens* Kins.
Similar gall, light straw tan to yellowish-brown, tending to brownish or purplish-olive, with conspicuous

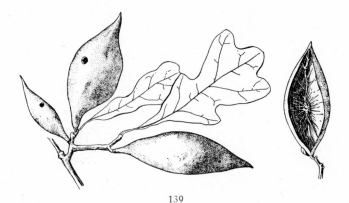

139

(Courtesy New York State Museum)

Fig. 139.—Scrub oak gall, *Amphibolips ilicifoliæ*. *(After Beutm.)*

bluish, diameter up to 1½ inches, average 1 inch, on
Q. conglomerata, gall wasp. Mex..............
.......................*Cynips spinifera* Kins.
Similar gall, deep rosy-brown-tan, unspotted, diameter
up to 1⅞ inches, average 1¼ inches, on *Q. intricata,
Q. pringlei*, gall wasp. Mex.......*Cynips vasta* Kins.
Similar gall, rosy-tan, unspotted, slightly shining, di-
ameter up to 1¾ inches, average 1¼ inches, on *Q.
potosina, Q. jaralensis, Q. chihuahuensis, Q. undata,
Q. sacame, Q. reticulata*, gall wasp. Mex..........
.......................*Cynips vulgata* Kins.
Gall, diameter up to 2¼ inches, average 1½ inches,
globular, abruptly truncate at base, light yellow to
pinkish or rosy-tan, spotted and striped with purple,
usually bluish, single rarely in two's and three's, on
main veins, on *Q. nudinervis*, gall wasp. Mex.......
.......................*Cynips tigrina* Kins.

Gall bulboid, with a short stalk or stem, mature, dark rosy-brown, usually unspotted, young galls often spotted with purple, diameter up to 2 inches, average 1¼ inches, on *Q. undata, Q. chihuahuensis, Q. sacame, Q. oblongifolia, Q. reticulata, Q. durangensis, Q. depressipes, Q. striatula,* gall wasp. Mex.........
.......................*Cynips bulboides* Kins.

Gall bulboid, rosy or yellow-brown, noticeably bluish, occasionally unspotted, mostly well marked with spots and ridges of purple, on *Q. læta, Q. polymorpha, Q. macrophylla, Q. sacame,* gall wasp. Mex...........
.......................*Cynips bulbacea* Kins.

Gall bulboid, rosy or yellow-brown, usually unspotted, sometimes well marked with purple, diameter up to 2 inches, average 1½ inches, on *Q. chihuahuensis,* gall wasp. Mex.................*Cynips bulbulus* Kins.

Gall bulboid, a peculiar dark rosy or dark yellow-brown, sometimes obscurely spotted, diameter up to 2 inches, average 1½ inches, on *Q. chihuahuensis, Q. jaralensis, Q. undata, Q. reticulata, Q. macrophylla,* gall wasp. Mex.................*Cynips bulla* Kins.

Gall, spherical, light straw yellow, touched with rose or brown, mottled with purplish, diameter up to 1¼ inches, average ⅞ inch, on *Q. chihuahuensis, Q. undata,* gall wasp. Mex.........*Cynips æqualis* Kins.

(2) Galls small, diameter less than 1 inch:

Almond-shaped, pointed, keeled bud or twig gall, color green or reddish, becoming brown, smooth, rather thick-shelled with filament supported cell, length ½ to ¾ inch, on black and Spanish oaks, in autumn, gall wasp. Pl. 31 (8), Fig. 140...................
.....Keeled oak apple, *Amphibolips tinctoriæ* Ashm.

Globose, slightly nippled, green, red-spotted, becoming brown, moderately thick-shelled bud gall with filament supported cell, diameter ¾ inch, on red and black oaks, wrinkles in drying, drops in September and October, gall wasp, Fig. 141...............
.......................*Amphibolips cookii* Gill.

PLATE 25. 1, Sulfured tube gall, *Andricus sulfurea* Weld, on *Q. arizonica.* 2, Gall of *Cynips bella* Bass. 3, Gall of *Cynips plumbea* Weld, on *Q. oblongifolia.* 4, Clustered urn gall, *Andricus tecturnarum* Kins. 5, Sparkling woolly gall, *Andricus crystallinus* Bass., on *Q. dumosa.* 6, Gall of *Amphibolips cinerea* Ashm., on blue jack oak. 7, Red sea urchin, *Acraspis echinus* O.S. ×3, on *Q. douglasii.* 8, Gall of *Cynips capillata* Weld, ×3, on white oak. 9, Gall of *Andricus lasius* Ashm., on canyon live oak. (*All after Weld*).

PLATE 25

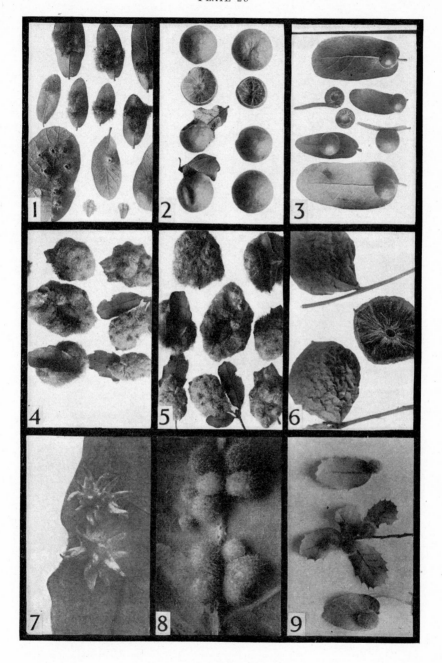

Globular, very thin-shelled leaf gall with filament supported cell, diameter ⅓ inch, on willow, laurel-leaved
oaks, gall wasp.........*Andricus femoratus* Ashm.

140

(Courtesy New York State Museum)

FIG. 140.—Keeled oak apple, *Amphibolips tinctoriæ*. (*After Beutm.*)

Globular, smooth, green, about half showing on upper
surface of leaf, diameter ¼ to ½ inch, on red oak,
gall wasp. Pl. 26 (4), Fig. 143.................
.........Small oak apple, *Andricus singularis* Bass.
Globular, thin-shelled leaf gall, spotted and sometimes
tinged with pink and covered with a white bloom, internally a filament supported cell, diameter ½ to ¾
inch, on under side of leaf of post oak, fall, gall wasp.
Pl. 24 (3), Fig. 132...........................
.........Spotted oak apple, *Cynips centricola* O.S.

Similar if not identical gall on post oak, gall wasp.
Fig. 133.................*Cynips rubræ* Karsch
Similar gall, always unspotted, on post oak, gall wasp
.......................*Cynips clivorum* Kins.
Similar gall, almost always well spotted with brown-
ish purple, on post oak, gall wasp..............
.......................*Cynips strians* Kins.
Globose or ovate, yellowish-green or brown, glossy
when dry, thin-shelled, slightly nippled, axillary bud
gall, diameter $\frac{1}{4}$ to $\frac{1}{2}$ inch, on water oak, gall wasp.
Fig. 135...........*Amphibolips melanocera* Ashm.

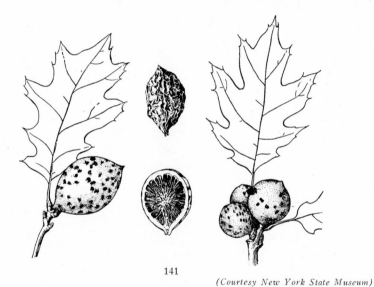

141

(Courtesy New York State Museum)

FIG. 141.—Gall of *Amphibolips cooki*. (*After Beutm.*)

Similar gall, diameter $\frac{1}{4}$ inch, smooth, shining, on
white and yellow chestnut oaks, rarely on burr oak
and *Q. michauxii*, gall wasp....................
.......................*Cynips canadensis* Kins.
Hemispherical or subhemispherical pale brown, minutely crackled vein gall, diameter $\frac{1}{6}$ inch, height
$\frac{1}{10}$ inch, gall wasp....*Neuroterus cockerelli* Beutm.
Globular, grayish-brown or black, pubescent, thin-
shelled leaf gall, the larval cell filament supported,
diameter $\frac{1}{4}$ to $\frac{1}{3}$ inch, on under surface of white,
burr and chinquapin oaks, Sept., Oct., gall wasp. Pl.

31 (1), Fig. 131..........*Cynips fulvicollis* Fitch
(*Philonix niger* Gill.)

Similar gall, diameter ¾ inch on *Q. gambelii*, gall
wasp...................*Cynips insulensis* Kins.

Similar gall on Utah oak......*Cynips latigenæ* Kins.

Similar gall, quite pubescent, on white and post oaks,
gall wasp.................*Cynips rubricosa* Kins.

Similar gall, to nearly ¾ inch in diameter, pubescent,
on burr and swamp white oaks, gall wasp..........
.........................*Cynips vorisi* Kins.

Similar gall, diameter to nearly ½ inch, on white,
burr and yellow chestnut oaks and *Q. michauxii*, gall
wasp......................*Cynips major* Kins.

Similar gall, quite pubescent, diameter to ⅘ inch, on
overcup and yellow chestnut oaks and *Q. michauxii*,
gall wasp...................*Cynips gigas* Weld

(3) Galls small, 1 inch in diameter or less, leaf present
and gall usually on the underside and solitary:

Globose, yellowish, yellowish-brown and brown
spotted when dry, single or clustered, with filament
supported cell, diameter ½ to 1 inch, on under surface of leaf of *Q. undulata*, *Q. wrightii*, gall wasp. Pl.
25 (3), Fig. 136..............*Cynips bella* Bass.
(*maculipennis* Gill.)

Similar gall, yellowish or bright rosy tan, diameter
1¾ to 2 inches, on *Q. depressipes*, *Q. potosina*, gall
wasp. Mex.................*Cynips occidua* Kins.

Similar gall, yellow or rosy-tan, diameter 1 inch, on *Q.
polymorpha*, gall wasp. Mex...*Cynips oriunda* Kins.

Similar gall, light olive tan, sometimes browner, unspotted, diameter up to 1¼ inches, average 1 inch,
on *Q. repanda*, gall wasp. Mex.....*Cynips pusa* Kins.

Irregular, subglobose, depressed, usually clustered,
straw-colored or brown leaf gall, ⅓ inch long, containing a fiber supported cell, occurs on both surfaces
of the leaf and on twigs on *Q. gambelii*, *Q. grisea*, *Q.
undulata*, gall wasp. Fig. 93...................
.....................*Dryophanta eburnea* Bass.

Gall similar to *D. eburnea*, rounded, much distorted,
flattened on bottom, compressed, mostly smooth, in
clusters on leaf blades, petioles or stems, on *Q. pringlei*, *Q. cordifolia*, gall wasp. Mex..............
.....................*Biorhiza innocens* Kins.

Similar gall, regularly hemispherical, flattened on bottom, usually scattered on leaves, on *Q. repanda*, gall wasp. Mex.................*Biorhiza nitellina* Kins.

Subglobose, one-celled, brown, thin-shelled, solitary or clustered, diameter ⅒ to ⅙ inch, on upper or under surface of leaf of *Q. emoryi*, gall wasp. Fig. 142 ....*Dryophanta emoryi* Ashm.

Globular, minutely pubescent, reddish, greenish or brownish, diameter ⅙ to ¼ inch, on *Q. grisea*, gall wasp..............................*Cynips sp.*

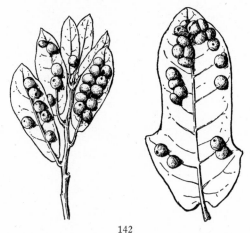

142

(Courtesy New York State Museum)

FIG. 142.—Gall of *Dryophanta emoryi*. (*After Beutm.*)

Globose, somewhat oblong, hollow, pale greenish-yellow, with filament supported cell, diameter ⅓ inch, about ¼ showing on upper surface of leaf, on pin, scarlet, shingle and scrub oaks, spring, gall wasp. Pl. 1 (5)................*Andricus ostensackeni* Bass.

Subglobular, sessile, thin-shelled, on lower side of leaf, about size of a pea, pointed at apex, cell supported by radiating fibers, fall, on *Q. douglasii*, gall wasp...... ....*Andricus brunneus* Full.

Globose, one-celled, leaf blade gall about equally developed on each surface, diameter ⅓ to ⅕ inch, yellowish-brown when dry, within a thin-walled black larval cell surrounded by fibers, on *Q. douglasii*, gall wasp............... *Andricus atrimentus* Kins.

Gall, dome shaped with broadly flattened base,

shrivelling, purplish-brown, diameter average about ⅕ inch on *Q. grisea,* gall wasp.................
.........................*Acraspis arida* Kins.

Gall, pointed, dome-shaped, with relatively broad base, light reddish-brown with whitish scurf, diameter under ⅙ inch, on *Q. repanda,* gall wasp. Mex.....
.......................*Acraspis contacta* Kins.

Gall, dome-shaped, base broadly flattened, shrivelling, purplish-brown, average diameter ¼ inch, on *Q. undata, Q. potosina, Q. chihuahuensis,* gall wasp. Mex
.........................*Acraspis eluta* Kins.

Gall, dome-shaped or irregularly hemispherical with broad base, hardly shrivelling with low irregular points or ridges, a row surrounding the circular base, light red-brown, with whitish base, diameter up to ¼ inch, on *Q. texcocana,* gall wasp. Mex...............
.......................*Acraspis eminula* Kins.

Gall, spherical, base but little flattened, surface minutely wrinkled or smooth, light red-brown, sometimes purplish-brown, average diameter about ⅙ inch, on *Q. conglomerata, Q. peduncularis, Q. nudinervis, Q. macrophylla,* gall wasp. Mex.................
.......................*Acraspis flavida* Kins.

Gall, spherical with slightly flattened base, smooth, light gray-tan, average diameter about ¼ inch, on *Q. decipiens,* gall wasp. Mex...*Acraspis fugiens* Kins.

Gall, dome-shaped, with broadly flattened base, slightly shrivelling, purplish-brown, diameter up to ¼ inch, average ⅕ inch, on *Q. polymorpha,* gall wasp. Mex.
.......................*Acraspis saxifera* Kins.

Gall, dome-shaped with broadly flattened base, shrivelling, purplish-brown, average diameter ¼ inch, on *Q. undata, Q. oblongifolia, Q. chihuahuensis,* gall wasp. Mex...............*Acraspis saxulum* Kins.

Gall, dome-shaped with broadly flattened base, shrivelling, purplish-brown, average diameter ¼ inch,

---

PLATE 26. 1, Oak spindle gall, *Amphibolips cœlebs* O.S., on Spanish oak. 2, Spongy oak apple, *Amphibolips acuminata* Ashm., on Spanish oak. 3, Stemmed oak gall, *Andricus pedicellatus* Kins., on *Q. dumosa, Q. douglasii,* and valley oak. 4, Small oak apple, *Andricus singularis* Bass., on Spanish oak. 5, Scrub oak gall, *Amphibolips ilicifoliæ* Bass., on scrub oak. 6. Larger empty oak apple, *Amphibolips inanis* O.S., on Spanish oak. 7, Hairy oak gall, *Acraspis villosa* Gill., on burr oak. 8, Gall of *Callirhytis attigua* Weld. 9, Gall of *Dryophanta notha* O.S., on Spanish oak. (*All after Weld*).

PLATE 26

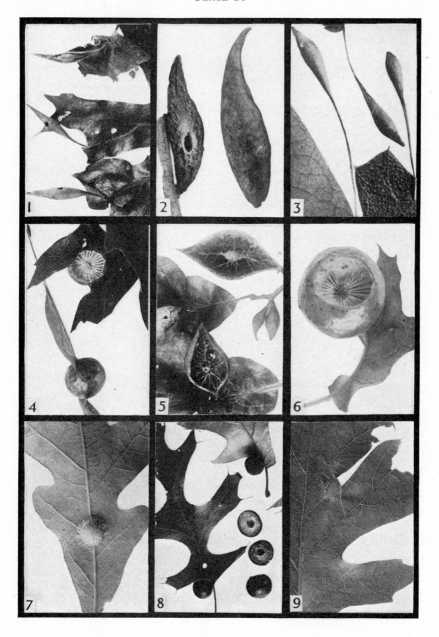

on *Q. chihuahuensis, Q. sacame, Q. grisea,* gall wasp. N.Mex., Mex.............*Acraspis tenebrica* Kins.

Gall, narrowly dome-shaped with a more narrow base, usually not shrivelling, purplish-brown, average diameter $\frac{1}{6}$ inch, on *Q. striatula,* gall wasp. Mex.....
...........................*Acraspis tholi* Kins.

(11) Galls small, the leaf present, they tend to occur in numbers on leaf:

   (a) Cells central in the gall:

      Globose, 1-20 on a leaf, on both surfaces, one-celled,

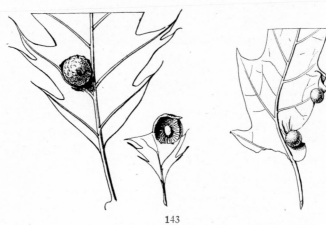

143

(Courtesy New York State Museum)

FIG. 143.—Gall of *Andricus singularis,* one gall in section and at right a smaller gall believed to be identical.

yellowish, thin-shelled, tinged with red or brown, a fiber supported cell, diameter $\frac{1}{4}$-$\frac{3}{4}$ inch, on post oak and *Q. chapmani,* summer, gall wasp. Fig. 144.............
...........Polished oak gall, *Dryophanta polita* Bass.

Globose, brown, wall very thin, opaque, with filament supported cell, diameter $\frac{1}{4}$ to $\frac{1}{3}$ inch, on canyon live oak, fall, gall wasp, Pl. 23 (5).......*Trichoteras coquilletti* Ashm.

Globose, diameter $\frac{1}{5}$-$\frac{1}{4}$ inch, white, smooth, on leaf vein beneath, one-celled, on post oak, fall, gall wasp. Pl. 23 (2)
.............................*Acraspis unica* Weld

   (b) Cell basal, against the leaf:

      Subglobose, flattened basally, usually on the midrib or on twigs, the shell thick, the interior filled with silvery-white hairs supporting a larval cell attached to the base of the gall, on both surfaces of the leaf of *Q. gambelii, Q. grisea,*

Q. undulata, gall wasp. Fig. 93......................
...........................*Dryophanta eburnea* Bass.

Gall similar to preceding but shining, brownish above and probably on a different species of oak, S. Utah, gall wasp
...........................*Dryophanta simillima* D.T.

Spherical, diameter ⅙ inch, subcoriaceous, reddish, one-celled vein gall developing in fissures of cross veins, on canyon live oak, gall wasp.............*Dryophanta sp.*

Ovate, small, one-celled, apical vein gall developing in a

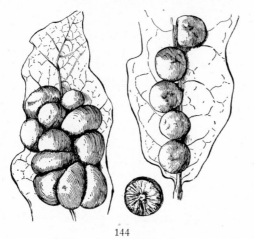

144   145

(Courtesy New York State Museum)

FIG. 144.—Polished oak gall, *Dryophanta polita.* (*After Beutm.*)
FIG. 145.—Gall of *Dryophanta pulchripennis.* (*After Beutm.*)

slit, woody, the walls thin, smooth, shining and reddish, gall wasp...............................*Cynips sp.*

(12) Galls small, thin-walled, globose or fusiform, usually marginal on the leaf and piercing the leaf blade:

Globose, densely pruinose, thin-walled, leaf or ament gall, diameter ⅛ inch, sometimes banded by a minute ridge, on post oak, gall wasp.......................*Andricus pruinosus* Bass.

Globular, green or purplish, pubescent, one-celled leaf and petiole gall, diameter ⅙ inch, on white oak, spring, gall wasp, Pl. 27 (4)..........................*Andricus utriculus* Bass.

Oval, thin-walled, one-celled vein swelling covered with a dense brown pubescence, on white oak, gall wasp...............
...........................*Neuroterus bassettii* D.T.

Hemispherical or subhemispherical, pale brown, minutely

crackled vein gall, diameter $\frac{1}{6}$ inch, height $\frac{1}{10}$ inch, Colorado, gall wasp, Fig. 100............*Neuroterus cockerelli* Beutm.

Small, round, thin-shelled galls on leaf blades, usually near the margin and always on the main leaf veins, projecting on both surfaces, diameter $\frac{1}{8}$ inch, on *Q. undulata*, gall wasp......... ....*Andricus pilulus* Bass.

Hemispherical, pale brown, reticulate, with minute reddish tubercles, diameter $\frac{1}{8}$ inch, on *Q. arizonica, Q. diversicolor, Q. grisea, Q. oblongifolia, Q. subturbinella,* and *Q. toumeyi,* gall wasp, Pl. 28 (4), Fig. 145...*Dryophanta pulchripennis* Ashm.

Gall similar to *D. pulchripennis,* light brown or straw brown, diameter $\frac{1}{8}$ inch, on *Q. microphylla,* gall wasp, Mex......... ....*Biorhiza socia* Kins.

Gall similar, light to rich brown, diameter $\frac{1}{6}$ inch, on *Q. macrophylla, Q. hæmatophlebia, Q. rhodophlebia, Q. chihuahuensis, Q. sacame, Q. undata, Q. reticulata, Q. potosina, Q. jaralensis, Q. microphylla,* gall wasp, Mex.........*Biorhiza solita* Kins.

Gall, similar, light brown, often straw brown, diameter $\frac{1}{7}$ inch, on *Q. rhodophlebia, Q. texcocana, Q. purpusii,* gall wasp, Mex. ....*Biorhiza stelis* Kins.

Gall similar, light to medium brown, diameter $\frac{1}{8}$ inch, on *Q. repanda,* gall wasp, Mex..............*Biorhiza tanos* Kins.

Gall similar, light yellow brown, diameter $\frac{1}{6}$ inch, on *Q. conglomerata,* gall wasp, Mex...........*Biorhiza tarasco* Kins.

Gall similar, light brown, often straw brown, diameter $\frac{1}{8}$ inch, on *Q. rhodophlebia, Q. texcocana,* gall wasp, Mex.......... ....*Biorhiza tricosa* Kins.

Gall similar, light to medium brown, diameter $\frac{1}{6}$ inch, on *Q. nudinervis, Q. macrophylla,* gall wasp, Mex............... ....*Biorhiza ulcus* Kins.

Gall similar, medium dark brown, diameter $\frac{1}{6}$ inch, on *Q. nudinervis,* gall wasp, Mex...............*Biorhiza urcea* Kins.

Gall similar but inverted flask-shaped with cylindrical base, medium to dark brown, diameter of gall $\frac{1}{8}$ inch, gall wasp, Mex...........................*Biorhiza zinzala* Kins.

Globose, green, with reddish excrescences at apex, fleshy, sessile on midrib or main vein, dropping in fall, diameter $\frac{1}{8}$ inch, on *Q. texana,* and red, scarlet, shingle, scrub, Spanish, turkey, black, black jack, blue jack, laurel-leaved and water oaks, gall wasp, Pl. 28 (9).........*Dryocosmus rileyi* Ashm.

Ellipsoidal, nearly one-half longer than thick, diameter $\frac{1}{25}$ inch, roughened, a blunt, slightly hairy tip, on valley oak and

?*Q. douglassii,* gall wasp. Pl. 29 (8); Fig. 146..............
.........................."Flea seeds", Jumping seed gall[1]
Neuroterus saltatorius H. Edw.

Gall ovoid, naked, broadly attached to the under surface of the leaf, cell diameter about ½ inch, thin, hard-walled, surface rough, usually many on a leaf, on *Q. macrophylla,* gall wasp, Mex...........................*Neuroterus tumba* Kins.

Spherical, slightly elongate, without an apical tip, very finely pubescent, on post oak, gall wasp........................
.............................*Neuroterus australis* Kins.

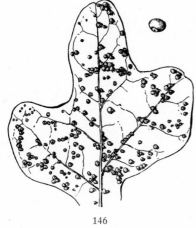 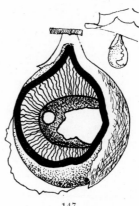

146   147
(Courtesy New York State Museum)

FIG. 146.—"Flea seeds," jumping bullet gall, *Neuroterus saltatorius. (After Beutm.)*
FIG. 147.—Gall of *Cynips maculosa,* natural size and one in section, enlarged. (*After Weld*)

Twice as long as wide, length ½ inch, surface rough with short pubescence, brownish or tinged with purplish red, on *Q. arizonica,* gall wasp..............*Neuroterus decrescens* Kins.

Globose, irregularly roughened, on live oak, gall wasp.......
.............................*Neuroterus texanus* Kins.

Seed-like, in cup-like depression on under surface, greenish-white, June-August, on burr oak, gall wasp. Pl. 28 (3).......
.............................*Neuroterus saltarius* Weld

Bulboid, diameter ¼ inch, on leaves of *Q. durata, Q. dumosa,* gall wasp. Pl. 39 (2)..................*Cynips tritior* Kins.

[1] This name was given to a western species and it has been applied erroneously to an eastern, similar gall. The two are probably different in the opinion of L. H. Weld. Dr. Kinsey is of the opinion that about seventy different species or varieties should occur in the United States.

Similar gall, on *Q. dumosa*, gall wasp. Pl. 23 (8); Fig. 147
..............................*Cynips maculosa* Weld

(13) Galls small, with peculiar or varied shapes, attached to the leaf blade:

Rounded or crown-shaped, ridged, apex pointed, pale green, soft when fresh, becoming hard after drying, thick-walled, diameter ¼ to ½ inch, length ⅓ to ½ inch, in clusters, on twigs and on young leaves of pin, water and willow oaks, spring, gall wasp.........Oak crown gall, *Andricus coronus* Beutm.

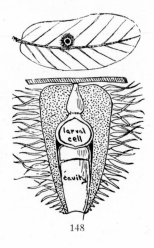 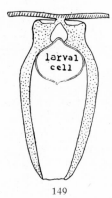

148   149

(Courtesy New York State Museum)

Fig. 148.—Sulfured tube gall, *Andricus sulfurea*. (*After Weld*)
Fig. 149.—Vase oak gall, *Andricus amphora*. (*After Weld*)

Gall, conical with broadened base, smooth, bearing spiny projections, mature gall variably conical, diameter up to ¼ inch high, sometimes with tip sharply pointed or recurved, base sometimes flaring, edge entire or with up to 6 short spiny projections, diameter up to ¼ inch, light pinkish brown, on *Q. subturbinella*, gall wasp.................*Acraspis conica* Kins.

Gall, a warped cone, base circular, flat or concave, diameter up to 1 inch, average ¾ inch, centrally with a short ridge or point of attachment, the conical body rising from the circular

Plate 27. 1, Succulent oak gall, *Andricus palustris* O.S., on black oak. 2, White oak club gall, *Callirhytis clavula* O.S. on white oak. 3, Leafy oak gall, *Andricus foliatus* Ashm., on live oak. 4, Gall of *Andricus utriculus* Bass., ×4, on white oak. 5, Oak petiole gall, *Andricus petiolicola* Bass. 6, Gall of *Cynips weldi* Beutm., on white oak. 7, Midrib tumor gall, *Plagiotrochus tumificus* O.S., on Spanish oak. 8, Gall of *Plagiotrochus scitulus* Bass., on scarlet oak. 9, *Neuroterus majalis* Bass., on white oak. (*All after Weld*).

PLATE 27

base with a long sharply pointed tip, the latter often bent, on
Q. sacame, gall wasp, Mex. . . . .*Cynips euconus* Kins.
A hollow cone, sessile, densely covered with sulfur-yellow spines,
height ¼ inch, diameter ⅙ inch, solitary, on under surface of
leaf, autumn, on *Q. arizonica, Q. grisea, Q. oblongifolia,* gall
wasp. Pl. 25 (1); Fig. 148. . . . .
. . . . .Sulfured tube gall, *Andricus sulfureus* Weld

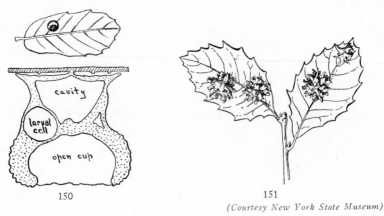

150

151

(Courtesy New York State Museum)

Fig. 150.—Gall of *Andricus sessilis. (After Weld)*
Fig. 151.—Red sea urchin, *Cynips echinus. (After Beutm.)*

Cylindric, fimbriate, bright red and yellow banded leaf gall,
height ⅙ to ¼ inch, diameter ⅛ inch, distal portion hollow,
the outer surface with numerous, long yellowish or reddish
processes, solitary, on *Q. grisea, Q. undulata,* fall, gall wasp.
Pl. 32 (9). . . . . . .Splendid tube gall, *Andricus splendens* Weld
Tubular galls in compact, convex mass to 1 inch in diameter,
galls ⅓ inch long, base slender, tip diameter ⅛ inch, white or
cream colored, on under side of leaf of Oregon oak, fall, gall
wasp. Fig. 155. . . . .*Xanthoteras tubifasciens* Weld
Cylindrical, height ⅕ inch, diameter ⅛ inch, somewhat swollen
in the middle, tapering apically, hollow with basal cell, red or
brownish, usually one or two on under side and near edge of
leaf, on *Q. undulata,* gall wasp, autumn. Fig. 149. . . . .
. . . . .Vase oak gall, *Andricus amphora* Weld
Cylindrical, with a deep cut at apex, diameter and height ⅕
inch, deep red, on under side of leaf, on *Q. arizonica,* autumn,
gall wasp. Fig. 150. . . . .*Andricus sessilis* Weld
Galls naked, cylindrical, upper third open, hollow, diameter
1/10 inch, height ⅕ inch, straw colored and light rose pink,

later reddish or brownish, usually on under surface of leaf, scattered or in dense masses, on *Q. texcocana*, gall wasp, Mex.
..........................*Xystoteras cylindratum* Kins.
Onion-shaped, tan-colored, single or clustered on under side of leaf, diameter $\frac{1}{10}$ inch, on *Q. undulata*, gall wasp, autumn.
Fig. 111..........................*Cynips cœpula* Weld
Squash-shaped or top-shaped leaf gall, the marginal ridge produced in 7 to 10 irregular tubercles, brown, with a lilac-gray bloom, diameter $\frac{1}{4}$ to $\frac{1}{2}$ inch, height $\frac{1}{4}$ inch, on *Q. douglasii, Q. dumosa*, gall wasp. Pl. 17 (9); Fig. 131..................
...............Spined turban gall, *Cynips douglasii* Ashm.
Gall deeply bowl-shaped or vase-shaped, without spines, light

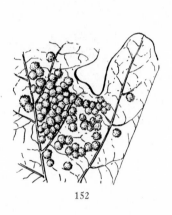 

152   153

(Courtesy New York State Museum)

FIG. 152.—Gall of *Neuroterus verrucarum*. (*After Beutm.*)
FIG. 153.—Gall of *Cynips clavuloides*. (*After Beutm.*)

yellow, tinged with purple, turning dark brown, on *Q. durata,* and *Q. dumosa*, gall wasp. Pl. 39 (3)....................
.............................*Cynips schulthessæ* Kins.
Small, wart-like, midrib galls on under surface of leaves and with corolla-like processes apically, on white oak, gall wasp
.............................*Andricus foliaformis* Gill.
Spindle-shaped or clavate leaf gall on under surface, length $\frac{1}{5}$ to $\frac{1}{4}$ inch, diameter of narrow portion $\frac{1}{25}$ inch, of inflated part $\frac{1}{20}$ inch, on valley oak, gall wasp, fall. Pl. 39 (5); Fig. 153.............Club oak-leaf gall, *Cynips clavuloides* Kins.
Similar gall, length $\frac{1}{4}$ inch, on *Q. dumosa, Q. durata*, gall wasp
.............................*Cynips hildebrandæ* Kins.
Fusiform, green, succulent, thin-shelled leaf gall with a free cell within, occurs singly on the acute lobes of several oaks,

gall wasp. Pl. 26 (9); Fig. 156..........................
..............Leaf lobe blister gall, *Dryophanta notha* O.S.
(*pusulatoides* Bass.)

Clavate or globular, stalked gall, length ¼ inch, diameter ⅒ inch, sparse, short white pubescence, single or few on under side of leaf, on Oregon oak, fall, gall wasp. Fig. 154........
...............................*Xanthoteras teres* Weld

Broadly crescentic or banana-shaped leaf gall attached laterally and sessile on under surface, length ⅒ inch, on yellow chestnut oak, gall wasp..............................?*Cynips sp.*

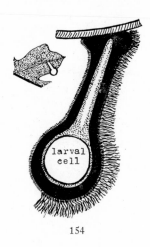
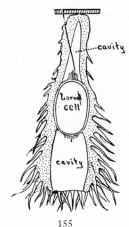

154   155

(Courtesy New York State Museum)

FIG. 154.—Gall of *Xanthoteras teres.* (*After Weld*)
FIG. 155.—Gall of *Xanthoteras tubifasciens.* (*After Weld*)

Cup-shaped spangle, edge thin, not inrolled, brown with whitish bloom, diameter ⅙ inch, on *Q. subturbinella,* gall wasp......
...............................*Andricus acutella* Weld

Cup-shaped black spangle, ⅒ inch in diameter, wall thick, edge inrolled, on both surfaces, falling with the leaves, on *Q. arizonica, Q. grisea, Q. subturbinella,* fall, gall wasp. Fig. 161................Oak cup gall, *Trigonaspis cupella* Weld

Round, flattened, disk-like, one-celled leaf galls, pinkish or purplish apically, sometimes yellowish, diameter ⅛ to ⅙ inch, on *Q. dumosa, Q. douglasii,* fall, gall wasp................
.........................*Xanthoteras californica* Beutm.

Small, circular, flattened, brown, one-celled, concave and with a minute conical elevation centrally, diameter 1/25 to 1/20 inch,

mostly on under surface of leaf, on swamp white oak, gall
wasp. Pl. 31 (5); Fig. 157, 158..........................
.............Oak button gall, *Neuroterus umbilicatus* Bass.
Disk-like, diameter ⅛ inch, on under surface of leaf, tan-
colored, margin crenate, convex on upper surface, concave on
under side, single or few on leaf, on *Q. subturbinella,* gall wasp,
fall. Pl. 31 (6); Fig. 159..Oak disk gall, *Andricus discalis* Weld
Disk-shaped, diameter ¼ inch, singly or few on under surface
of leaf, upper surface slightly concave, edge sinuate, margin
reflexed nearly to leaf surface, on Oregon oak, gall wasp, fall.
Fig. 160.......................*Andricus discularis* Weld
Disk-shaped, often flat, greenish leaf galls with a lilac center,
the margin irregular, diameter ¼ inch, on *Q. douglasii,* autumn,

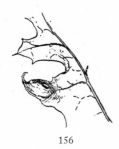

156   157

(Courtesy New York State Museum)

Fig. 156.—Leaf lobe blister gall, *Dryophanta notha. (After Beutm.)*
Fig. 157.—Oak button gall, *Neuroterus umbilicatus.*

gall wasp. Pl. 32 (2)..............*Andricus pattersonœ* Full.
Disk-shaped, convex above, hard, smooth, one-celled galls
sessile on under surface of leaf, diameter ⅕ inch, on canyon
live oak, gall wasp. Pl. 32 (1)....*Cynips guadaloupensis* Full.
Pouch or wedge-shaped, on under surface of leaf, length ½
inch, diameter about ⅕ inch, on canyon live oak, agamic form,
gall wasp. Fig. 162..................*Cynips insolens* Weld
Button-shaped vein gall with a depressed center and median
larval cell, having the smoothness and polish of bone, diameter
½ inch, height ¼ inch, on canyon live oak, gall wasp. Pl.
32 (8); Fig. 163.....Weld's cup gall, *Cynips patelloides* Weld
Saucer-like, small galls in numbers on underside of the leaves,
in fall, covered with a whitish bloom, diameter ⅛ inch, on
white, ? burr and ? post oaks, summer, gall wasp...........
................,.....Oak spangles, *Xystoteras poculum* Weld

Similar galls on oak, gall midge. Pl. 8 (1, 2); Fig. 164, 165, 166
............................*Cecidomyia poculum* O.S.
Saucer-shaped, sessile, minute, flat, red leaf galls on under
surface, diameter ⅛ inch, on valley oak, gall wasp. Pl. 32 (3);
Fig. 168...........Oak saucer gall, *Andricus parmula* Bass.
(*discus* Bass.)

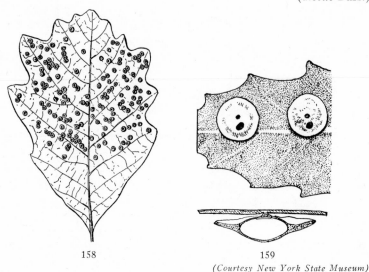

158   159

(Courtesy New York State Museum)

FIG. 158.—Oak button gall, *Neuroterus umbilicatus.* (*After Beutm.*)
FIG. 159.—Oak disk gall, *Andricus discalis,* underside and in section. (*After Weld*)

Broad, saucer-shaped, base terminating in a slender cone with
incurved sides, scarcely pubescent, reddish when growing,
smoky-gray, length ¼ inch, diameter ⅕ inch, on valley oak and
Q. douglasii, in fall, gall wasp. Pl. 33 (6)................
..................................*Andricus kingi* Bass.
Vase or urn-shaped, buff or reddish-brown midrib masses on
the under surface, often 1 inch to 1½ inches in diameter and
containing scores of hollow, urn-shaped, closely clustered,
galls, some ⅟₂₅ by ⅛ inch and consisting of a somewhat conical compressed tube, bearing a dense mass of crystalline hairs

PLATE 28. 1, Gall of *Callirhytis modesta* O.S., on Spanish oak. 2, Gall of *Xystoteras volutelæ* Ashm., on overcut oak. 3, Gall of *Neuroterus saltarius* Weld, on burr oak. 4, Gall of *Dryophanta pulchripennis* Ashm., on *Q. arizonica.* 5, Gall of *Callirhytis rugosa* Ashm., on willow oak. 6, Gall of *Neuroterus perminimus* Bass., on white oak. 7, Gall of *Belonocnema fossoria* Weld, on live oak. 8, Oak blister gall, *Neuroterus papillosus* Beut., ×4, on swamp white oak. 9, Gall of *Dryocosmus rileyi* Ashm., on Spanish oak. (*All after Weld*).

PLATE 28

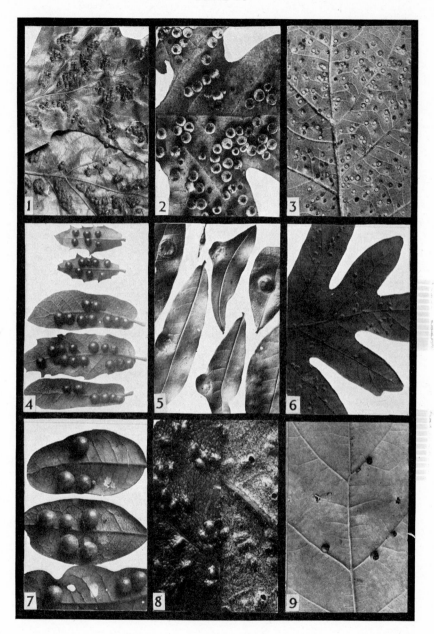

toward the tip, on *Q. arizonica, Q. grisea, Q. subturbinella,* gall wasp. Pl. 25 (4)...................................
................Clustered urn gall, *Dros tecturnarum* Kins.

Vase or urn-shaped, basal stalk slender, cylindrical, diameter $\frac{1}{10}$ inch, expanding gradually to cupped body of gall, no saucer-like base on the stalk, dull brownish red, diameter $\frac{1}{4}$ inch, height a little more, on *Q. conglomerata, Q. texcocana,* gall wasp, Mex....................*Dros moreliense* Kins.

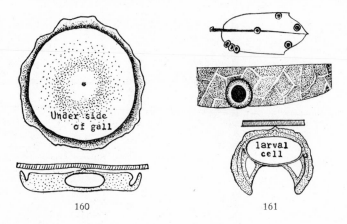

160   161

Fig. 160.—Gall of *Andricus discularis,* underside and in section. (*After Weld*)
Fig. 161.—Oak cup gall, *Trigonaspis cupella,* infested leaf, gall from below and in section, last two enlarged. (*After Weld*)

Vase or urn-shaped, basal stalk tapered to less than $\frac{1}{10}$ inch, the cupped body of the gall expanding gradually, the base wider than the stalk, edge of gall about $\frac{1}{15}$ inch wide, blood red to deep brownish red, diameter and height about $\frac{2}{5}$ inch, on *Q. macrophylla,* gall wasp, Mex......*Dros periscele* Kins.

Similar gall on *Q. macrophylla*..........*Dros picatum* Kins.

Similar gall on *Q. jaralensis, Q. microphylla, Q. sacame* and *Q. undata*........................*Dros repicatum* Kins.

Vase or urn-shaped, basal stalk slender, cylindrical, diameter $\frac{1}{10}$ inch, cupped body of gall expanding abruptly, yellowish brown and red, diameter nearly $\frac{1}{2}$ inch, height $\frac{1}{3}$ inch, on *Q. macrophylla,* gall wasp, Mex........*Dros perlentum* Kins.
                                                   Dros petasum Kins.

(14) Galls composed apparently of crystalline matter and attached to the leaves:

(a) Galls solitary, globular:

Globose, with 20 to 60 spiny projections, these broadest

where they are fewest in number, diameter ⅕ to ⅛ inch, bright or dark red with violet bloom, on *Q. douglasii*, gall wasp. Pl. 39 (8); Fig. 118, 119, 151.................
...............Red sea urchin gall, *Cynips echinus* O.S.
(*speciosus* Bass., *teste* Beutm. & Kins.)
Similar gall on *Q. douglasii*, gall wasp.................
................................*Cynips vicina* Kins.
Cynips incepta Kins.

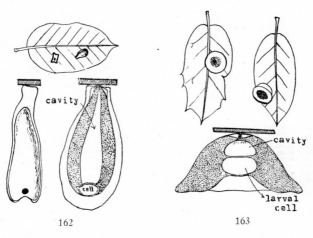

162   163

FIG. 162.—Gall of *Cynips insolens*. (*After Weld*)
FIG. 163.—Weld's cup gall, *Cynips patelloides*. (*After Weld*)

Similar gall but irregularly cushion-shaped with a few short, blunt projections, brick red, on *Q. dumosa* and *Q. turbinella,* gall wasp. Pl. 39 (1)....*Cynips dumosæ* Kins.
Gall closely similar to the preceding, yellowish and rose or brownish red, on *Q. dumosa*, gall wasp. Pl. 39 (4)....
................................*Cynips mista* Kins.
Hemispherical, diameter ⅛ inch, height ⅒ inch, with short, blunt crystalline spines and at base a circle of 12-15 star-like rays, yellowish-white, often red tinged on under side of leaf of Oregon oak, fall, gall wasp.............
.................Star oak gall, *Andricus stellaris* Weld
Subglobular, reddish-brown, covered with dense crystalline spicules, single or clustered, on under side of leaf, diameter ⅒ to ⅕ inch, on valley oak, gall wasp........
.................*Callirhytis trimaculosa* McC. & Egb.
(b) Galls often clustered, tubular:

Length ¼ to ½ inch, narrow basally, open apically, yellowish, the surface with numerous red spines, the interior divided by two horizontal partitions, the basal and distal cavities empty, the latter open, on post oak, fall, gall wasp ....Spined oak tube gall, *Callirhytis tubicola* O.S.[1]

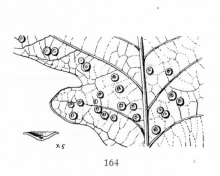
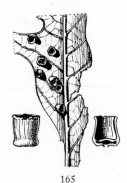

164   165

(Courtesy New York State Museum)

FIG. 164.—Oak spangles, *Cecidomyia sp.*, on white oak, one gall in section.
FIG. 165.—Oak spangles, *Cecidomyia sp.*, on burr oak, one in section.

Clustered, woolly, bright pinkish, fusiform leaf galls, the wool crystalline, semitransparent, diameter ⅛ to ⅓ inch, on *Q. douglasii, Q. dumosa, Q. durata*, gall wasp. Pl. 25 (5) ....Sparkling woolly gall, *Andricus crystallinus* Bass.

166

(Courtesy New York State Museum)

FIG. 166.—Oak spangles, *Cecidomyia sp.*, on yellow chestnut oak, one in section.

Galls cylindrical, tip flaring, crystalline processes, a few broad filaments, most of the fibers hair-like, purple rose and light brown, later darker, in clusters with diameter up to 1⅛ inch and height ½ inch, on *Q. texcocana*, gall wasp, Mex. ....*Feron tibiale* Kins.
Similar gall with practically no broad filaments and in

[1] See also *A. splendens* on p 228.

masses with diameter up to 1¼ inch, height ½ inch, on
Q. chihuahuensis, Q. sacame, gall wasp, Mex. . . . .
. . . .*Feron tostum* Kins.
Similar gall on *Q. chihuahuensis,* gall wasp, Mex. . . . .
. . . .*Feron uterinum* Kins.
Similar galls with blunt crystalline processes in spiny
clusters with diameter up to 1¼ inches, bright purple rose
and straw color when fresh, on *Q. texcocana,* gall wasp,
Mex. . . . .*Feron validum* Kins.

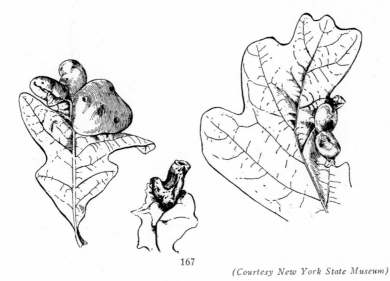

167

(Courtesy New York State Museum)

Fɪɢ. 167.—Gall of *Neuroterus majalis. (After Beutm.)*

Similar galls in clusters with diameter of 2¼ inches on
Q. macrophylla, gall wasp, Mex. . . .*Feron verutum* Kins.
Similar galls in clusters with diameter of 1½ inch, on *Q.
rhodophlebia* (and *Q. texcocana?*), gall wasp, Mex. . . . .
. . . .*Feron vitreum* Kins.

(15) Small fleshy galls clustered on leaves:

(a) Galls split midvein in their growth:

Clusters of seed-like bodies, often 30 or 40 together occur
on the underside of the midvein, the larger cells smooth,
greenish-white, with an enlarged apex and about the size
of grains of wheat, on black, red and scrub oaks, gall wasp.
Pl. 3 (1). . . . . .Deciduous oak gall, Black oak wheat,
Dryocosmus deciduus Beutm.

Clustered, pubescent, globular, drab or brownish-red midvein galls frequently splitting and extending along the vein.

1 to 4 inches, diameter ⅛ to ⅓ inch, occur in clusters of 10 to 100 or more, on red oak, fall, gall wasp. Pl. 32 (6)....
......................*Dryocosmus piperoides* Bass.
Pyriform, usually clustered, reddish-brown leaf gall with a minute whitish pubescence and arising from a slit in the basal ⅔ of the midvein, height ⅕ to ⅓ inch, gall wasp
......................................*Andricus sp.*

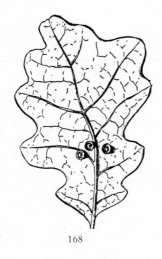 

168   169
(Courtesy New York State Museum)

Fig. 168.—Gall of *Dryophanta discus*. (*After Beutm.*)
Fig. 169.—Bell-shaped oak gall, *Zopheroteras vaccinii*. (*After Beutm.*)

(b) Galls do not split midvein in growing:

Galls in rounded masses, a few to 30 in each, closely packed, clustered on the under side of the midrib or petiole, one-celled, globose, pointed basally, greenish, tinged with pink when fresh, grayish when old, individual galls, diameter ¹⁄₁₀ to ⅛ inch, diameter of masses from ¼ to ½ inch, on white, burr and chestnut oaks, fall, gall wasp. Pl. 22 (8)...Clustered midrib gall, *Cynips dimorphus* Beutm.

PLATE 29—CYNIPID GALLS. 1, Gall of *Andricus wiltzæ* Full., ×3, on valley oak. 2, Jumping ribbed gall, *Trisoleniella saltatus* Ashm., ×3, on Spanish oak. 3, Gall of *Neuroterus fragilis* Bass., ×3, on *Q. dumosa*. 4, Gall of *Neuroterus decipiens* Kins. ×3, on on *Q. dumosa*. 5, Noxious oak gall, *Neuroterus noxiosus* Bass., woody gall of agamic generation on stem and succulent gall of sexual generation on leaves, on swamp white oak. 6, Gall of *Callirhytis balanosa* Weld, ×3, on scarlet oak. 7, Gall of *Disholcaspis plumbella* Kins., on *Q. dumosa*. 8, "Flea seed," jumping bullet gall, *Neuroterus saltatorius* Hy. Ed., ×3 on valley oak. 9, Gall of *Biorhiza cœpuliformis* Beutm., on Spanish oak. (*All after Weld*).

PLATE 29

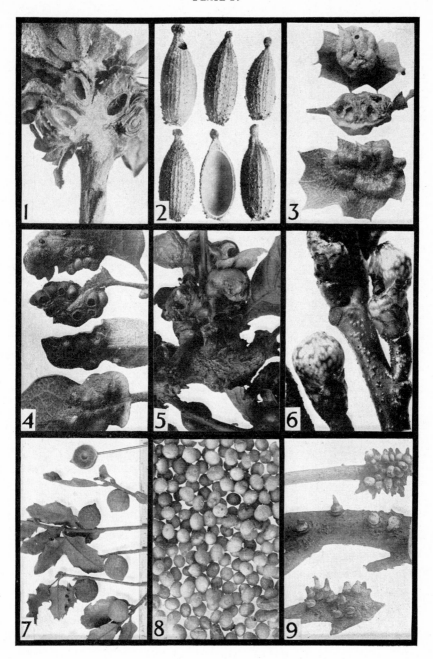

Clustered, bell-shaped, one-celled greenish or reddish leaf vein gall shaped somewhat like a huckleberry blossom, length ⅛ to ⅙ inch, on post oak, gall wasp. Fig. 169....
.......Huckleberry oak gall, *Callirhytis lustrans* Beutm.
(*impositus* Beutm.)

Clustered, conical leaf gall attached to the under surface of the midrib, on swamp white oak, gall wasp. Pl. 22 (9)
.............................*Cynips nigricens* Gill.

(16) Woolly galls attached to the leaves and covered with woolly fibers:

(a) Galls composed of small cells, each with a separate crown of wool:

170   171

(Courtesy New York State Museum)

Fig. 170.—Gall of *Neuroterus minutissimus*. (*After Beutm.*)
Fig. 171.—Gall of *Neuroterus clarkeœ*. (*After Beutm.*)

Globose leaf gall densely covered with close, brown, moss-like wool, diameter ¹⁄₁₀ inch, on under side of leaf of live oak, gall wasp. Fig. 170.............................
.....................*Neuroterus minutissimus* Ashm.

Globose leaf gall, smooth above, thickly covered with white wool below, single or confluent, diameter ⅛ inch, on swamp white oak, gall wasp. Pl. 31 (2); Fig. 103.............
.............Oak flake gall, *Neuroterus floccosus* Bass.

Light brown, bud-like, thin-shelled, marginal leaf gall covered with short wool, length ¹⁄₁₀ to ⅛ inch, on white oak, gall wasp. Fig. 171.....*Neuroterus clarkeœ* Beutm.

Globose, brown-haired, clustered vein galls, each one-celled, diameter ¹⁄₁₀ inch, on upper surface, usually 2 or 3 in a cluster and not showing on the lower surface, on Spanish oak, September, gall wasp.........*Cynips sp.*

(b) Galls composed of seed-like cells in groups and covered by wool:

Woolly, whitish mass on underside of the leaves, usually along the midrib, diameter ⅓ inch, containing a mass of small one-celled galls, on white oak, fall, gall wasp. Pl. 1 (2, 4).......................*Andricus flocci* Walsh

(*lana* Fitch)

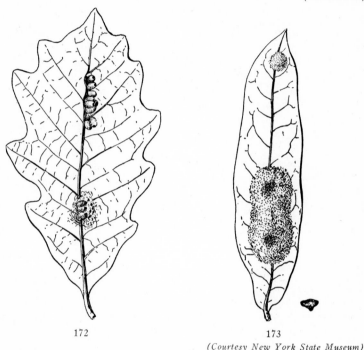

172

173

(*Courtesy New York State Museum*)

Fig. 172.—Gall of *Dryophanta ignota*. (*After Beutm.*)
Fig. 173.—Gall of *Neuroterus laurifoliæ*. (*After Beutm.*)

Clustered larval cells along the midvein, the cells hidden in short, dense, brownish wool, with largest clusters often more than half the length of the leaf, on post oak, fall, gall wasp.....................*Andricus pattoni* Bass.

Hemispherical or irregular tufts ½ inch long of rather long, whitish or reddish wool covering, 2 to 6 irregular brown, seed-like kernels on under side of midrib, diameter $\frac{1}{12}$ inch, on live oak, summer, gall wasp. Pl. 31 (7)........

..........Wool-bearing gall, *Andricus lanigerus* Ashm.

Oval, rather thick-shelled, brown leaf vein gall, at first woolly, later naked, length ⅛ inch, diameter $\frac{1}{16}$ inch, on

swamp white oak, gall wasp. Fig. 172.................
.........................*Dryophanta ignota* Bass
Clustered, hard, woody, cylindrical, wedge-shaped, or sub-
triangular, one-celled, leaf galls, each densely covered with
short, coarse, whitish, woolly fibers, the clusters appearing
as one large gall, on post oak, gall wasp..............
.........................*Andricus texanus* Beutm.
Creamy white or yellowish, hairs straight, not long, close,
3 or fewer slender cells in a compact circular cluster with
a diameter of nearly $\frac{1}{2}$ inch, on *Q. oleoides,* gall wasp,
Mex..........................*Druon linaria* Kins.
Buff or tan brown, hairs tangled, masses irregular, length
up to $1\frac{1}{2}$ inches, height $\frac{1}{3}$ inch, or oval masses $\frac{1}{2}$ by $\frac{1}{3}$
inch, larval cells average diameter $\frac{1}{8}$ inch and 3 to 6 in
a cluster, on *Q. polymorpha,* gall wasp, Mex...........
.........................*Druon malinum* Kins.
Light gray to buff brown, hairs long, tangled, clusters
rounded, compact, diameter $\frac{1}{2}$ inch, height $\frac{1}{3}$ inch, compound masses up to $1\frac{1}{4}$ inches, on *Q. polymorpha,* gall
wasp, Mex.................*Druon polymorphœ* Kins.
Brownish yellow, russet or bright purplish brown, hairs
short, densely matted, single clusters with diameter of
nearly $\frac{1}{2}$ inch, compound clusters up to $1\frac{1}{4}$ inches, on
Q. conglomerata, gall wasp, Mex...*Druon protagion* Kins.
Grayish yellow-brown, hairs very long, tangled, clusters
oval, dense, diameter $\frac{4}{5}$ inch, height $\frac{1}{2}$ inch, compound
masses up to $1\frac{1}{2}$ inches, on *Q. rhodophlebia,* gall wasp,
Mex..........................*Druon receptum* Kins.
Cream white to tan and russet brown, hairs not long,
straight, in masses up to 1 inch, average about $\frac{1}{2}$ inch,
on *Q. macrophylla,* gall wasp, Mex.................
.........................*Druon rusticum* Kins.

(c) Galls with large cells, not seed-like but clustered under
wool as before:

Globose, kernel-like leaf galls occurring singly or in clusters and covered with long, loose, fawn-colored wool,
diameter of kernel $\frac{1}{10}$ inch, on laurel-leaved, shingle and
willow oaks, gall wasp. Fig. 173.........*Callirhytis sp.*[1]
Globose, fleshy, one-celled leaf gall with dense yellow wool,
diameter $\frac{1}{5}$ to $\frac{1}{4}$ inch, on upper surface, on blue jack,
black jack, laurel-leaved and turkey oaks and *Q. myrti-*

---

[1] This gall does not produce a *Neuroterus,* though according to Weld, it is commonly
known as *N. laurifoliœ* Ashm.

folia, fall, gall wasp........*Callirhytis infuscata* Ashm.
Conical, truncate and slightly convex above, tapering to a
point of attachment, as broad as high, ¼ inch, larval
cavity large, evidently once covered with wool, probably
from a leaf cluster, unknown oak, Missouri, gall wasp....
.........................*Andricus perplexus* Ashm.
Bunches of pale brown wool on undersurface of leaf, each
with 2 to 8 triangular or irregularly conical cells, diameter

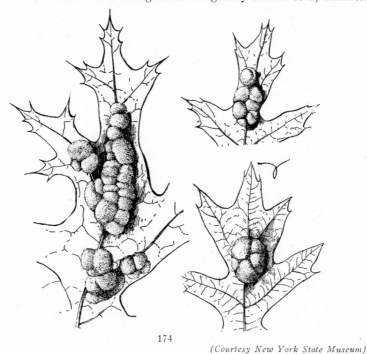

174

(Courtesy New York State Museum)

FIG. 174.—Wooly oak gall, *Callirhytis lanata.* (*After Beutm.*)

⅕ to ⅗ inch, on scarlet, black, black jack, Spanish and
scrub oaks and *Q. texana,* fall, gall wasp. Fig. 174......
...............Woolly oak gall, *Callirhytis lanata* Gill.
Globular or hemispherical, densely haired, pinkish-red
clusters of galls, each with 1 to 5 larval cells, diameter
⅕ to ½ inch, on *Q. arizonica, Q. oblongifolia, Q. toumeyi,*
gall wasp. Fig. 175.............*Acraspis nubila* Bass.
Central core red brown, with short, dense, clubbed hairs
and long, dense, hair-like wavy spines, light straw white
tinged with yellow, on *Q. sacame,* gall wasp, Mex.......
.............................*Acraspis lanaris* Kins.

Central core tan or brown, with dense, short, hair-like cells and long, wavy, hair-like spines, light straw white, tinged with yellow, golden tan near tips, on *Q. reticulata*, *Q. polymorpha*, gall wasp, Mex. .*Acraspis molucrum* Kins.

Similar gall, the core straw to dirty brown, the hair-like spines mostly whitish or yellowish, the tips yellowish-russet, the base of the spines somewhat swollen, on *Q. arizonica* and *Q. oblongifolia*, gall wasp. Fig. 176.......

..............................*Acraspis russa* Kins.

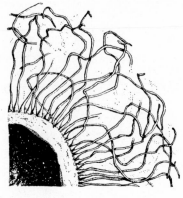

175   176

(Courtesy New York State Museum)

FIG. 175.—Gall of *Acraspis nubila*. (*After Beutm.*)
FIG. 176.—Gall of *Acraspis russa*, section of a part, greatly enlarged. (*After Kinsey*)

Similar gall, the core yellowish to rich red-russet color, the spines yellowish-white with golden-yellow tips, bases not swollen, on *Q. potosina*, *Q. jaralensis*, *Q. sacame*, *Q. chihuahuensis*, *Q. texcocana*, *Q. centralis*, *Q. macrophylla*, *Q. undata*, gall wasp, Mex. Pl. 39 (7)...............

...........................*Acraspis incompta* Kins.

Gall, reddish or dirty brown, the long hair-like spines whitish straw to light yellow, weathering to dirty brown or black on *Q. læta*, *Q. polymorpha*, *Q. macrophylla*, gall wasp, Mex. ....*Acraspis nigricula* Kins.

PLATE 30—CYNIPID GALLS. 1, Gall of *Neuroterus contortus* Weld, on *Q. breviloba*. 2, Gall of *Callirhytis floridana* Ashm., on post oak. 3, Gall of *Andricus atrimenta* Kins., on *Q. douglasii*. 4, Gall of *Heterœcus chrysolepidis* Ashm., on canyon live oak. 5, Gall of *Andricus rugatus* Weld, ×4, on overcup oak. 6, Gall of *Andricus fimbrialis* Weld, on *Q. dumosa*. 7, Gall of *Cynips corallina* Bass., on *Q. douglasii*. 8, Gall of *Plagiotrochus suttoni* Bass., on coast live oak. 9, Gall of *Andricus howertoni* Bass., on *Q. undulata*. (*All after Weld*).

PLATE 30

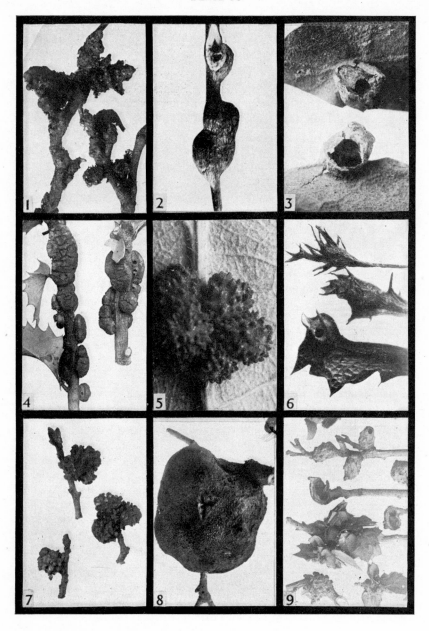

Gall, brick or brownish-red, the long hair-like spines light brownish-orange, clusters often $3\frac{1}{3}$ inches, on *Q. conglomerata, Q. convallata, Q. rodophlebia*, gall wasp, Mex. ....*Acraspis chica* Kins.

Gall, with long hair-like spines, nearly white, the tips orange-pink or rosy when young, becoming rosy-orange or brownish-orange when old, on *Q. undata*, gall wasp, Mex. ....*Acraspis radialis* Kins.

Gall, the long hair-like spines white, their tips orange-pink or rosy becoming rosy-orange or brownish, on *Q. undata*, gall wasp, Mex. ....*Acraspis rufula* Kins.

Gall, long hair-like spines, nearly white at base, pinkish-orange to bright orange at tips, on *Q. sacame, Q. durangensis, Q. depressipes*, gall wasp, Mex. ....*Acraspis subtincta* Kins.

Gall, long hair-like spines nearly white at base, purplish-pink when young, yellow-brown or light rosy-brown when mature, on *Q. sacame, Q. chihuahuensis*, gall wasp, Mex. ....*Acraspis tincta* Kins.

Clustered, thin-shelled, reddish, woolly oak leaf gall, individual galls diameter $\frac{1}{25}$ to $\frac{1}{16}$ inch, height $\frac{1}{10}$ inch, on valley oak, gall wasp......*Andricus fullawayi* Beutm.

Subelliptical or subcylindrical yellowish vein gall with long yellowish hairs, ordinarily in clusters of 2 to 3, length about $\frac{1}{3}$ inch, differs from *Callirhytis infuscata* by the greater thickness of the walls, gall wasp.....*Andricus sp.*

(d) Galls with small cells and bonded together by a hard substance:

Hemispherical, hard, many-celled leaf gall covered with pale yellowish wool, more or less wrinkled, with ferruginous stem entirely rust-red, resembles *A. floccus*, diameter $\frac{1}{5}$ to $\frac{1}{3}$ inch, occurs on both surfaces of canyon live oak, gall wasp. Pl. 25 (9)........*Andricus lasius* Ashm.

Similar gall presumably on same oak, gall wasp........ ....*Andricus areolaris* Kins.

Similar gall, presumably on same oak, gall wasp........ ....*Andricus sublasius* Kins.

Densely haired, russet-colored, hemispherical masses attached by a small point to the upper or lower surface of the leaf, diameter $\frac{1}{2}$ to $\frac{3}{4}$ inch, on *Q. arizonica*, gall wasp ....*Bassettia tenuicornis* Bass.

(e) Galls many-celled and under wool:

Woolly, rusty, yellowish-brown, many-celled, midvein gall,

dimensions $\frac{1}{10}$ to $\frac{1}{8}$ inch, on *Q. macrophylla,* gall wasp
. . . .*Andricus mexicanus* Bass.

Red or brown, silky haired, many-celled, on the upper side of the leaf, usually on a vein, diameter $\frac{1}{25}$ inch, on scarlet and scrub oaks, gall wasp. . . . .*Cynips ? cristata* Steb.

(17) Galls with a stem or petiole, or an extension of a vein above or beyond the leaf surface, attached to the leaves:

Elongate or fusiform, pointed leaf or twig gall, usually with a long pedicel, the prolongation of a leaf vein, pale green, thin-shelled and with an oblong, thin larval cell supported by radiating fibers, length $\frac{4}{5}$ to 1 inch, diameter $\frac{1}{6}$ to $\frac{1}{3}$ inch, on scarlet and red oaks, summer, gall wasp. Pl. 26 (1); Fig. 177. . . . . .
. . . . .Oak spindle gall, *Amphibolips coelebs* O.S.

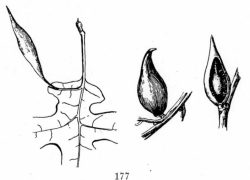

177

(Courtesy New York State Museum)

FIG. 177.—Oak spindle gall, *Amphibolips coelebs. (After Beutm.)*

Slender, globe-shaped leaf gall, nearly $\frac{1}{2}$ inch long, the stalk twice as long as the swelling, the surface pubescent, on white, swamp white, burr, chestnut and post oaks, spring, gall wasp. Pl. 22 (1). . .Small oak spindle gall, *Andricus chinquapin* Fitch
(*capsulus* Bass., *fusiformis* O.S.)

Elongate capsule attached by a slender thread near the edge of the leaf, dimensions of the thin-walled, hollow capsules $\frac{1}{5}$ to $\frac{1}{4}$ inch by $\frac{1}{25}$ to $\frac{1}{16}$, of the stem $\frac{1}{5}$ to $\frac{1}{2}$ inch, on valley oak and *Q. dumosa, Q. douglasii,* gall wasp. Pl. 26 (3). . . . . .
. . . . .Stemmed oak gall, *Andricus pedicellatus* Kins.

Fusiform, stemmed, green or dark olive brown leaf gall with a free cell within, length $\frac{1}{6}$ to $\frac{1}{5}$ inch, diameter $\frac{1}{8}$ inch, on scarlet, red and black oaks, gall wasp, spring. Fig. 178. . . .
. . . .*Dryophanta pedunculata* Bass.

Fusiform, stemmed, smooth, reddish-brown vein gall, length

⅓ to ⅖ inch, the stem slender, smooth, gall wasp...........
......................*Andricus pseudo-callidoma* Trott.

(18) Marginal folds of leaves or leaf rolls:

Fusiform, marginal, smooth, solitary fold, length ¼ inch, diameter ¹⁄₁₀ inch, walls somewhat thickened, on live oak, gall wasp
....................................*Dryophanta sp.*

Ovate, pocket-shaped, marginal, pilose leaf fold, usually clustered, sometimes single, length ⅙ inch, diameter ⅛ inch, on live oak, gall wasp......................*Dryophanta sp.*

178   179
(Courtesy New York State Museum)

FIG. 178.—Gall of *Dryophanta pedunculata.* (*After Beutm.*)
FIG. 179.—Oak flower stem gall, *Neuroterus pallidus.* (*After Beutm.*)

Ovate, pocket-shaped, marginal leaf fold with greatly thickened walls, solitary, sometimes in pairs, length ⅕ to ⅓ inch, gall midge.........................*?Diplosis silvestrii* Trott.

A folded leaf edge between serrations, gall midge. Pl. 8 (5)...
.............Marginal fold gall, *Itonida foliora* Rsll. & Hkr.
Cecidomyia erubescens O.S.

Leaf lobes folded, white oak, gall midge. Pl. 8 (6)........
....*Cecidomyia sp.*

Toothed, marginal, poddy thickenings, dimensions ³⁄₁₆ inch, canyon live oak.........................*Cecidomyia sp.*

(19) Presumably leaf galls, the gall unknown:

Reared from oak, presumably from a gall resembling that made by Cynips, gall midge.........*Thecodiplosis quercifolia* Felt

Probably reared from oak leaves, gall midge...............
.............................*Dicrodiplosis quercina* Felt

Flower or Catkin Galls

The blossoming period of the oak is a restricted one and the aments or catkins drop within a short time. These limitations, however, do not prevent a series of gall wasps developing successfully and sometimes in large numbers in flower galls. The large woolly mass of *Callirhytis operator* has a similarity in appearance to the beautiful gall produced by the wool sower. It is quite different in that it is a modification of the aments, the individual mass being some two or three inches in diameter and containing possibly 150 cells or more. Another of these flower infesting gall wasps produces rounded, shot-like enlargements, in other cases the catkins are thickly distorted or even seriously deformed by the numerous abnormal growths. The remarkable feature in these infestations is that the gall wasps must issue or emerge from some other gall at just about the right time and deposit their eggs within a short period, and the young or larvae must complete their growth before or soon after the catkins drop, as is the case with the oak flower gall produced by *Callirhytis pulchra* Bass. This means a short and active period of development.

All of these staminate flower galls produce the sexual generation of adults, both males and females.

6. Galls of the Aments, Catkins or Peduncles

    a. Irregular, woolly or hairy flower galls on the stems or peduncles of the pistillate flowers:

        Oval masses 2 to 3 inches in diameter, hairs greenish white or rose tinted, sometimes deep red, there may be 150 or more cells each less than $\frac{1}{10}$ of an inch in diameter, on scarlet, scrub, black jack, red and pin oaks, gall wasp. Pl. 36 (2) . . . . .Woolly catkin gall, *Callirhytis operator* O.S.

        Similar to above, on scarlet, black jack and black oaks, gall wasp . . . .*Callirhytis consobrina* Kins.

        Similar to above, on scrub oak, gall wasp . . . . . .*Callirhytis falsa* Kins.

        Similar gall on *Q. schumardii,* gall wasp . . . .*Callirhytis austrior* Kins.

        Globular, woolly gall, diameter $\frac{1}{2}$ inch, on water oak, gall wasp . . . .*Callirhytis turneri* Ashm.

    b. Axis or stem of staminate flowers enlarged and containing or bearing the cells or galls; large galls, at least $\frac{1}{2}$ inch in diameter:

        Irregular, rugose, yellowish-brown, many-celled, enlargement of staminate flower stem, length 1 to 2 inches, on coast and interior live oaks, gall wasp. Pl. 19 (3) . . . .*Callirhytis congregata* Ashm.

        Nodula, fusiform, succulent enlargements of flower axis containing many cells and soon drying and shriveling, on post oak, occurs in fall on swamp white and burr oaks, gall wasp. Pl. 31 (2); Fig. 103 . . . . .Oak flake gall, *Neuroterus floccosus* Bass.

        Cells in swollen staminate flower stems, the catkins shortened and

thickened, aborting the entire ament and producing an ovoid mass with a diameter of nearly ¼ inch and covered closely with clustered but otherwise normal anthers, on *Q. breviloba*, gall wasp..........
.............................*Neuroterus evanescens* Kins.
Irregular swellings of the flower stems beset with dwarfed clusters of stamens, affecting twigs, leaf blades and petioles to a minor degree, length 1¼ inch, diameter ⅔ inch, on valley oak, gall wasp........
...............................*Neuroterus pacificus* Kins.

c. Axis or stem of staminate flowers normal in size although often shortened, bearing numbers of individual galls which are modified anthers or filaments, the individual galls rarely over ¼ inch in diameter, often clustered into masses:

Globular, greenish white, coarsely pubescent, diameter ⅛ inch, on staminate flowers of shingle oak...........*Callirhytis parva* Weld

180

Fig. 180.—Gall of *Disholcaspis pedunculoides.* (*After Weld*)

Clavate, irregular, angulate, thin-shelled, each 1-2-celled, clustered, dark brown, diameter ⅙ inch, on coast live oak, gall wasp........
................................*Dryophanta dubiosa* Full.
Dense ½ inch clusters of yellowish or yellowish-brown, two-celled grain-like galls, the whole rounded or elongate, oval and containing 20-40 or more cells, on coast and interior live oaks, gall wasp. Pl. 36 (8)..............................*Andricus serricornis* Kins.
Rounded, shot-like, green-white, soft, spongy, many-celled, on scarlet, red and black oaks, gall wasp. Pl. 2 (7); Pl. 33 (5)..........
......................Oak flower gall, *Callirhytis pulchra* Bass.

Plate 31—Cynipid Galls. 1, Gall of *Philonix nigra* Gill., on white oak. 2, Oak flake gall, *Neuroterus floccosus* Bass., on burr oak. 3, Gall of *Callirhytis futilis* O.S., sexual generation on white oak. 4, Gall of *Dryophanta cinereæ* Ashm., ×4, on Spanish oak. 5, Oak button gall, *Neuroterus umbilicatus* Bass., ×4 on swamp white oak. 6, Oak disk gall, *Andricus discalis* Weld, ×4, on *Q, toumeyi.* 7, Wool patch gall, *Andricus lanigera* Ashm., on live oak. 8, Keeled oak apple, *Amphibolips tinctoriæ* Ashm., on black oak. 9, Oak hedgehog gall, *Acraspis erinacei* Beutm., agamic form, on white oak. (*All after Weld*).

PLATE 31

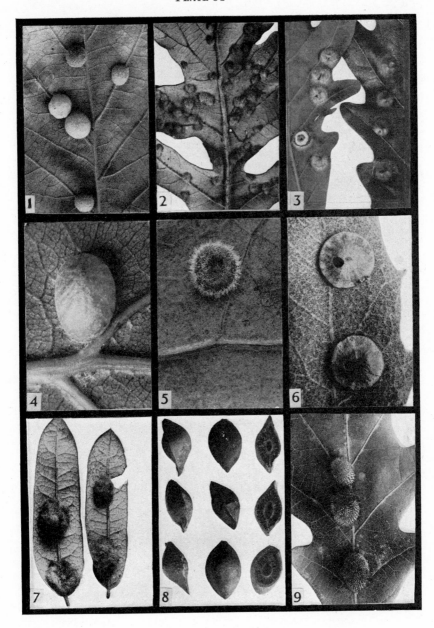

Conical, one-celled, dark brown or black when dry, length $\frac{1}{8}$ inch, on *Q. myrtifolia*, gall wasp. . . . . *Callirhytis myrtifoliæ* Beutm.

Ovate, smooth, diameter $\frac{1}{25}$ inch, on blue jack oak, gall wasp. . . . . *Callirhytis blastophaga* Ashm.

Ovate, small, short, dark, slate-colored, length $\frac{1}{20}$ inch, on post oak, gall wasp. . . . . *Neuroterus exiguus* Bass.

Small, black, many-celled galls in sterile florets of scrub oak, making aments look like elongated blackberries, occasionally very abundant, diameter $\frac{1}{10}$ inch, gall wasp. . . . . *Callirhytis clarkei* Bass.

Globose, one-celled, pale wood-colored, densely clustered at ends of aments, on swamp white oak, gall wasp. Fig. 179. . . . . Oak flower stem gall, *Neuroterus pallidus* Bass.

Similar gall on post oak, gall wasp, spring. . *Neuroterus exiguus* Bass.

Minute, ovate, one-celled, light colored, pointed capsules, diameter $\frac{1}{16}$ inch, on *Q. douglasii*, gall wasp. . . . . . . *Neuroterus floricola* Kins.

Ovate, brown, scattered, thin-walled, pointed cells, diameter $\frac{1}{10}$ inch, on *Q. douglasii*, gall wasp. Pl. 21 (4). . . . . *Andricus gigas* Kins.

Reared from undescribed oak blossom galls, gall midge. . . . . *Lasioptera querciflorœ* Felt

d. Galls clasping the stem or peduncle, 2 to 20:

Galls slender, conical, sharp at tip, $\frac{1}{2}$ inch long, basal diameter $\frac{1}{8}$ inch, one-celled, brown, on *Q. arizonica, Q. grisea, Q. oblongifolia, Q. subturbinella*, fall, gall wasp. Fig. 180. . . . . *Disholcaspis pedunculoides* Weld

Acorn Galls

More than twenty species of cynipid galls originate in the pistillate flowers and develop within the acorn, some producing characteristic large growths known as "plum galls," on the side of the acorn cup. These drop off in the fall. Others develop in cells more or less imbedded in the tissues of the cup. Another series produces what is known as "pip galls," tooth-like or wedge-shaped growths which are somewhat common between the acorn and the cup and another series develops within the acorn itself, sometimes without producing an appreciable deformation.

7. Acorn Galls

a. Galls of the acorn cup (cupule) and not involving the acorn itself:

(1) Large, globose, thick-walled, hard, mottled, brownish or reddish galls on the side of the acorn cup, easily detached and dropping to the ground in the fall, always on red oaks:

Pink when fresh, becoming yellow and then blood-red, diameter $\frac{1}{2}$ to 1 inch, on black, red, scarlet, Spanish and scrub oaks, August and September, shrivels, and becomes very hard, gall

wasp. Pl. 34 (3); Fig. 181............................
..............Acorn plum gall, *Amphibolips prunus* Walsh
Densely corky, rusty brown internally, diameter 1 to 1½ inches,
does not shrivel, on black jack oak, gall wasp. Pl. 21 (7); Fig.
182...........................*Amphibolips gainesi* Bass.

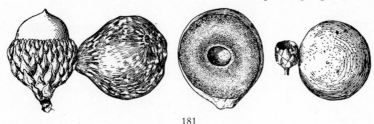

181

(Courtesy New York State Museum)

FIG. 181.—Acorn plum gall, *Amphibolips prunus*. (*After Beutm.*)

Globose, smooth, corky, reddish brown with a large central cell,
dropping to ground in fall, diameter ⅓ to ½ inch, on willow
and laurel-leaved oaks, gall wasp...........................
..........................*Amphibolips fuliginosa* Ashm.

(2) Smaller galls more or less imbedded in the tissue of the cup,
often falling to the ground in the fall when mature:

182

(Courtesy New York State Museum)

FIG. 182.—Gall of *Amphibolips gainesi*. (*After Beutm.*)

Ellipsoidal white cell, ⅙ to ¼ inch in diameter and almost hidden in the fimbriate recess in the side of the cup, on swamp
white oak, gall wasp. Pl. 35 (2)........*Andricus incertus* Bass.
(*fimbriatus* Weld)
Irregular, one-celled, conical swellings of the cupule, length ¼
inch, on burr, chinquapin and basket oaks, gall wasp..........
..............................*Callirhytis glandula* Beutm.
Cell, diameter 1/10 inch, walls hard, sometimes a slight swelling

of cupule, on valley oak, gall wasp. . . .*Neuroterus varians* Kins.

Gall subglobular, green, one-celled, with blunt, warty elevations, apex slightly prolonged, diameter ¼ inch, probably an acorn gall, on willow oak. Pl. 19 (4). . . . .
. . . . .Warty oak gall, *Callirhytis middletoni* Weld

b. Galls inside the acorn:

(1) Cells in the cluster, confluent or protruding, a stony mass more or less filling the interior and which may be lifted out intact, often can be detected only by cutting acorns open:

On black jack oak, gall wasp. . . . .*Callirhytis fruticola* Ashm.

On scarlet and red oaks and *Q. texana,* gall wasp. Pl. 36 (1)
. . . .*Callirhytis fructuosa* Weld

On blue jack oak, gall wasp. . . . .*Callirhytis petrosa* Weld

On coast and interior live oaks, and California black oak, gall wasp. Pl. 19 (1). . . . .*Callirhytis milleri* Weld

On swamp white oak, separable cells at base of cotyledons. Pl. 36 (7). . . . .*Callirhytis lapillula* Weld

On *Q. hypoleuca,* gall wasp. . . . .*Callirhytis petrina* Weld

On canyon live oak, cells contiguous on one side of acorn, fall, gall wasp. . . . .*Loxaulus trizonalis* Weld

On black oak, gall unknown, gall wasp. . . . .
. . . .*Callirhytis corrugis* Bass.
(*defecta* Kieff.)

(2) Cells single, not confluent nor separable from the wall of the acorn:

On canyon live oak, cell horizontal, at base of young acorns, midsummer, gall wasp. . . . .*Andricus chrysobalani* Weld

On coast and interior live oaks and California black oak, fall, gall wasp. . . . .*Biorhiza eldoradensis* Beutm.

On *Q. dumosa,* acorns lopsided, undersized, one or two cells at base, Fig. 183. . . . .*Andricus albobalani* Weld

Reared from larvae between the seed coats of an acorn, gall midge. . . . .*Dasyneura glandis* Felt

On acorns of chinquapin oak, gall wasp. . . . .
. . . .*Callirhytis glandula* Beutm.

Seed-like, conical galls partly imbedded in the cup, dropping in autumn, on burr, white, chestnut, yellow chestnut and basket oaks, gall wasp, never reared. Pl. 3 (4). . . . .
. . . .*Cynips glandulosus* Beutm.

Cell buried in wood of acorn cup, oftenest at the base, on valley oak, gall wasp. . . . .*Neuroterus cupulœ* Kins.

(3) Galls known as "pip galls" produced between the acorn and the cup:

Flattened, tooth-like or wedge-shaped galls on the outside of the acorn, the ends usually protruding more or less beyond the cupule, on black, red, scarlet, scrub and Spanish oaks, gall wasp, fall form of *Andricus operator* O.S. Pl. 35 (1)..............
............................*Callirhytis operatola* Bass.

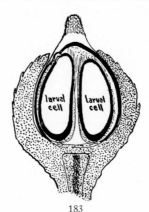

183

(Courtesy New York State Museum)

FIG. 183.—Gall of *Andricus albobalani*. (*After Weld*)

(4) Galls beside immature acorns of red oak:

Fleshy, smooth, greenish, purple mottled, flattened galls, blunt at apex, on one-year old acorns of scarlet oak, in early spring, secrete honeydew, gall wasp. Pl. 29 (6).....................
...............................*Callirhytis balanosa* Weld

Triangular, flattened, cell in upper part of gall, produces honeydew, in fall alongside immature acorns, on black oak, gall wasp. Pl. 35 (3).....................*Callirhytis balanoides* Weld

Longer than broad, deeply imbedded beside immature acorns, the cup twice normal size, occur in fall and secrete honeydew, on black jack oak, gall wasp. Pl. 34 (2)....................
............................*Callirhytis balanaspis* Weld

Green, smooth, laterally compressed, slightly elongate basally, about as broad as long, mostly protruding, from young, normal sized acorn cups, occur in fall, secrete honeydew, on black jack oak, gall wasp..................*Callirhytis balanopsis* Weld

On one year old acorns in spring, secreting honeydew, on scrub oak, gall wasp. Pl. 1 (7)............*Callirhytis perditor* Bass.

Smooth, green, often laterally compressed, about ¼ inch long, dropping in May, secretes honeydew, on coast and interior live oaks, gall wasp. Pl. 36 (3).......*Callirhytis carmelensis* Weld

Apparently normal, under-sized acorns showing slight elevations of the surface and containing 6-20 kernels or cells, in a stony-hard mass, on coast and interior live oaks and California black oak, gall wasp...............*Callirhytis milleri* Weld
(*essigi* McC. & Egb.)

Nettle Family (*Urticaceæ*)

The elms are attacked by several gall insects, especially plant lice. The leaves of the common American elm, particularly those of small trees, are sometimes rather seriously deformed by coxcomb elm galls or very badly curled and twisted, with more or less yellowish discoloration by hosts of a mealy covered plant louse. The latter is hardly an insect gall in the strict sense of the word. The slippery elm is infested by another plant louse which produces upon the upper surface of the leaves a spindle-shaped, hollow gall variable in size and frequently about half an inch long. A smaller pouch-like gall occurs on the English elm. It is widely established in this country.

The hackberry is a prime favorite with certain jumping plant lice or Psyllids belonging to the genus *Pachypsylla,* insects related to the destructive and well known pear psylla. The jumping plant lice produce galls upon the twigs, buds and foliage, those on the leaves varying from subglobular to somewhat disk-shaped and may even resemble a star or flower. The *Pachypsylla* bud galls give a characteristic appearance to a badly infested hackberry. Several gall midges also find suitable conditions in this plant, the hackberry flask gall being one of the more common.

The witch's broom, produced by a mite or a fungus, is a striking feature when abundant on hackberry.

Elm (*Ulmus*)

Knotty growths on trunk and branches, midsummer. Fig. 184.......
.....................Woolly elm louse, *Schizoneura rileyi* Thos.

Blasted buds, immature leaf clusters, or swollen seeds of slippery elm midge, spring. Pl. 10 (3); Pl. 11 (6); Fig. 185..*Dasyneura ulmea* Felt
Phytophaga ulmi Beutm.

Green or reddish coxcomb-shaped ridges between leaf veins, length ½ inch, aphid, summer. Fig. 186...Coxcomb elm gall, *Colopha ulmicola* Fitch

---

PLATE 32—CYNIPID GALLS. 1, Gall of *Cynips guadaloupensis* Full., ×3, on canyon live oak. 2, Gall of *Andricus pattersonæ* Full., ×3 on *Q. douglasii*. 3, Oak saucer gall, *Andricus parmula* Bass., ×3, on valley oak. 4, Gall of *Acraspis carolina* Ashm., ×3, on post oak. 5, Double oak gall, *Heterœcus sanctæ-claræ* Full., ×3, on canyon live oak. 6, Gall of *Dryocosmus piperoides* Bass., ×3, on Spanish oak. 7, Oak trumpet gall, *Andricus tubalis* Weld, ×3, on *Q. oblongifolia*. 8, Weld's cup gall, *Cynips patelloides* Weld, ×3, on canyon live oak. 9, Splendid tube gall, *Andricus splendens* Weld, ×3. (*All after Weld*).

PLATE 32

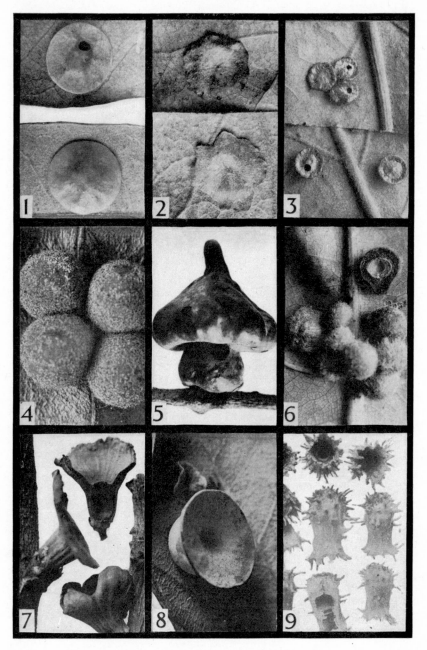

Spindle-shaped hollow leaf gall, length ½ inch, aphid, summer......
...............Slippery elm pouch gall, *Gobaishia ulmifusus* Walsh
Marginal leaf roll on slippery elm, aphid, summer................
....*Georgiaphis ulmi* Wilson
Globose, yellowish-green, pink-tinted leaf gall, diameter ¼ to ½ inch, on
U. montana, aphid, summer...............................
....................Elm sack gall, *Tetraneura ulmisacculi* Patch

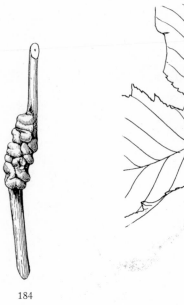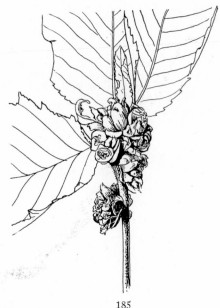

184   185
(Courtesy New York State Museum)

Fig. 184.—Woolly elm louse gall, *Schizoneura rileyi*.
Fig. 185.—Aborted buds of slippery elm, caused possibly by *Dasyneura ulmea*.

Globular leaf gall, on upper surface, on *U. americana*, mite........
....*Eriophyes ulmi*
Curled, twisted, lousy leaves, aphid, summer....................
...................Elm leaf aphid, *Schizoneura americana* Riley
Oval, brown leaf spots, diameter ⅛ inch, midge, spring....*Cecidomyia sp.*
Green or yellowish pocket galls or pile on leaves, mite, summer......
....*Eriophyes sp.*

Hackberry *(Celtis)*

"Witch's broom" on branches and twigs, mite, summer.....*Eriophyes sp.*
Sphærotheca phytophila

Hollow twig swellings, length ½ to 2¼ inches, midge.............
.....................................*Cecidomyia deserta* Patt.
Fusiform bud gall, length ¾ to 1½ inches, caterpillar. Fig. 189......
.....................................*Proteoteras œsculana* Riley
Twig galls resembling seed capsules of Rumex, diameter ¼ inch, midge,
summer.........................*Cecidomyia semenrumicis* Patt.
Subcortical twig swellings, diameter ⅛ inch, midge........*Lasioptera sp.*
Bud-shaped, polythalamus twig gall, psyllid, summer. Fig. 191......
...................Hackberry bud gall, *Pachypsylla gemma* Riley

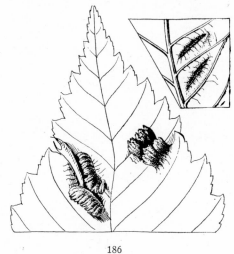

186   187
(Courtesy New York State Museum)

FIG. 186.—Cockscomb elm gall, *Colopha ulmicola,* showing upper and lower leaf surface.
FIG. 187.—Elm sack gall, *Tetraneura ulmisaccula.*

Conical slightly-ribbed leaf or twig gall, diameter ⅛ inch, midge, summer.
Pl. 40 (5), Fig. 192....................................
.................Hackberry flask gall, *Phytophaga celtiphylla* Felt
Globose, polythalamus twig galls, diameter ¼ inch, midge..*Cecidomyia sp.*
Conical spine-shaped leaf gall, height ⅙ inch, midge, summer........
...............Spiny hackberry gall, *Cecidomyia spiniformis* Patt.
Small globular subsessile leaf gall, psyllid, summer...............
.....................................*Pachypsylla globulus* Riley
Top-shaped, moderately thick leaf gall, diameter ⅙ inch, midge, summer
....*Phytophaga wellsi* Felt

Rosette-shaped rib leaf gall, diameter ⅛ inch, midge, summer......
...............................*Cecidomyia capsularis* Patt.

Large reniform petiole gall at base of leaf, an opening, psyllid, summer
................Hackberry petiole gall, *Pachypsylla venusta* O.S.

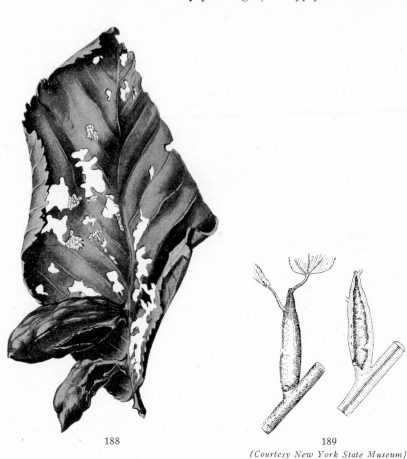

188

189

(Courtesy New York State Museum)

Fig. 188.—Slippery elm pouch gall, *Gobaishia ulmifusus.*
Fig. 189.—Gall of *Proteoteras æsculana.* (*After Wells*)

Large mammiform leaf gall, diameter ⅙ inch, psyllid, summer. Pl. 14 (2);
Fig. 193..........Hackberry nipple gall, *Pachypsylla mamma* Riley

Elevated mammiform gall with long process, diameter ¼ inch, psyllid,
summer.............................*Pachypsylla rohweri* Ckll.

Small subglobular hairy leaf gall, diameter ⅛ inch, psyllid, summer..
..................................*Pachypsylla pubescens* Riley

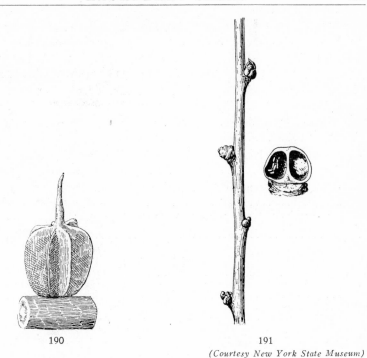

190   191

(Courtesy New York State Museum)

FIG. 190.—Winged twig gall, *Cecidomyia sp.* (*After Wells*)
FIG. 191.—Hackberry bud gall, *Pachypsylla gemma.*

Without the cup-shaped depression of the preceding, midge, summer. Pl.
40 (9)............................*Cecidomyia pubescens* Patt.
Circular flattened leaf gall, diameter ¼ inch, psyllid, summer.......
...............Hackberry button gall, *Pachypsylla umbilicus* Riley

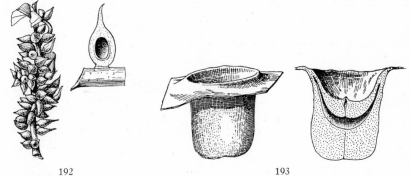

192   193

(Courtesy New York State Museum)

FIG. 192.—Hackberry flask gall, *Phytophaga celtiphyllia.*
FIG. 193.—Hackberry nipple gall, *Pachypsylla mamma,* one in section. (*After Weld*)

Circular, white-haired leaf gall, diameter ⅛ inch, midge, summer. Pl. 40 (7)..............................*Phytophaga painteri* Felt

Star-shaped or flower-shaped leaf gall, diameter ¼ inch, psyllid, summer ....Hackberry star gall, *Pachypsylla asteriscus* Riley

Blister-like yellowish leaf gall, psyllid, summer................... ....Hackberry blister gall, *Pachypsylla vesiculum* Riley

Globose, smooth, sessile, much flattened leaf gall, psyllid, summer.... ....Hackberry melon gall, *Pachypsylla cucurbita* Riley

Capsule-shaped, peduncled vein gall, usually basal, height ⅙ inch, midge, summer.............................*Phytophaga texana* Felt

Subconical leaf gall on under surface, length ⅛ inch, midge, summer.. ....*Cecidomyia unguicula* Beutm.

Subconical leaf stem, petiole or fruit gall, diameter ⅙ inch, midge, summer ....*Cecidomyia sp.*

Hop *(Humulus)*

Swollen stems, 2 to 25 inches long, midge, summer. Fig. 194........ ....Hop stem gall, *Lasioptera humilicaulis* Felt

Nettle *(Urtica)*

Hoary yellowish-white gall, diameter ⅙ inch, midge, summer. Pl. 7 (8) ....Nettle bullet gall, *Cecidomyia sp.*

Pale green midrib or vein gall, subsessile, diameter ⅛ inch, midge, summer ....Nettle urn gall, *Cecidomyia urnicola* O.S.

Wood Nettle *(Laportea)*

Irregular oval stem gall, midge, summer. Fig. 195........*Cecidomyia sp.*

Irregular, presumably bud gall, midge, summer..........*Cecidomyia sp.*

False Nettle *(Boehmeria)*

Fusiform stem gall, length ½ inch, midge, summer. Fig. 196........ ....*Cecidomyia boehmeriœ* Beutm.

Fig *(Ficus)*

Reared from fruits, midge, summer.........*Ficiomyia perarticulata* Felt

Reared from fruits of *Ficus populina (brevifolia)....Ficiomyia birdi* Felt

PLATE 33—CYNIPID GALLS. 1, Gall of *Callirhytis enigma* Weld, on *Q. myrtifolia*. 2, Gall of *Callirhytis ellipsoida* Weld, on swamp white oak. 3, Gall of *Holocynips badia* Bass., on swamp white oak. 4, Gall of *Callirhytis ovata* Weld, on *Q. lœvis*. 5, Gall of *Callirhytis pulchra* Bass., on scarlet oak. 6, Gall of *Andricus kingi* Bass., ×4, on valley oak. 7, Gall of *Callirhytis similis* Bass., on scrub oak. 8, Gall of *Callirhytis crypta* Ashm., on black jack oak. 9, Gall of *Neuroterus batatus* Fitch, summer form, on white oak. (*All after Weld*).

PLATE 33

Birthwort Family *(Aristolochiaceæ)*

Birthwort ovate leaf gall, diameter ⅙ inch, midge, summer..........
.....................................*Cecidomyia hageni* Aldr.
Woolly capsule on under surface of leaf, mite, summer......*Eriophyes sp.*

Buckwheat Family *(Polygonaceæ)*

Only four genera are infested by gall insects and most of these are

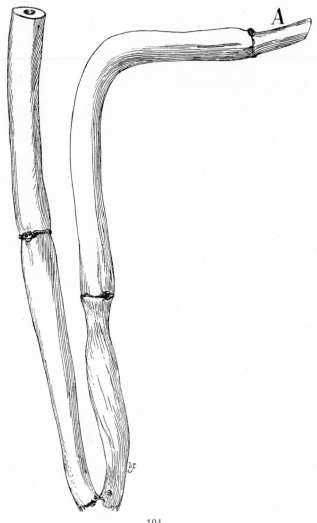

194

(Courtesy New York State Museum)

FIG. 194.—Hop stem gall, *Lasioptera humulicaulis.*

midges. The family is not a favorite with gall makers, though large numbers of midges may be reared from reddish dock seeds. An exceptionally interesting species produces a blister leaf gall on sea grape.

Eriogonum

Elongate bud swelling, midge, spring.................*Cecidomyia sp.*

Dock, Sorrel *(Rumex)*

Deformed reddish seeds, summer.............................
.....................Dock seed midge, *Contarinia rumicis* Loew

195   196   197

(Courtesy New York State Museum)

FIG. 195.—Bud gall of *Cecidomyia sp.* on *Laportea.*
FIG. 196.—Stem gall of *Cecidomyia boehmeriæ.*
FIG. 197.—Sea grape blister gall, *Ctenodactylomyia watsoni.*

Sea Grape *(Coccolobis)*

Dark green blister leaf gall, diameter ¼ inch, midge, summer. Fig. 197
.................Sea grape blister, *Ctenodactylomyia watsoni* Felt
Slight swellings in young branches, caterpillar.....*Hexeris enhydris* Grote

Knotweed *(Polygonum)*

Ovate stem galls, green to reddish-brown, length ½ inch, beetle, summer
....*Lixus musculus* Say
Variable marginal leaf rolls, often involving leaf to midrib, on *P. lapathi-folium*, midge.................................*Cecidomyia sp.*
Ovate stem gall, ½ by ³⁄₁₆ inch, brownish in fall, on *Polygonum scandens*, midge..*Lasioptera sp.*

Goosefoot Family *(Chenopodiaceæ)*

The plants of this family are not favorites with gall makers, though certain southwestern species, especially greasewood and Atriplex, support

an interesting and somewhat abundant fauna, this being particularly true
of the last named.

Mexican Tea *(Chenopodium ambrosioides)*

Fusiform stem enlargement, length ½ to ¾ inch, midge....*?Lasioptera sp.*

Eurotia

Irregular bud gall, midge, spring......................*Cecidomyia sp.*

Greasewood *(Sarcobatus)*

Oval bud gall, length ½ inch, midge, spring. Fig. 198..............
..................Greasewood bud gall, *Onodiplosis sarcobati* Felt
Axillary rosette bud galls, length ¾ inch, fly, spring...........*Trypetid*

 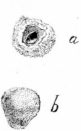

198   199

(Courtesy New York State Museum)

Fig. 198.—Greasewood bud gall, *Onodiplosis sarcobati.*
Fig. 199.—Gall of *Atriplex* bud midge, *Asphondylia neomexicana.*

Swollen folded leaflets, length ½ inch, midge, spring..............
..................Greasewood leaf gall, *Protaplonyx hagani* Felt
Oval leaf swelling, midge, early summer.........*Aplonyx sarcobati* Felt
Irregular stem swelling, length ½ to 2 inches, midge, summer.......
....*Lasioptera sp.*

Atriplex

Hairy bud galls, diameter ⅓ inch, midge, spring. Fig. 199........
..............Atriplex bud midge, *Asphondylia neomexicana* Ckll.
Tumor-like twig galls, length ½ inch, midge, summer. Fig. 200.....
..................Atriplex tumor gall, *Asphondylia atriplicis* Ckll.
Irregular twig gall, length ¾ inch, midge, summer. Fig. 201........
.................................*Lasioptera willistoni* Ckll.
Circular pustulate leaf gall, diameter ⅛ inch, midge, summer........
.............Atriplex leaf blister, *Cecidomyia atriplicicola* Ckll.

Woolly masses on stems, ½ to 1 inch long, midge, summer.........
.................................*Asphondylia ? atriplicis* Ckll.

Subglobose or lenticular apposed leaf galls, diameter ⅛ inch, scale insect, summer. Fig. 202....................*Atriplicia ? gallicola* Ckll.

Longitudinally curled, apposed leaves, length ¼ inch, scale insect. Fig. 203...*Coccid sp.*

Sea Blite *(Suaeda or Dondia)*

Blackish globose leaf galls, diameter ⅛ inch, midge, summer........
....................................*Asphondylia dondiæ* Felt

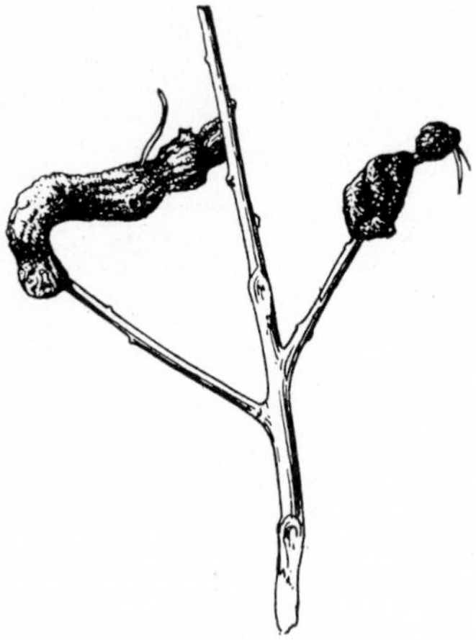

200    201

(Courtesy New York State Museum)

FIG. 200.—*Atriplex* tumor gall, *Asphondylia atriplicis.*
FIG. 201.—Gall of *Lasioptera willistoni.*

Amaranthus Family *(Amaranthaceæ)*

Amaranthus

Galls in dry stem, *A. palmeri,* midge, summer...*Cecidomyia palmeri* Ckll.

Aborted and elongate ovary, *A. blitoides,* midge, spring............
....................................*Asphondylia amaranthi* Felt

Pokeweed Family *(Phytolaccaceæ)*

Rouge Plant *(Rivina)*

Bud gall, midge, spring.......................*Schizomyia rivinæ* Felt

Four O'Clock Family *(Nyctaginaceæ)*

Oxybaphus

Stem gall, length ¾ to 1 inch, midge, summer.....*Lasioptera allioniæ* Felt

Crowfoot Family *(Ranunculaceæ)*

Present records indicate a far from general infestation by gall makers among these plants, the insects being all gall midges and mostly upon virgin's bower. There are, in addition, several gall mites.

Meadow Rue *(Thalictrum)*

Enlarged seed pods, length ⅓ inch, midge, spring...............

...............Meadow rue seed midge, *Asphondylia thalictri* Felt

  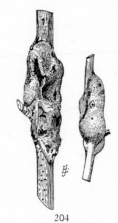

202   203   204

(Courtesy New York State Museum)

FIG. 202.—Coccid gall on *Atriplex.*
FIG. 203.—Coccid gall on *Atriplex.*
FIG. 204.—Spice stem gall, *Lasioptera linderæ.*

Anemone

Loose bud gall, midge, spring....................................

....................Anemone bud gall, *Dasyneura anemone* Felt

Golden-brown leaf pile, mite.........................*Eriophyes sp.*

Virgin's Bower *(Clematis)*

Oval stem gall, length 1 inch, fly. Pl. 2 (1)...............*Agromyza sp.*

PLATE 34—CYNIPID GALLS. 1, Gall of *Andricus stropus* Ashm., ✕4, on post oak. 2, Gall of *Callirhytis balanaspis* Weld, ✕4, on black jack oak. 3, Acorn plum gall, *Amphibolips prunus* Walsh, on black oak. 4, Gall of *Callirhytis gemmiformis* Beutm., ✕4, on white oak. 5, Hard oak bud gall, *Acraspis gemula* Bass., ✕4, on white oak. 6, Gall of *Callirhytis mamillaformis* Weld, on white oak. 7, Gall of *Neuroterus vesicula* Bass., ✕4, on swamp white oak. 8, Gall of *Acraspis erinacei* Beutm., ✕4, galls of sexual generation on bud scales of white oak. 9, Gall of *Neuroterus escharensis* Weld, ✕4, on swamp white oak. *(All after Weld).*

PLATE 34

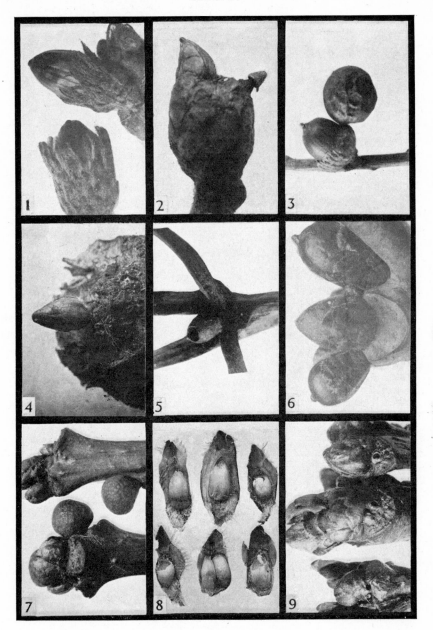

Subglobular bud gall, diameter ½ inch, midge, spring. Pl. 41 (9)....
....................Clematis bud gall, *Asphondylia clematidis* Felt
Pl. 9 (4) *Contarinia clematidis* Felt
Dasyneura clematidis Felt
Reddish-brown axillary bud gall, diameter ⅙ inch, midge, spring.....
...............................*Neolasioptera clematidis* Felt
Enlarged reddish flower buds, midge, spring.....................
..................Clematis flower midge, *Prodiplosis floricola* Felt
Small patches of short whitish tubes on leaves, bud stalks and buds, spring
and summer....................Clematis mite gall, *Eriophyes sp.*

Larkspur *(Delphinium)*

Loose leaf and blossom bud deformations, diameter ¼ to 1 inch, mite,
summer...............Cyclamen mite, *Tarsonemus pallidus* Banks

Laurel Family *(Lauraceæ)*

Two of the four native genera are hosts to gall midges, the more
common being a small species which produces a swelling upon the stems
of spicebush.

Sassafras

Curling leaves of *S. variifolium*, midge, summer..................
..................Sassafras leaf midge, *Dasyneura sassafras* Felt

Spice Bush *(Benzoin)*

Rolled leaf margins, midge, summer...................*Cecidomyia sp.*
Subcortical stem gall, length ¼ to 1 inch, midge, summer. Fig. 204...
.................Spice bush stem gall, *Lasioptera linderæ* Beutm.

European Bay Tree *(Laurus)*

Irregular, mostly marginal leaf rolls, foliage sometimes badly deformed,
summer......................Laurel psyllid, *Trioza alacris* Flor.

Persea

Irregular, mostly marginal leaf rolls, length frequently ½ inch.......
...........................Laurel psyllid, *Trioza alacris* Flor.
Marginal, reniform leaf rolls, length ¼-1 inch...............*Aphis sp.*
Irregularly ovate or globose leaf gall, frequently marginal, diameter ⅛ to
⅕ inch, mite...................................*Eriophyes sp.*

Magnolia Family *(Magnoliaceæ)*

The tulip spot gall is a somewhat common and characteristic species in
the south, occasionally being so numerous as to conspicuously mark a very

considerable proportion of the leaves of the smaller trees. There are on this tree, in addition, two midrib or vein galls, all the work of gall midges.

Magnolia

Large, greenish, with a bluish bloom, when mature opens along the side as a large curved lip.........Magnolia psyllid, *Trioza magnoliæ* Ashm.

Tulip Tree

Globular midrib or vein gall, length ¼ inch, midge, summer........
...............................Tulip vein gall, *Cecidomyia sp.*
Irregular midrib gall, length ¾ inch, midge, summer.............
...................Tulip midrib gall, *Cecidomyia tulipiferæ* O.S.
Purplish leaf blisters, diameter ⅛ inch, midge, summer. Pl. 10 (7)...
...................Tulip spot gall, *Thecodiplosis liriodendri* O.S.

Poppy Family *(Papaveraceæ)*

Poppy *(Papavera)*

Poppy stem gall, midge, summer............*Clinodiplosis caulicola* Coq.

Mustard Family *(Cruciferæ)*

Only 5 of the 30 genera in this large family are hosts for gall makers and these apparently to only a very limited extent, excepting possibly the peppergrass seed midge which develops in the seed capsules. All are native gall midges, aside from the introduced *Curculionid,* attacking the tubers or roots of turnip.

Peppergrass *(Lepidium)*

Swollen discolored seed capsules, midge, summer.................
................Peppergrass seed midge, *Dasyneura lepidii* Felt
Subglobose stem or root swellings, diameter ¼ to ½ inch, midge.....
....*Cecidomyia sp.*
Irregular stem swelling, ½ to ⅛ inch, scale insect, summer.........
..........................*Asterolecanium ? fimbriatum* Fonsc.

Hedge Mustard *(Sisymbrium)*

Bud gall, diameter ⅓ inch, midge, spring....*Dasyneura ? sisymbrii* Schr.

Stanleya

Swollen flowers, thickened enlarged sepals, midge.................
.....................................*Dasyneura stanleyæ* Ckll.

Turnip *(Brassica)*

Nodular enlargements of tubers or roots, beetle.................
..............................*Ceutorhynchus sulcicollis* Payk.

Bitter Cress *(Cardamine)*

Irregular, conical flower deformations, length ½ to ¾ inch, midge...
....*Dasyneura sp.*

Orpine Family *(Crassulaceæ)*

Red Orpine *(Clementsia)*

Reddish deformed flower heads, mite....................*Eriophyes sp.*

Caper Family *(Capparidaceæ)*

Stinking Clover *(Cleome)*

Enlarged seed pods, midge...............*Cecidomyia peritomatis* Ckll.

Saxifrage Family *(Saxifragaceæ)*

The currant and the closely related gooseberry are hosts for a series of gall midges, the buds and the fruits being favored. The buds of the wild hydrangeas are also affected. Otherwise, members of the entire plant family, *Saxifragaceæ*, to which the currant belongs, appear to be exempt from attack by gall makers.

Wild Hydrangea

Bud gall, length ½ inch, midge................................
..............Hydrangea bud gall, *Asphondylia hydrangeæ* Felt

Currant, Gooseberry *(Ribes)*

Arrested gooseberry bud, midge. Pl. 12 (8).....................
............Gooseberry bud midge, *Rhopalomyia grossulariæ* Felt

Red, prematurely ripe currants, midge, summer..................
..................Currant midge, *Dasyneura grossulariæ* Fitch

Greenish or brownish leaf blister, diameter ⅛ inch, midge.........
..........................Currant leaf blister, *Cecidomyia sp.*

Probably leaf gall, on *R. menziesii*, midge....*Phytophaga californica* Felt

Irregular stem gall, length ¾ inch, diameter ½ inch, on *R. grossularia*, midge.......................................*Cecidomyia sp.*

Arrested and deformed buds and bud parts.....................
.....................Gooseberry gall mite, *Eriophyes ribis* Nal.

Subglobose leaf and bud galls, usually sparsely white woolly, simple or compound, maximum diameter ¾ inch, on *R. divaricatum*, mite..
....*Eriophyes sp.*

Greenish erineum on leaf surface of *R. odoratum*, mite......*Eriophyes sp.*

Witch-Hazel Family *(Hamamelidaceæ)*

Two galls produced by plant lice on witch hazel are of more than ordinary interest on account of later generations establishing themselves upon a very different tree.

The many-spined, green or reddish, oval bud enlargement known as the spiny witch-hazel gall, with a length of approximately one inch, occurs upon this plant in early summer, the migrating plant lice producing a thickly corrugated series of somewhat lobed deformations upon the leaves of birch. The witch-hazel cone gall, a greenish or reddish conical deformation on the upper surface of the leaf, is about half an inch long and is very common and sometimes exceedingly abundant. The plant lice issuing therefrom migrate, like the preceding species, to the birch, establish themselves upon the under side of the leaves, and though they produce no marked deformity, they are unusually interesting because of the marked differences in form presented by the series of generations.

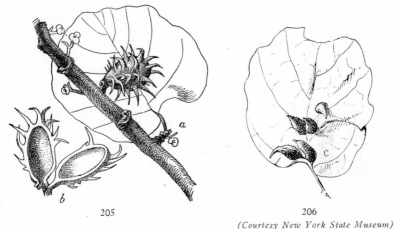

205   206

(Courtesy New York State Museum)

Fig. 205.—Spiny witch-hazel gall, *Hamamelistes spinosus*. (*Reduced from Pergande*)
Fig. 206.—Witch-hazel cone gall, *Hormaphis hamamelidis*. (*After Pergande*)

There is also the sometimes abundant leaf galls on sweet gum produced by a scale insect.

Witch-Hazel *(Hamamelis)*

Many-spined oval bud gall, length 1 inch, aphid, spring. Fig. 205. . . .
. . . . .Spiny witch-hazel gall, *Hamamelistes spinosus* Shim.
Fleshy vein folds, length 1 inch, midge. . . . .*Cecidomyia sp.*
Purplish corrugated intervenal folds, midge. . . . .*Cecidomyia sp.*
Green leaf blister, diameter ⅛ inch, midge. . . . . . .*Asteromyia nigrina* Felt
Purplish leaf blister, diameter ¼ inch, midge. . . . .*Cecidomyia sp.*
Conical greenish or reddish leaf galls, length ½ inch, aphid, summer. Fig. 206. . . . . .Witch-hazel cone gall, *Hormaphis hamamelidis* Fitch

Sweet Gum *(Liquidambar)*

Brownish leaf pile in vein angles, mite. . . . .*Eriophyes sp.*

A globose or bluntly conical leaf gall, diameter $\frac{1}{25}$ inch, scale insect..
..........................*Cryptophyllaspis liquidambaris* Kot.

Plane Tree Family *(Platanaceæ)*

Buttonwood (Platanus)

Marginal, irregularly browned leaf rolls, one to two inches long and about
$\frac{1}{4}$ of an inch wide, midge, summer...............*Cecidomyia sp.*

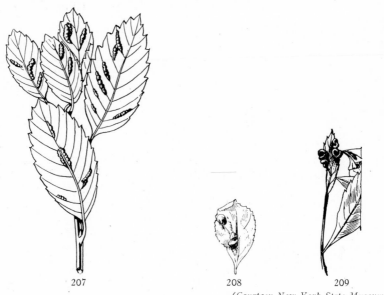

207   208   209

(Courtesy New York State Museum)

Fig. 207.—Mite or *Eriophyes* gall on *Exochorda*.
Fig. 208.—Leaf cone gall, *Cecidomyia sp.*
Fig. 209.—Spirea leaf roll, *Parallelodiplosis spiræ*.

Exochorda

Small, confluent, lobed vein swelling, diameter $\frac{1}{25}$ of an inch long, $\frac{1}{6}$ to $\frac{1}{4}$
of an inch wide, mite.............................*Eriophyes sp.*

PLATE 35—CYNIPID GALLS. 1, Galls of *Callirhytis operator* O.S., gall of agamic generation, on Spanish oak. 2, Gall of *Andricus incertus* Bass., on swamp white oak. 3, Gall
of *Callirhytis balanoides* Weld, on black oak. 4, Marbled oak gall, *Andricus pisiformis*
Beutm., on white oak. 5, Gall of *Callirhytis difficilis* Ashm., on willow oak. 6, Ridged
bunch gall, *Callirhytis gemmaria* Ashm. 7, Rough bud gall, *Callirhytis rugulosa* Beutm.,
on scarlet oak. 8, Gall of *Neuroterus minutus* Bass., ×4, on white oak. 9, Ellipsoidal
bud gall, *Amphibolips ellipsoidalis* Weld, ×4, on pin oak. (*All after Weld*).

PLATE 35

Rose Family *(Rosaceæ)*

The rose family comprises a long series of somewhat dominant plants and naturally one would expect to find a somewhat abundant gall fauna. This is particularly marked in the spireas or meadowsweets, the Juneberry or *Amelanchier, Cratægus* or wild thorn, strawberry and cinquefoil, brambles and roses, each with a peculiar and in some instances abundant population of gall producers. This is especially true of the rose, a marked favorite of certain gall wasps which, it may be remembered, are rather closely limited to the oaks.

Spirea or Meadowsweet Galls

The spireas are favorites with certain gall midges and are occasionally somewhat abundantly infested, this being particularly marked in the case of the spirea pod gall, really deformed leaflets which have swollen so enormously as to resemble pods. Occasionally most of the terminal leaves of a bush may be affected.

Even the flower buds do not escape. One midge develops in unopened, apparently normal flowers and another species causes enlarged blossoms with a reddish discoloration. The flower buds are also attacked by a plant mite, the infestation resulting in an arrested growth. There is little difference between flower buds and leaf buds so far as insects are concerned. There are several bud galls which are common upon spireas, their general characters being indicated by the common names, namely the lobular bud gall, the clustered bud gall, and the "cabbage" or "lettuce" bud gall.

The opened leaves are also affected, one species producing a blister-like condition, another a conical leaf gall above and a pustule-like swelling on the under surface, while the larvae of a third inhabit marginal leaf rolls.

Meadowsweet *(Spirea)*

Slightly enlarged reddening flowers, midge, spring...............
.................·....Spirea flower midge, *Itonida spireafloræ* Felt
In unopened flowers, midge....................*Prodiplosis floricola* Felt
Globose axillary bud gall, midge. Pl. 14 (9).....................
................................Spirea bud gall, *Cecidomyia sp.*
Reddish, purplish or greenish leaf buds, length ½ inch, midge......
....*Asphondylia sp.*
Globose greenish bud gall, diameter ¼ inch, midge, spring..........
.................Lobular bud gall, *Trishormomyia clarkeæ* Felt
Oval brown bud gall, diameter ⅛ inch, midge, spring..............
....*Itonida spiræina* Felt
Terminal clustered bud galls, diameter ⅛ inch, midge, spring........
..................Clustered bud gall, *Parallelodiplosis clarkei* Felt
Terminal "cabbage or lettuce" bud galls, midge, spring............
..................Spirea cabbage gall, *Contarinia spiræina* Felt

Bud gall, leaflets fringed, diameter ⅛ inch, midge, spring..........
...........................Fringed bud gall, *Cecidomyia sp.*
Arrested flower buds, mite, spring......................*Eriophyes sp.*
Conical leaf cone, diameter ⅙ inch, midge, early summer. Fig. 208....
.............................Leaf cone gall, *Cecidomyia sp.*
Yellowish-brown leaf blister, diameter ⅛ inch, midge, early summer..
.................................*Lasioptera spiræafolia* Felt
Thickened greenish midrib fold, length ½ to ¾ inch, midge, early summer. Pl. 12 (1)........Spirea pod gall, *Rhabdophaga salicifolia* Felt

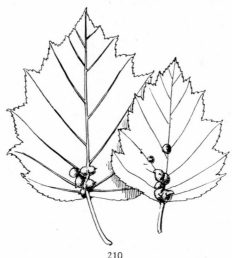

210

(Courtesy New York State Museum)

FIG. 210.—Globular leaf gall, *Cecidomyia sp.*

Marginal leaf roll, length ⅛ inch, midge, early summer. Fig. 209.... ..
.....................Spirea leaf roll, *Parallelodiplosis spiræ* Felt
Flask-shaped, flower bud enlargement, length ½ inch, mite.........
....*Eriophyes sp.*

Apple, Pear (*Pyrus*)

Deformed globose young pears, early summer...................
.........................Pear midge, *Contarinia pyrivora* Riley
Deformed young apples and infertile seed, summer................ ,
....................Pear seed wasp, *Syntomaspis druparum* Boh.
Sinuous elevations on trunk and branches, beetle................
......................Sinuate pear borer, *Agrilus sinuatus* Oliv.
Inrolled, swollen apple leaves....Apple leaf midge, *Dasyneura mali* Kieff.
Partly rolled or folded pear leaves..Pear leaf midge, *Dasyneura pyri* Kieff.

Brownish leaf blister on both pear and apple, summer..............
.........................Pear blister mite, *Eriophyes pyri* Pgst.
Pile on American crabapple, mite, summer................*Eriophyes sp.*
Circular reddish brown leaf Erineum, smooth above, crinkly hairy below, diameter ⅛ inch, on *P. sambucifolia*, mite, summer.....*Eriophyes sp.*
Leaf gall on *Pyrus arbutifolia*. Pl. 16 (4).............. *Eriophyes sp.*

Cercocarpus

Bud gall, midge, spring....................*Dasyneura cercocarpi* Felt

Black Chokecherry (*Aronia*)

Speck-like capsule leaf galls, mite......................*Eriophyes sp.*
Small pouch gall on underside of leaf of *A. arbutifolia*, mite........
....*Eriophyes sp.*

Mountain Ash (*Sorbus*)

Infertile seeds.............Pear seed wasp, *Syntomaspis druparum* Boh.
Megastigmus brevi_audis Ratz.
Brownish leaf blister, summer......Pear blister mite, *Eriophyes pyri* Pgst.
Greenish, dimpled, pouch galls, diameter ¹⁄₂₅ inch, mite......*Eriophyes sp.*
Brown or whitish leaf pile, mite.....................'.....*Eriophyes sp.*

Cratægus or White Thorn Galls

Cratægus or white thorn is very common in portions of the northeastern United States and is represented by a considerable series of similar species. These trees or shrubs are favorites with certain gall midges, the thorn cockscomb gall being a characteristic and somewhat common deformation on the leaves, and the same is true of the thorn vein gall, the latter really little more than globular or pod-like swellings along the veins. The galls of both of these are occasionally extremely abundant on one or more shrubs and rarely noticed on others, in some cases this condition persists for a series of years. The tufted thorn gall and the fringed cup gall are both peculiar, the latter broadly open at the tip and affording practically no protection to the exposed, reddish orange extremity of the maggot. The purple leaf blotch, a condition suggesting infestation by fungus, is really produced by a gall midge and like some of the preceding noticed, is usually abundant on only a few plants here and there.

Thorn twigs half an inch in diameter or thereabouts frequently develop oval swellings, as a result of infestation by two borers, one producing a rather characteristic oval gall with longtitudinal fissures in the more swollen parts. The cedar rust develops upon the thorn, causing an irregular twig swelling resembling the black knot of plums, though easily recognized, by the bright red spores.

Several plant mites find the foliage of thorn well adapted to their needs and produce such deformities as leaf curls, sometimes leaf folds, capsule galls and even a spinulose, blackish deformation upon the upper surface of the leaf.

White Thorn (*Cratægus*)

Globose twig swelling, diameter ¾ inch, beetle...................
........................Thorn limb borer, *Agrilus politus* Say
Oval fissured twig gall, length 1½ to 2 inches, beetle.............
....Thorn limb borer, *Saperda fayi* Bland.
Black knot-like plum twig swelling............................
.................Cedar rust, *Gymnosporangium globosum* Farlow

211   212
(Courtesy New York State Museum)

FIG. 211.—Slender leaf fold, *Cecidomyia sp.*
FIG. 212.—Thorn vein gall, *Lobopteromyia venæ.*

Coxcomb leaf gall, green and red, length ½ inch, midge, summer....
..............Thorn coxcomb gall, *Trishormomyia cratægifolia* Felt
Filamentous, subglobular vein gall, length ½ inch, midge, summer....
.... Tufted thorn gall, *Cecidomyia bedeguar* Walsh
Globose, greenish, frequently pointed vein gall, diameter ⅛ inch, midge, summer. Fig 210.............................*Cecidomyia sp.*
Fusiform, greenish or reddish vein fold, length ½ inch, midge, summer. Fig. 211......................................*Cecidomyia sp.*
Cup-shaped, fringed leaf gall, midge, summer. Pl. 11 (2)...........
....................Fringed cup gall, *Winnertzia hudsonici* Felt
Cylindrical, fringed leaf gall, length ⅙ inch, midge, summer.......
.....................................*Rhizomyia absobrina* Felt

Oval fleshy vein gall, length ¼ inch, midge, summer. Pl. 10 (9); Fig. 212
.... Thorn vein gall, *Lobopteromyia venæ* Felt
Dicrodiplosis venitalis Felt

213

(Courtesy New York State Museum)

Fig. 213.—Cinquefoil axil gall, *Gonaspis potentillæ*, various types. (*After Beutm.*)

Purplish blister leaf mine, diameter ⅓ inch, midge, summer.......
.... Purple leaf blotch, *Lasioptera excavata* Felt
Rhizomyia hirta Felt
Spinose blackish leaf gall, leaf curls, capsule galls and leaf folds on various
thorns, mite.................................... *Eriophyes sp.*

PLATE 36—CYNIPID GALLS. 1, Gall of *Callirhytis fructuosa* Weld, ×3, on scarlet oak.
2, Gall of *Callirhytis operator* O.S., on staminate flowers of black oak, producing the
sexual generation. 3, Gall of *Callirhytis carmelensis* Weld, ×3, on coast live oak. 4, Gall
of *Disholcaspis eldoradensis* Beutm., on coast live oak, left row, interior live oak, right
row. 5, Fig root gall, *Trigonaspis radicola* Ashm., on white oak. 6, Tubular twig gall,
Andricus tubularius Weld on *Q. undulata.* 7, Gall of *Callirhytis lapillula* Weld, on
swamp live oak. 8, Gall of *Andricus serricornis* Kins., ×3, on coast live oak. 9, Honeycomb twig gall, *Dryocosmus favus* Beutm., developing gall on Spanish oak. (*All after
Weld*).

PLATE 36

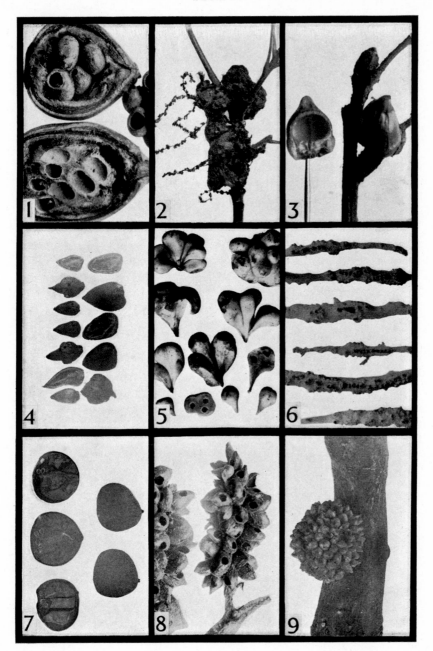

Intervenal, convolute, pale green folds, ½ to two inches long, on *C. brevispina*, mite..*Eriophyes sp.*

Intervenal, irregular, reddish brown erineum, length ½ inch to one inch, mite..*Eriophyes sp.*

Cotoneaster

Blister leaf gall, summer..........Pear blister mite, *Eriophyes pyri* Pgst.

Strawberry and Cinquefoil Galls

One hardly thinks of galls in connection with strawberry plants, yet two species find the leaf stems suitable for their requirements, one producing a cylindrical enlargement some half an inch long and containing a number of white maggots and the other a reniform swelling on the leaf petiole from a third to about three-quarters of an inch in length, the latter the work of a gall midge.

The closely related cinquefoil or potentilla is subject to attack by gall wasps and gall midges closely related to those affecting the strawberry, one, however, producing a bud enlargement in the axil of the leaf and another, oval, blister-like swellings on the stalks and midribs.

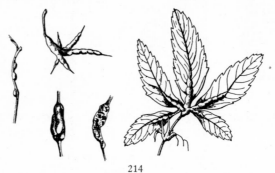

214

(Courtesy New York State Museum)

Fig. 214.—Gall of *Diastrophus niger*. (*After Beutm.*)

Strawberry (*Fragaria*)

Cylindrical petiole swelling, length ½ inch, gall wasp, summer......
..........Cylindrical strawberry gall, *Diastrophus fragariæ* Beutm.

Reniform petiole gall, length ⅓ to ¾ inch, midge, summer..........
............Reniform strawberry gall, *Cecidomyia reniformis* Stebb.

Cinquefoil (*Potentilla*)

Swollen bud, diameter ⅓ to ½ inch, gall wasp, spring. Pl. 38 (4); Fig. 213.
..................Cinquefoil axil gall, *Gonaspis potentillæ* Bass.

Much enlarged stem, midge, summer..........................
...........Internodal stem gall, *Cecidomyia potentillæcaulis* Stebb.
Spindle-shaped or blister-like swelling on stalk and midrib, gall wasp, sum-
mer. Fig. 214..........................*Diastrophus niger* Bass.
Long stalk swelling, length ½ to 1½ inches, gall wasp, summer. Fig 215.
...............Fusiform stem gall, *Diastrophus fusiformans* Ashm.
Nodular, polythalamous stem swelling, ½ inch long, on *P. monspeliensis v.
norvegica,* gall wasp, summer.........*Diastrophus tumefactus* Kins.
Whitish leaf pile, mite, summer......................*Eriophyes sp.*

Bramble Galls

The brambles, blackberries and raspberries, are rather commonly infested by several gall insects. Two gall wasps cause irregular, brown or
greenish swellings on the roots or the stem close to the surface of the
ground. Two small beetles, the raspberry girdler and the gouty gall beetle
produce characteristic swellings on the stems of the raspberry and blackberry respectively.

215

216

(*Courtesy New York State Museum*)

Fig. 215.—Fusiform stem gall, *Diastrophus fusiformans.* (*After Beutm.*)
Fig. 216.—Blackberry root gall, *Diastrophus radicum.* (*After Beutm.*)

One of the most peculiar deformations known as the blackberry seed
gall, suggests thick clusters of more or less hairy, seed-like growths along
the stems, the masses frequently exceeding an inch and a half in length.
These peculiar developments are really groups of individual galls usually
spined at the tip and sometimes thickly clothed with long, hair-like growths.

Galls also occur upon the leaves, the mealy leaf galls being somewhat warty, mealy-like vein swellings with dimensions varying from about half an inch to an inch and a half. They are produced by small gall midges and the same is true of the mossy vein galls, hairy globose enlargements of the leaf veins. One midge is found in a marginal leaf roll.

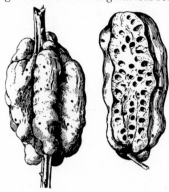

217

(Courtesy New York State Museum)

FIG. 217.—Blackberry knot gall, *Diastrophus nebulosus*. *(After Beutm.)*

Bramble *(Rubus)*

Rounded, brown clustered root galls, diameter ¼ to 1 inch, gall wasp, summer. Fig. 216 . . . . Blackberry root gall, *Diastrophus radicum* Bass.

Globose, greenish or reddish root or stalk swellings, diameter ½ to 1 inch, gall wasp, summer. Fig. 218 . . . .
. . . . Bassett's blackberry gall, *Diastrophus bassetti* Beutm.

Variable stem swelling girdled above and below, length 1 to 1½ inches, beetle, summer. Fig. 219 . . . .
. . . . Raspberry cane girdler, *Oberea bimaculata* Oliv.

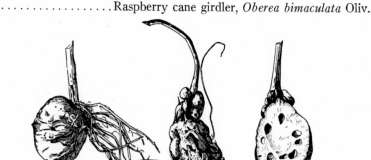

218

(Courtesy New York State Museum)

FIG. 218.—Bassett's blackberry gall, *Diastrophus bassetti*. *(After Beutm.)*

Ridged cane gall, length 1 inch, summer.......................
......................Gouty gall beetle, *Agrilus ruficollis* Fabr.

Rounded or long stem swellings, sometimes with 4 or 5 deep longitudinal furrows, length 2 to 6 inches, on *R. villosus*, gall wasp, summer, Fig. 217..............Blackberry knot gall, *Diastrophus nebulosus* O.S.

Abrupt, pithy, sometimes spined stem swellings, length 2 to 6 inches, on *R. strigosus*, gall wasp, summer. Fig. 222..*Diastrophus turgidus* Bass.

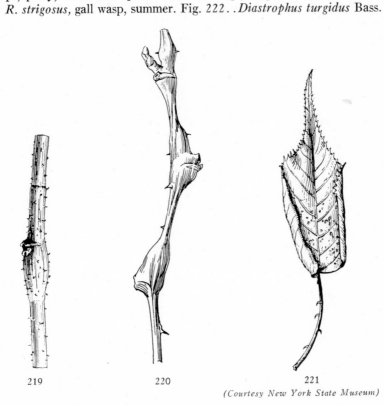

219　　　　　　　　　　220　　　　　　　　　　221

(Courtesy New York State Museum)

FIG. 219.—Raspberry cane girdler, *Oberea bimaculata.*
FIG. 220.—Nodular stem galls, *Lasioptera nodulosa.*
FIG. 221.—Leaf roll of *Camptoneuromyia rubifolia.*

Similar to preceding, irregular, filled with hard larval chambers, length 2 to 5 inches, on *R. nutkanus, R. parviflorus*, gall wasp, summer. Pl. 37 (7); Fig. 223....................*Diastrophus kincaidii* Gill.[1]

Irregular stem gall, length 1 inch, midge, summer. Fig. 220.........
.................Nodula stem gall, *Lasioptera nodulosa* Beutm.

Globose branch enlargement, diameter ¼ inch, gall wasp, summer....
..................................*Diplolepis rubicola* Kieff.

[1] A variety, *austrior* Kins., has been described from a similar gall.

Infested blossoms, spring. . . . .
. . . . .Blackberry blossom midge, *Dasyneura rubiflorœ* Felt
Warty, mealy vein gall, length ½ to 1½ inches, midge, summer. . . . . .
. . . . .Mealy leaf gall, *Lasioptera farinosa* Felt
Globose, filamentus vein gall, on *R. nigrobaccus,* midge, summer. . . .
. . . . .Mossy vein gall, *Cecidomyia muscosa* Stebb.
Marginal leaf roll, length ¼ inch, midge, summer. Fig. 221. . . . .
. . . .*Camptoneuromyia rubifolia* Felt

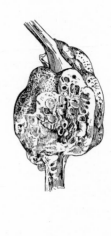

222   223
(Courtesy New York State Museum)

Fig. 222.—Gall of *Diastrophus turgidus.* (*After Beutm.*)
Fig. 223.—Gall of *Diastrophus kincaidi.* (*After Beutm.*)

Clustered, spined, seed-like greenish or reddish galls, gall wasp, summer.
Fig. 224. . . . . . .Blackberry seed gall, *Diastrophus cuscutæformis* O.S.

Agrimony (*Agrimonia*)

Reared from florets, midge, summer. . . . .*Contarinia agrimoniœ* Felt

Juneberry or Amelanchier Galls

This small tree bears several very interesting galls. One is a thickly
massed leaf swelling of numerous cells, each with a truncate, usually red

PLATE 37—CYNIPID GALLS. 1, Tufted rose gall, *Diplolepis weldi* Beutm., X3 on
Rosa sp. 2, Mossy rose gall, *Diplolepis rosae* L., on *Rosa rubiginosa* L. 3, Mealy rose gall,
Diplolepis ignotus O.S. 4, Gall of *Diplolepis utahensis* Bass. 5, Gall of *Diplolepis cali-
fornicus* Beum. 6, Gall of *Diplolepis multispinosus* Gill. 7, Gall of *Diastrophus kincaidii*
Gill., on *Rubus nutkanus.* 8, Gall of *Aulacidea tumida* Bass., on *Lactuca canadensis.*
9, Gall of *Antistrophus silphii* Gill., on *Silphium perfoliatum.* (*All after Weld*).

PLATE 37

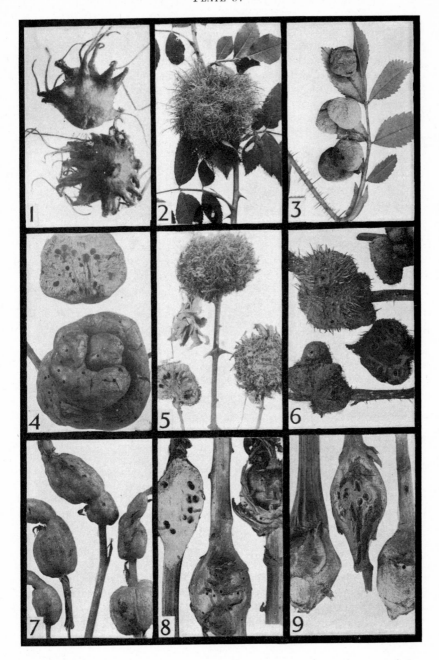

lipped tip. This gall is known as the Juneberry lipped gall and is occasionally so numerous as to deform entire leaves or even groups of leaves.

Another characteristic growth has been designated as the toothed purse gall, a flattened, white, pouch-like leaf swelling with a toothed margin. It is rather common, though rarely abundant and attracts notice because of its unusual shape and delicate white and pink coloration. There are on this tree, as on the spireas, thickened, oval vein swellings produced by a gall

224

(Courtesy New York State Museum)

FIG. 224.—Blackberry seed gall, *Diastrophus cuscutæformis*. (*After Beutm.*)

midge and also in the early spring prematurely enlarged fruit which, on examination are found literally packed with small, white maggots and suggesting, in a general way at least, the work of the midge in pears.

Juneberry (*Amelanchier*)

Prematurely enlarged fruit containing white maggots, midge, spring. .
. . . .*Cecidomyia sp.*
Tapering, truncate, red-lipped leaf gall, length ¼ inch, midge. Fig. 225.
. . . . .Juneberry lipped gall, *Trishormomyia canadensis* Felt
Subglobose, white, woolly, basal leaf or petiole gall, diameter ¹⁄₁₀ inch, midge, summer. . . . .*Cecidomyia sp.*
Subglobose, greenish or pinkish petiole and midrib swelling, the tip frequently prolonged, diameter ¹⁄₁₀ inch, midge, summer. .*Cecidomyia sp.*

Ovate, flattened, minutely-toothed pouch leaf gall, yellowish-white and purplish-red, height ⅕ inch, midge, summer....................
............................Toothed purse gall, *Cecidomyia sp.*

Slender, conical, yellowish, red-tipped leaf gall, length ¼ inch, midge, summer..*Cecidomyia sp.*

Yellowish vein gall, usually basal with numerous white hairs, length ½ to ¾ inch, midge, summer. Fig. 226......................
.....................Juneberry vein gall, *Itonida canadensis* Felt.

Sub-ovoid on upper surface, flattened laterally, the sides paralleling secondary veins, length ⅛ inch, upper surface yellow or red, lower yellowish, truncate with slit-like opening, midge, summer...............
................................*Trishormomyia canadensis* Felt

Stout, balloon-shaped, reddish-purple leaf gall with slender tip, midge, summer...*Cecidomyia sp.*

225   226

(Courtesy New York State Museum)

Fig. 225.—Juneberry lipped gall, *Trishormomyia canadensis.*
Fig. 226.—Juneberry pouch gall, *Trishormomyia? canadensis.*

Stout, curved, tubular reddish purple leaf gall, length ⅛ inch, mostly on upper surface, midge.............................*Cecidomyia sp.*

Leaf fold, midge, summer..........................*Cecidomyia sp.*

Globose, enlarged fruit, diameter ⅕ inch, midge, summer..........
....*Cecidomyia sp.*

Phrygian, cap-like dimple, mite, summer.................*Eriophyes sp.*

Dark brown pocket leaf galls, diameter ⅟₁₀ inch, mite, summer......
................................*Eriophyes amelanchier* Stebb.

Rose (*Rosa*)

A considerable series, more than forty species or varieties, of gall wasps occur upon roses and produce a variety of deformations. The relation between the insects and the host is so close that one genus of gall wasp, *Diplolepis* (widely known as *Rhodites*), is limited mostly to roses.

Several of the species of *Diplolepis* produce root galls. The rose root gall is an irregularly rounded, brownish swelling an inch and a half to three inches in diameter being typical.

The rose twig gall or bedeguar is a common twig deformity which, like similar growths on other plants, consists of a thick mass of individual hairy cells, all so closely united as to give the appearance of a homogeneous swelling.

The spiny rose gall and the mealy rose gall, the former globular or nearly so and the latter irregular, are both common and frequently come to the notice of gardeners.

The leaves of roses may bear blister-like swellings showing on both surfaces, the rose blister gall, or more conspicuous deformations such as the regal rose gall, the latter a somewhat globular enlargement with a series of crown-like spines around the margin. The tufted rose gall is quite similar and has been characterized as shaped like a miniature simlin squash with numerous long, slender, scaly processes.

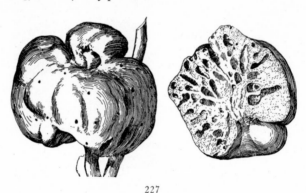

227

Fig. 227.—Rose root gall, *Diplolepis radicum*. (*After Beutm.*)

The buds of roses by no means escape, the rose bud midge and the rosette midge both producing characteristic effects. The former blasts buds and developing leaves and the latter produces a loose bud or rosette gall, an inch to an inch and a quarter long. The nomenclature of Kinsey has been closely followed in the rose galls.

Root Galls

Brownish tomato-shaped, diameter 1½ to 2½ inches, gall wasp. Fig. 227.
. . . . Rose root gall, *Diplolepis radicum var. radicum* O.S.
Somewhat smaller gall. . . . . *var. johnsoni* Kins.

Gall somewhat larger. Pl. 37 (4); Fig. 228........*var. utahensis* Bass.

Gall not peculiar...............................*var. plana* Kins.

Gall not peculiar............................*var. divergens* Kins.

Single or clustered root nodules, diameter ¼ inch, on sweet briar, gall wasp.
    Fig. 229...........................*Diplolepis semipiceus* Harr.

Stalked root nodules, diameter ½ to ¾ inches, on *R. nutkana*, gall wasp.
...................................*Diplolepis ostensackeni* Beutm.

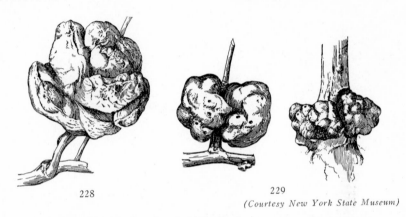

228

229

(Courtesy New York State Museum)

Fig. 228.—Gall of *Diplolepis utahensis*. (*After Beutm.*)
Fig. 229.—Gall of *Diplolepis fulgens*. (*After Beutm.*)

Twig Galls

Oval, filamentaceous, diameter 2 to 4 inches, gall wasp, summer. Pl. 37 (2);
    Fig. 230....Mossy rose gall, or rose bedeguar, *Diplolepis rosæ* Linn

Mossy cluster of woody cells, each with a diameter ⅛ to ⅙ inch, on *R.
    nutkana*, gall wasp, summer............*Diplolepis bassetti* Beutm.[1]

Filaments, finer, denser, curled ....*var. bassetti* Beutm.

Filaments rather stout, straight,...................*var. lucida* Kins.

Masses of spherical spined cells or twig galls, size from 1 inch to 4 inches,
    gall wasp, summer.......................*Diplolepis mayri* Schl.

Globular reddish or greenish galls, diameter ¼ to ½ inch, gall wasp, sum-
    mer. Pl. 38 (8); Fig. 231....Spiny rose gall, *Diplolepis bicolor* Harr.

Globular, yellowish, pinkish or purplish, diameter 1 to 1½ inches, gall wasp,
    summer. Fig. 232.................*Diplolepis tuberculatrix* Ckll.

Very similar gall.................................*var. similis* Ashm.

Smaller spineless gall. Fig 233..................*var. arefacta* Gill.

[1] Variety *lucida* Kins. produces a gall with heavier, broader, straighter filaments, there
are usually 30 or fewer larval cells, each more or less separate, maximum diameter 1 inch.

Similar densely spined gall. Pl. 37 (6); Fig. 234.............
......................................*var. multispinosa* Gill.
Similar gall mostly smooth, short spined........*var. coloradensis* Kins.
Gall similar with short spines. Fig. 235............*var. tumida* Bass.

230   231

Fig. 230.—Mossy rose gall, *Diplolepis rosæ*. (*After Beutm.*)
Fig. 231.—Spiny rose gall, *Diplolepis bicolor*. (*After Beutm.*)

Similar gall, spineless......................*var. wasatchensis* Kins.
Similar gall with mossy spines. Pl. 37 (5)......*var. californica* Beutm.
Resembling preceding.........................*var. versicolor* Kins.
Similar to preceding, spines rigid, sparse.........*var melanderi* Kins.

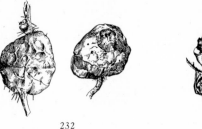

232   233

Fig. 232.—Gall of *Diplolepis tuberculatrix*. (*After Beutm.*)
Fig. 233.—Gall of *Diplolepis arefactus*. (*After Beutm.*)

Plate 38—Cynipid Galls. 1, Gall of *Aylax glechomæ* L. on *Nepeta hederacea*. 2, Gall of *Aylax taraxaci* Ashm., on *Taraxacum officinale*. 3, Gall of *Antistrophus pisum* Walsh, on *Lygodesmia juncea*. 4, Gall of *Gonaspis potentillæ* Bass., on *Potentilla canadensis*. 5, Gall of *Aylax gillettei* Kieff., on *Silphium laciniatum*. 6, Gall of *Aylax laciniatus* Gill., on *Silphium laciniatum*. 7, Gall of *Disholcaspis sileri* Bass., on *Q. undulata*. 8, Spiny rose gall, *Diplolepis bicolor* Harr. 9, Gall of *Diplolepis fusiformans* Ashm. (*All after Weld*).

PLATE 38

Gall similar with short spines or filaments........*var. rubriderma* Kins.

Gall like preceding...........................*var. sierranensis* Kins.

Gall similar..............................*var. descansonis* Kins.

Reddish stem swellings, length ½ inch, gall wasp, summer. Fig. 236..
........................Knotty rose gall, *Diplolepis vernus* O.S.

Globose swellings, length ¼ to ½ inch, gall wasp, summer. Pl. 38 (9);
Fig. 237.........................*Diplolepis fusiformans* Ashm.

Stem swelling, slight, length ¾ inch...............*var. minuta* Kins.

Swelling, moderate, length 1¼ inch..........*var. mendocinensis* Kins.

Globose, smooth, length 1½ inch, diameter ½ to 1 inch, gall wasp, summer.
Fig. 238..........Globular rose gall, *Diplolepis globuloides* Beutm.

 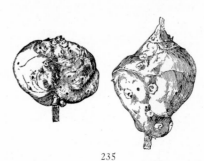

234   235

(Courtesy New York State Museum)

Fig. 234.—Many spined twig gall, *Diplolepis multispinosus.* (*After Beutm.*)
Fig. 235.—Gall of *Diplolepis tumidus.* (*After Beutm.*)

Fusiform, smooth or prickly, length ½ to 2 inches, diameter ¼ to ¾ inches,
gall wasp, summer. Fig. 239.................................
....................Long rose gall, *Diplolepis dichlorcerus* Harr.

Slight twig swelling, length ½ inch, gall wasp, summer.............
.................Nodula twig gall, *Diplolepis nodulosus* Beutm.

Stem swellings, length ½ to 1¼ inches, gall wasp, summer.........
.................................*Diplolepis ashmeadi* Beutm.

Globose powdered twig or leaf gall, diameter ⅙ to ½ inch, gall wasp, summer. Pl. 37 (3); Fig. 240....Mealy rose gall, *Diplolepis ignotus* O.S.

Similar but without the white powder, gall wasp, summer..........
...............................*Diplolepis variabilis* Bass.

Irregular stem gall, length ¾ to 1 inch, beetle........*Agrilus viridis* Linn.

Leaf Galls

Lentil shaped, diameter ⅛ inch, gall wasp, summer. Fig. 241........
....................Rose blister gall, *Diplolepis rosæfolii* Ckll.

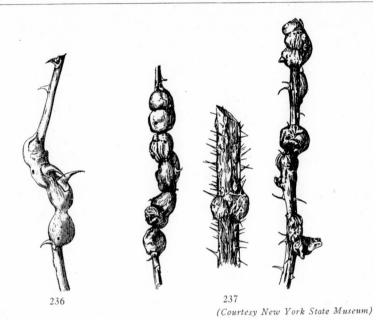

236   237

(Courtesy New York State Museum)

Fig. 236.—Knotty rose gall, *Diplolepis vernus*. (*After Beutm.*)
Fig. 237.—Gall of *Diplolepis fusiformans*. (*After Beutm.*)

Globular spinose gall, diameter ¼ inch, gall wasp, summer. Fig. 242..
. . . .*Diplolepis nebulosus* Bass.
Similar to preceding, on wild rose, gall wasp, summer. . . . .
. . . .*Diplolepis pustulatoides* Beutm.

238   239

(Courtesy New York State Museum)

Fig. 238.—Globular rose gall, *Diplolepis globuloides*. (*After Beutm.*)
Fig. 239.—Long rose gall, *Diplolepis dichlocerus*. (*After Beutm.*)

Small gall, possibly *D. nebulosus,* gall wasp, summer..............
................................*Diplolepis politus* Ashm.
Ovate, smooth, brown, gall, diameter ½ to 1 inch, gall wasp, summer.
Fig. 243...........................*Diplolepis variabilis* Bass.
Gall similar.................................*var. sculpta* Kins.

240   241

(Courtesy New York State Museum)

Fig. 240.—Mealy rose gall, *Diplolepis ignotus.* (*After Beutm.*)
Fig. 241.—Rose blister gall, *Diplolepis rosæfolii.* (*After Beutm.*)

Gall similar.................................*var. rufopicea* Kins.
Gall somewhat smaller.......................*var. lutescens* Kins.
Obconical leaf gall with short obtuse processes, diameter ⅛ inch, gall wasp,
summer. Fig. 244..........Regal rose gall, *Diplolepis gracilis* Ashm.
Gall like a miniature simlin squash, with long slender processes, diameter
⅙ inch, gall wasp, summer. Pl. 37 (1).....................
.......................Tufted rose gall, *Diplolepis weldi* Beutm.

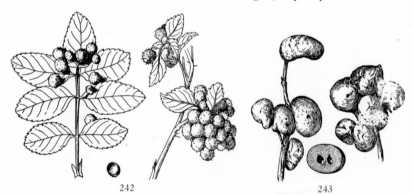

242   243

(Courtesy New York State Museum)

Fig. 242.—Gall of *Diplolepis nebulosus.* (*After Beutm.*)
Fig. 243.—Gall of *Diplolepis variabilis.* (*After Beutm.*)

Globose with circle of slender fleshy appendages, diameter ¼ inch, gall wasp, summer.................................*Diplolepis sp.*

Globose ridged gall, diameter ⅛ inch, gall wasp, summer...........
...................................*Diplolepis silvestrii* Trott.

Curled or folded terminal leaves. Pl. 10 (1)...................
.................:......Rose leaf midge, *Dasyneura ? rosarum* Hardy

Bud Galls

Malformed buds sometimes hairy, gall wasp, spring...............
.................................*Diplolepis oregonensis* Beutm.

244    245

(Courtesy New York State Museum)

Fig. 244.—Regal rose gall, *Diplolepis gracilis*.
Fig. 245.—Rosette midge, *Rhabdophaga rosacea*.

Enlarged terminal or lateral buds, length ¼ to ¾ inches, gall wasp, spring
.................................Rose bud wasp, *Diplolepis sp.*

Buds and developing leaves blasted...........................
.................Rose-bud midge, *Dasyneura rhodophaga* Coq.

Loose bud or rosette gall, length 1 to 1¼ inches. Fig. 245.......
.......................Rosette midge, *Rhabdophaga rosacea* Felt

Reared from infertile seeds..................................
..................Rose seed wasp, *Megastigmus aculeatus* Swed.

Cherry and Plum Galls

Insect galls are rather common on wild cherry. The chokecherry midge produces characteristic swollen or deformed cherries, the affected fruits being simply bladdery expansions containing a number of yellowish maggots. The conditions are so favorable that some six or seven different species of gall midges have been reared from such fruits.

The wild black cherry is occasionally attacked by gall midges, the terminal shoot or bud developing into an oval swelling about three-quarters of an inch in diameter and containing a number of yellowish orange maggots. This is known as the wild cherry bud gall.

A number of species of plant mites develop upon cherry and plum foliage, producing a variety of pocket or pouch galls and occasionally occurring in considerable numbers.

The domesticated plum is commonly affected by black twig swellings known as black knot, a gall produced by a fungus. This deformation presents conditions favorable for the development of a number of insects and occasionally they are erroneously considered as the causal agents.

Peach (*Amygdalus*)

A silvery sheen on the leaf, mite, summer . . . .*Phyllocoptes cornutus* Bnks.

Plum, Cherry (*Prunus*)

Greatly enlarged, bladdery, infertile fruit, on *P. maritima, P. virginiana*, fungus, spring. . . . .*Exoascus sp.*

Swollen, deformed chokecherries, spring. Pl. 9 (6). . . . .
. . . . .Chokecherry midge, *Contarinia virginianiæ* Felt

Guest flies. . . . .*Itonida canadensis* Felt

Guest flies. . . . .*Rhizomyia absobrina* Felt

Guest flies. . . . .*Dasyneura pergandei* Felt

Guest flies. . . . .*Cecidomyia cerasiphila* Felt

Guest flies. . . . .*Arthrocnodax apiphila* Felt

Raceme axis gall, length 1 inch, midge, spring. Pl. 7 (5). . . . .
. . . .*Cecidomyia racemi* Stebb.

Terminal shoot and bud gall on wild black cherry, midge, spring. Pl. 7 (6)
. . . . .Wild cherry bud gall, *Cecidomyia serotinæ* O.S.

Oval twig gall on wild black cherry, midge. . . . .*Cecidomyia sp.*

Irregular black twig swelling, length ½ to 1½ inches. . . . .
. . . . .Black knot, *Plowrightia morbosa* Schw.

Conical leaf stalk swelling, length ¾ inch, midge. . . . .*Cecidomyia sp.*

PLATE 39—CYNIPID GALLS. 1, Gall of *Cynips dumosæ* Kins. 2, Gall of *Cynips tritior* Kins. 3, Gall of *Cynips schulthessæ* Kins. 4, Gall of *Cynips mista* Kins. 5, Club oak-leaf gall, *Cynips clavuloides* Kins. 6, Gall of *Andricus marmoreus* Kins. 7, Gall of *Cynips incompta* Kins. 8, Red sea urchin gall, *Acraspis echinus* O.S. 9, Gall of *Disholcaspis fungiformis* Kins. (*All after Kinsey*).

PLATE 39

Thickened folded chokecherry leaf, midge, summer. Pl. 11 (4)......
....*Mycodiplosis cerasifolia* Felt
Green or reddish stemmed leaf galls, length ½ inch, mite, summer. Pl. 15 (2); Figs. 247, 248.... Wild cherry pouch gall, *Eriophyes padi* Nal.
Pale greenish tubular leaf galls ⁹⁄₁₆ inch x ¹⁄₂₅ inch tapering to a slender stem, on plum, summer. Mich.....................*Eriophyes sp.*

246   247

(Courtesy New York State Museum)

Fɪɢ. 246.—Mite or *Eriophyes* gall on wild plum.
Fɪɢ. 247.—Mite pouch gall of *Eriophyes padi*, on wild cherry.

Tubular growths at base of buds and shoots of plum..............
....*Eriophyes phlœocoptes* Nal.
Pouch galls on leaves of wild cherry, beech and plum........*Eriophyes sp.*

Adenostoma
Reared from seeds, midge...............*Asphondylia adenostoma* Felt

Pulse Family (*Leguminosæ*)

The *Leguminosæ* or pulse family comprises a long series of somewhat dominant plants, some of which are hosts mostly to gall midges, the exceptions being a scale insect, a small moth and one of the plant mites. The locusts, both honey and black, the clovers and the closely related lupines are more abundantly infested by gall makers than other plants in this family.

Mimosa biuncifera
Fusiform or conical bud or pod gall, length ¼ inch, midge. Pl. 41 (5, 6)
....*Asphondylia mimosæ* Felt
Globose, many-celled stem swellings on one side of twigs, diameter ⅘ inch, covered with normal bark (*Myrtopsen mimosæ* Weld, a guest fly)
....Probably Chalcid

Acacia greggii
Narrowly oval, stem swellings, the surface of the gall with party ruptured

irregularly-ridged bark, length about ½ of an inch, diameter about ¼ of an inch, one cell, Chalcid. Pl. 2 (1)......................
...............................*Tanaostigmodes howardi* Ashm.

Globular, narrowly attached, woody, pebbled, 2 to 3 celled, purplish-gray stem, probably bud gall, single or clustered, diameter ¼ of an inch, gall wasp (*Myrtopsen mimosœ* Weld, a guest fly). Chalcid. Pl. 2 (2)
...............................*Tanaostigmodes howardi* Ashm.

Globose, thickly tubercled, about ⅛ of an inch in diameter, each tubercle with a slender, yellowish-orange process, giving a distinctly spiny or flower-like appearance to the one-celled, thin-walled gall, fly. Pl. 2 (3) ....Probably dipterous

Albizzia

Circular twig elevations, diameter ¼ inch, a central depression, scale insect
.... *Coccid*

Mesquite (*Prosopis*)

Aborted fruit and bud gall, midge. Pl. 41 (7) ....
...............................*Asphondylia prosopidis* Ckll.

Honey Locust (*Gleditsia*)

Twig gall ....*Neolasioptera sp.*

In folded leaflets or marginal leaf rolls, midge, early summer. Pl. 9 (8).
...............Honey locust pod gall, *Dasyneura gleditschiœ* O.S.

Wild Sensitive Plant (*Cassia*)

Stem gall, length 1½ inches, midge, summer.......*Lasioptera cassiœ* Felt

Thermopsis montana

Thickened terminal leaf pods, midge ....*Cecidomyia sp.*

Rattlebox (*Crotalaria*)

Fusiform stem swelling, midge, summer......*Cecidomyia crotalariœ* Stebb.

Woad-Waxen (*Genista*)

Folded apical leaflets, midge, summer..*?Dasyneura genistamtorquens* Kieff.

Lupine (*Lupinus*)

Fusiform stem galls, length ¾ to 1¼ inches, midge, summer. Fig. 248.
.........................Lupine stem gall, *Dasyneura lupini* Felt

From undescribed gall, midge, summer.........*Lasioptera lupini* Felt

Folded leaflets, summer........Clover leaf midge, *Dasyneura trifolii* Loew

Clover (*Trifolium*)

Yellowish larvae in heads of red clover, summer ....
................Clover seed midge, *Dasyneura leguminicola* Lintn.
Folded, discolored, white clover leaves, summer ....
....................Clover leaf midge, *Dasyneura trifolii* Loew

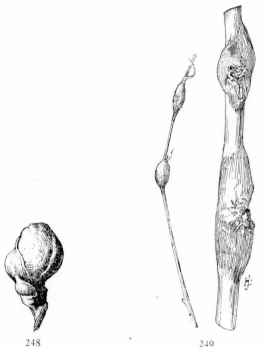

248   249

(Courtesy New York State Museum)

Fig. 248.—Lupine stem gall, *Dasyneura lupini.*
Fig. 249.—Tick trefoil stem gall, *Lasioptera desmodii.*

Alfalfa (*Medicago*)

Aborted seed pods, midge, summer ....*Asphondylia websteri* Felt

Milk Vetch (*Astragalus*)

Irregular, warty stem deformation, length ½ to 1 inch, diameter ½ inch,
    midge, summer ....*Cecidomyia sp.*

Locust, Black (*Robinia*)

Small "witch's broom" on twigs, mite ....*Eriophyes sp.*
Fusiform stem swellings, length ⅓ inch, caterpillar, summer. Pl. 4 (7).
    ....Locust twig gall, *Ecdytolopha insiticiana* Zell.

Folded leaflets, summer......Locust midge, *Dasyneura pseudacaciœ* Fitch
Rolled leaf margins, midge, summer...........*Obolodiplosis robiniœ* Felt

Tick Trefoil (*Desmodium*)

Stem gall, length 1 inch, midge, summer. Fig. 249. ....
.................Tick trefoil stem gall, *Lasioptera desmodii* Felt
Similar gall, midge, summer. Fig. 250 ....*Neolasioptera hamata* Felt
Bud gall, midge, spring ....*Hyperdiplosis meibomiifoliœ* Beutm.
Clustered bud gall, length ⅓ to 1 inch, midge, spring ....
....................................*Dasyneura meibomiœ* Felt

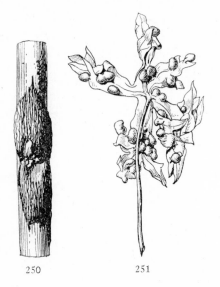

250   251   252
(Courtesy New York State Museum)

FIG. 250.—Gall of *Neolasioptera hamata*.
FIG. 251.—Mite or *Eriophyes* gall on geranium.
FIG. 252.—Creosote bush gall, *?Asphondylia*.

Bush Clover (*Lespedeza*)

Stem gall, length ¼ inch, midge, summer ....*Cecidomyia sp.*
Swollen seed heads, length ¼ to ⅛ inch, midge, summer...........
....*Cecidomyia sp.*
Deformed leaflets, midge, summer...................*Youngomyia sp.*

Beach Pea (*Lathyrus*)

Rolled leaflets, length ½ to 1 inch, midge, spring...............
....................................*Dasyneura maritima* Felt

Hog Peanut (*Amphicarpa*)

Stem gall, length ¾ inch, midge, summer................*Lasioptera sp.*

Lead Plant (*Amorpha*)

Oval stem gall, length 1½ inch, diameter ½ inch, on *A. fruticosa*, caterpillar, summer.....................*Walshia amorphella* Clem.

Conical leaf gall, ⅙ to ½ inch long, reddish, on *A. canescens*, midge..
....*?Diarthronomyia sp.*

Yellowish, marginal leaf gall, ⅛ to ¼ inch long, on *A. canescens*, midge
....*Cecidomyia sp.*

Geranium Family (*Geraniaceæ*)

Crane's-Bill

Blister stem enlargement, midge, summer...............*Cecidomyia sp.*

Pinkish pouch leaf gall, diameter ⅛ inch, on *G. richardsonii*, mite summer. Fig. 251.......................................*Eriophyes sp.*

Flax Family (*Linaceæ*)

Flax (*Linum*)

Irregular swellings of the crown and upper portion of the root, length 1 to 1½ inches, diameter ½ inch, eel worm............*?Tylenchus sp.*

Caltrop Family (*Zygophyllaceæ*)

Creosote Bush (*Covillea*)

Probably a bud gall, midge, spring. Fig. 252....*Asphondylia auripila* Felt

Globose, filamentous, woody gall, diameter ½ to 1 inch, midge......
...................................*Asphondylia ?auripila* Felt

Kallstroemia intermedia

Enlarged stems about 3 times normal size, the gall subconial, major diameter ¼ inch, midge, summer. Pl. 40 (2)......*Lasioptera kallstroemia* Felt

---

PLATE 40—MIDGE GALLS. 1, Gall of *Walshomyia texana* Felt. 2, Gall of *Lasioptera kallstroemia* Felt. 3, Gall of *Asphondylia autumnalis* Beutm. on *Helenium microcephalum*. 4, Horseweed blister midge, *Neolasioptera erigerontis* Felt. 5, Hackberry flask gall, *Phytophaga celtiphyllia* Felt. 6, Gall of *Eutreta sparsa* Wied. on *Vernonia*. 7, Gall of *Phytophaga painteri* Felt on *Celtis*. 8, Weevil gall on *Solanum*, maker unknown. 9, Gall of a midge, possibly *Cecidomyia pubescens* Patt., on *Celtis reticulata*. (*All after Painter*).

PLATE 40

Rue Family (*Rutaceæ*)

Orange, Lemon

Lobulate woody bud galls on navel orange, length ¾ inch, mite....
....*Eriophyes sp.*
Brownish rust spots on orange and curled dull leaves, mite.........
.............................*Phyllocoptes oleiovorus* Ashm.
Whitened or silvery spots on lemon and curled leaves, mite.........
.............................*Phyllocoptes oleiovorus* Ashm.

253   254

(Courtesy New York State Museum)

FIG. 253.—Gall of box leaf midge, *Monarthropalpus buxi.*
FIG. 254.—Sumac bud gall, *Asphondylia integrifoliæ.*

Spurge Family (*Euphorbiaceæ*)

The plants grouped in this family are not favorites with gall makers, possibly on account of the usual milky acrid juice. The four species recorded are infested almost exclusively by gall midges, but one plant mite being recorded. The tropical cassava is probably more abundantly infested than any of the others.

Cassava (*Manihot*)

Leaf galls, midge..*Itonida manihot* Felt
Lasiopteryx manihot Felt

Three-Seeded Mercury (*Acalypha*)

Reddish brown bud gall, diameter ⅙ inch, midge........*Cecidomyia sp.*

Otaheite Gooseberry (*Phyllanthus*)

Reared from fruit, midge......................*Asphondylia siccæ* Felt

Spurge (*Euphorbia*)

Cylindrical fruit gall, length ¼ inch, midge.....................
...........................Spurge fruit gall, *Cecidomyia sp.*
Deformed leaves and flower buds, *E. corollata*, mite........*Eriophyes sp.*

Box Family (*Buxaceæ*)

One species, European in origin, is known as a serious pest of ornamental box in gardens.

Boxwood

Oval, yellowish or brownish blister leaf galls, diameter ⅛ inch, midge, summer. Fig. 253.......Box leaf midge, *Monarthropalpus buxi* Lab.
Cup-shaped deformations of terminal leaves, plant louse, summer...
...........................Boxwood Psyllid, *Psylla buxi* Linn.

Cashew Family (*Anacardiaceæ*)

Sumac Galls

The various sumacs, in spite of their milky, acrid juice and the distinctly toxic properties (to man at least) of the poison oak, support a considerable series of gall midges and gall mites. The poison oak is of particular interest because of its two root galls produced by midges, one is presumably a subterranean bud gall. There is also the peculiar red pouch gall of a plant louse found in September on sumac leaves, a seed wasp, and two gall midges on the related tropical mango.

Mango (*Mangifera*)

Bark gall, midge...........Mango bark midge, *Asynapta mangiferæ* Felt
Blister leaf gall, midge....Mango blister midge, *Erosomyia mangiferæ* Felt

Sumac (*Rhus*)

Globose root gall on rootlets, midge, summer...................
.....................Poison oak root gall, *Dasyneura rhois* Coq.

Mossy, subterranean bud gall, diameter ½ inch, midge, summer......
....*Cecidomyia sp.*
Stem swelling, midge, summer.........................*Cecidomyia sp.*
Reared from dead twigs, midge, summer...*Parallelodiplosis cinctipes* Felt
Infertile seeds, seed wasp, summer.............*Eurytoma rhois* Crosby
Deformed heads, the leaflets almost curled, about ½ inch long, the
    mass 6 by 4 inches, mite, summer. Pl. 16 (7)..*Eriophyes rhoinus* Ckll.

255   256

(Courtesy New York State Museum)

Fig. 255.—Sumac leaves deformed by a mite, *Eriophyes sp.*
Fig. 256.—Gouty vein midge, *Dasyneura communis.*

Flower bud gall, diameter ⅛ inch, midge, spring, Fig. 254........
...................Sumac bud gall, *Asphondylia integrifoliæ* Felt
Pear-shaped reddish leaf gall, length ¾ to 1½ inches, aphid, summer.
    Pl. 19 (5)...................Red pouch gall, *Melaphis rhois* Fitch
Reddish pouch leaf gall with coxcomb effect, *R. diversiloba*, mite, summer
..............................*Phyllocoptes toxicophagus* Ewing
Pubescent leaf corrugations, *R. radicans, R. toxicodendron*, mite, summer.
    Fig. 255..............................*Eriophyes rhois* Stebb.
Green, reddish or purplish pouch or cylindrical leaf galls or a leaf pile, mite.
    Pl. 16 (6)......................................*Eriophyes sp.*

Holly Family (*Aquifoliaceæ*)

Cassena, Yaupon (*Ilex vomitoria*)

Young leaves folded to form hollow, pod-like structures containing white
waxy matter, length ¼ to ½ inch, Texas, summer, aphid......
....?*Tamalia sp.*
Midvein leaf fold, length ⅛ to ⅕ inch, midge, summer....*Cecidomyia sp.*

Mountain Holly (*Nemopanthus*)

Oval bud gall, length ¼ inch, midge, spring....*Asphondylia ilicoides* Felt

Staff Tree Family (*Celastraceæ*)

Pachistima myrsinitis

Dark red, folded, terminal leaves, midge, summer........*Cecidomyia sp.*

Climbing Bittersweet (*Celastrus*)

Irregular root gall, length 1¼ inches, midge, summer............
................................*Cecidomyia celastri* Stebb.
Irregular, subcortical stem gall, midge, summer..........*Cecidomyia sp.*
Variable, globose, light green, sack-like leaf gall, diameter ⅛ inch, mite,
summer......................................*Eriophyes sp.*

Maple Family (*Aceraceæ*)

The gall insects of the various maples most frequently come to notice
through the maple leaf spot, a brilliant yellowish red-margined blister leaf
gall on red maple, the maple bladder gall, a small greenish or reddish
bladder-like gall with a diameter less than an eighth of an inch, sometimes
extremely abundant upon the leaves of soft maple, and the work of the
gouty vein midge, somewhat characteristic pocket-like swellings along the
veins of the red and sugar maples. The box elder or ash leaved maple sometimes has the foliage greatly deformed by the globose swellings of the
box elder leaf gall or seriously marred by the whitish or brownish patches
of plant hairs on the under side of the leaf and inhabited by tiny plant
mites belonging to the genus Eriophyes.

Red Maple (*Acer rubrum*)

Irregular twig swelling, beetle...Maple twig gall, *Xylotrechus aceris* Fisher
Rough branch swellings, length 5 to 7 inches, caterpillar, summer....
.............................Maple Sesian, *Sesia acerni* Clem.
Pustular areas on smooth bark, mite..*Anthocoptes transitionalis* Hodgk.
Pouch-like leaf swellings, diameter 1/12 inch, scale insect, summer....
...........................*Cryptophyllaspis liquidambaris* Kot.

Green or red vein galls, length ¼ inch, midge, summer. Fig. 257...
.....................Gouty vein gall, *Dasyneura communis* Felt
Bladder-like leaf galls, diameter ⅛ inch. Pl. 15 (1); Pl. 16 (9); Fig. 257
.................Maple bladder gall, *?Phyllocoptes quadripes* Shim.
Yellow, red-margined blister leaf gall, diameter ⅛ inch. Fig. 258....
.....................Maple leaf spot, *Cecidomyia ocellaris* O.S.

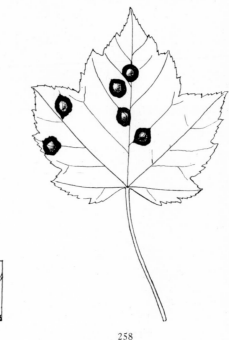

257   258
(Courtesy New York State Museum)

Fig. 257.—Bladder maple gall, *Phyllocoptes? quadripes.*
Fig. 258.—Maple leaf spot, *Cecidomyia ocellaris.*

Irregular leaf folds, midge, summer.........*Rhabdophaga rileyana* Felt
Distorted rolled leaves, midge, summer.................*Dasyneura sp.*
Fusiform leaf galls, length ¼ inch, mite, summer...............
.............Maple spindle gall, *Phyllocoptes aceris-crumena* Riley

PLATE 41—MIDGE GALLS. 1, Apical bud gall of *Lasioptera vernoniæ* Beutm. 2, Midrib gall of *Lasioptera vernoniæ* Beutm. 3, Gall of *Neolasioptera eupatorii* Felt. 4, Gall of *Asphondylia bumeliæ* Felt. 5, Gall of *Asphondylia mimosæ* Felt, in buds. 6, Gall of *Asphondylia mimosæ* Felt, in fruits. 7, Gall of *Asphondylia prosopidis* Ckll., summer form on the left, winter form on the right. 8, Gall of *Asphondylia ratibidæ* Felt. 9, Clematis bud gall, *Asphondylia clematidis* Felt. (*All after Painter*).

PLATE 41

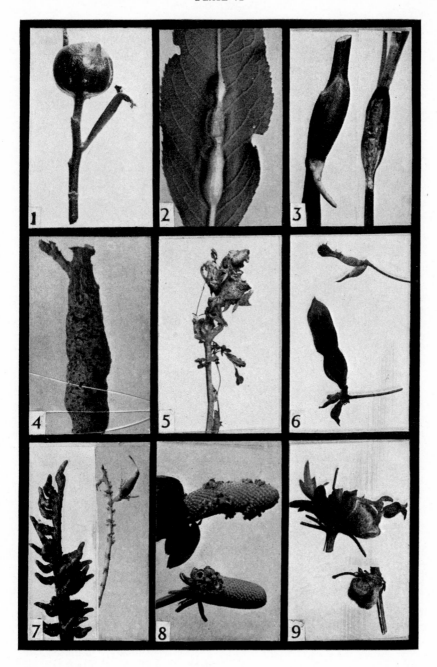

Red pile on upper leaf surface, mite, summer....................
......................*Phyllocoptes minutissimus* Hodgk.
Pinkish pile on under leaf surface, mite, summer..*Eriophyes major* Hodgk.
Eriophyes ornatus Hodgk.
Phyllocoptes quinquilobus Hodgk.
Yellowish brown, whitish or frost-like pile, mite, summer...*Eriophyes sp.*

White or Silver Maple (*Acer saccharinum*)

Irregularly distorted leaves, midge, summer.....................
.....................Maple leaf midge, *Rhabdophaga aceris* Felt
Fusiform leaf galls, length ¼ inch, mite, summer...............
.............Maple spindle gall, *Phyllocoptes aceris-crumena* Riley

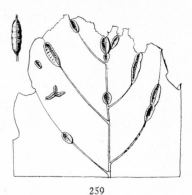

259

(Courtesy New York State Museum)

FIG. 259.—Gouty vein midge, *? Dasyneura communis* on sugar maple.

Bladder-like, greenish or reddish leaf galls, diameter ⅛ inch, mite, spring.
Fig. 260..........Maple bladder gall, *Phyllocoptes quadripes* Shim.
Eriophyes confusus Hodgk.
Yellow or brown pile on under leaf surface, mite, summer....*Eriophyes sp.*

Sugar or Rock Maple (*Acer saccharum*)

Vein galls, length ⅛ to ¼ inch, midge, summer. Fig. 259..........
.....................Gouty vein gall, *?Dasyneura communis* Felt
Fusiform leaf galls, length ¼ inch, midge, summer..............
.............Maple spindle gall, *Phyllocoptes aceris-crumena* Riley
Red pile on upper leaf surface, mite, summer..*Eriophyes elongatus* Hodgk.
Eriophyes maculatus Hodgk.
Eriophyes regulus Hodgk.
Phyllocoptes constrictus Hodgk.
Phyllocoptes variabilis Hodgk.

Greenish pile on under leaf surface, mite, summer.................
....................................*Eriophyes modestus* Hodgk.
Whitish or brownish leaf pile, mite, summer..............*Eriophyes sp.*

Norway Maple *(Acer platanoides)*

Hairy growths in vein axils on under leaf surface, mite, summer.....
..............................*Phyllocoptes magnificus* Hodgk.

260

(Courtesy New York State Museum)

FIG. 260.—Maple bladder gall, *Phyllocoptes quadripes,* on soft maple, several galls enlarged.

White-Barked Maple *(Acer leucoderme)*

Fusiform leaf galls, length ¼ inch, mite, summer................
.............Maple spindle gall, *Phyllocoptes aceris-crumena* Riley
Leaf pile in scattered patches, mite, summer..............*Eriophyes sp.*

Mountain Maple *(Acer spicatum)*

Whitish pile on upper leaf surface, mite, summer..................
...................................*Eriophyes parallelus* Hodgk.
Purplish leaf pile in large patches, mite, summer...........*Eriophyes sp.*

Maple, Species Indeterminate *(Acer)*

Rolled leaf margin, the edges yellow, the center crimson, midge.....
....*Cecidomyia sp.*

Irregular, nodular twig swelling, diameter $\frac{1}{10}$ inch.........*?Hemipteron*
Black velvety leaf pile, mite, summer...................*Eriophyes sp.*
Obscurely lipped, flattened, greenish pouch gall on under side of veinlets,
major dimension $\frac{1}{8}$ inch, Packenham, Ont., midge, summer.....
....*Cecidomyia sp.*

Box Elder *(Acer negundo)*

Swollen terminal buds, diameter $\frac{1}{2}$ to 1 inch, midge, spring.........
.................Box elder bud gall, *Cecidomyia negundinis* Gill.
Subglobose leaf gall, diameter $\frac{1}{10}$ inch, midge, spring, summer......
..................Box elder leaf gall, *Contarinia negundifolia* Felt
Whitish leaf pile on shallow dimple, mite.................*Eriophyes sp.*
Warty leaf swellings, mite, summer...........*Eriophyes negundi* Hodgk.
Phyllocoptes splendidus Hodgk.
Irregular stem enlargement, a canker-like swelling, length 1 to $1\frac{1}{2}$ inches,
midge, summer...............................*Cecidomyia sp.*

Balsam Family *(Balsaminaceæ)*

Impatiens, more commonly known as balsam or jewel weed, frequently
has a thickened midrib fold in the leaf, inhabited by yellowish midge larvae
and occasionally the flower buds may become enlarged to globose swellings
half an inch in diameter—the work of another gall midge. The stems of
this plant are sometimes swollen because of a fungus infestation, certain
midge maggots finding these abnormal growths admirable for their own
development.

Balsam, Jewel Weed *(Impatiens)*

Globular flower bud, length $\frac{1}{2}$ inch, midge, summer. Pl. 7 (4)......
.................Touch-me-not gall, *Cecidomyia impatientis* O.S.
Midrib fold, length $\frac{1}{4}$ inch, midge, summer. Pl. 10 (8)...........
.............................*Lasioptera impatientifolia* Felt
Subglobular stem gall, midge, summer.........*Lasioptera fulva* Beutm.
Stem swollen by *Aecidium impatientis*, midge, summer............
.............................*Mycodiplosis impatientis* Felt
Oval, nodal swellings, length $1\frac{1}{2}$ to 2 inches, diameter 1 to $1\frac{1}{2}$ inches,
caterpillar, summer...............................*Lepidopteron*

Buckthorn Family *(Rhamnaceæ)*

New Jersey tea or redroot, also well known as *Ceanothus*, supports an
interesting gall fauna, a bud midge, a leaf midge, a *Lepidopterous* stem
gall producer and a species of gall mite.

Red Root *(Ceanothus)*

Loose terminal bud gall, length 1 inch, midge, spring. . . . .
. . . . .Red root bud gall, *Asphondylia ceanothi* Felt
Stem enlargement, length ½ inch, caterpillar, summer. . . . .
. . . . .Red root stem gall, *Stagmatophora ceanothiella* Cosens
Thickened vein fold, length ¼ inch, midge, summer. . . . . . .*Cecidomyia sp.*
Globose fuzzy leaf galls, diameter ½ inch, mite, summer. . . . .*Eriophyes sp.*

Vine Family *(Vitaceæ)*

The various species of grape support a somewhat abundant gall midge fauna, some ten species occurring in diverse petiole or tendril galls and several others produce characteristic leaf deformities. Four species of gall midges inhabit grape buds, including those of the blossoms, while the seeds may produce two species of seed wasps. There are, in addition, the well known and sometimes exceedingly abundant *Phylloxera* galls, two species of plant mites and a small weevil that produces swellings in the canes. The gall insect fauna of the Virginia creeper or woodbine is similar, though less extensive than that of the grape, while the related *Cissus* is host to at least one gall midge which produces an irregular stem swelling.

Virginia Creeper, Woodbine *(Psedera)*

Infertile seeds, summer. . . . .
. . . . .Woodbine seed wasp, *Prodecatoma phytophaga* Crosby
Swollen midrib leaf gall, length ½ inch, midge, summer, Fig. 261. . . .
. . . . .Woodbine vein gall, *Dasyneura parthenocissi* Stebb.
Irregular petiole swelling, caterpillar, summer. . . .*Adela ? ridingsella* Clem.
"Nail gall" or pouch leaf gall, mite, summer. . . . .*Eriophyes sp.*
Stem gall, beetle, summer. . . . .*Ampeloglypter ater* Lec.
Irregular root gall, diameter ½ inch, length 1 inch, midge, summer. . .
. . . . .Woodbine root gall, *Lasioptera psederæ* Felt

Grape *(Vitis)*

Fruit and Bud Galls

Shriveled berries and enlarged seed, summer. . . . .
. . . . .Grape seed wasps, *Evoxysoma vitis* Saund.
Decatomidea cooki How.
Enlarged blossom buds, diameter ⅛ inch, early summer. . . . .
. . . . .Grape blossom midge, *Contarinia johnsoni* Sling.
Nut-like bud gall, diameter ¾ inch, midge, early summer. . . . .
. . . . .Grape apple gall, *Schizomyia pomum* Walsh & Riley
Possibly from same gall, midge. . . . .*Rhabdophaga hirticornis* Felt

261

(Courtesy New York State Museum)

FIG. 261.—Woodbine vein gall, *Dasyneura parthenocissi.*

Clustered woolly bud galls, diameter ½ to ¾ inch, midge, early summer.
Pl. 13 (6). . . . Grape filbert gall, *Schizomyia coryloides* Walsh & Riley

Leaf or Tendril Galls

Oval petiole or tendril gall, length ⅛ inch, midge, summer. Fig. 262 . . .
. . . . Grape petiole gall, *Schizomyia petiolicola* Felt
Asteromyia petiolicola Felt

Lasioptera riparia Felt
Neolasioptera vitinea Felt

Cylindrical petiole gall, length ¾ to 2 inches, midge, summer........
....*Cecidomyia sp.*

Irregular, green or reddish leaf or tendril gall, diameter ¼ to ¾ inches, midge, summer. Fig. 263.....Grape tomato gall, *Lasioptera vitis* O.S.
Dasyneura vitis Felt
Rhizomyia vitis Felt
Brachyneura vitis Felt
Janetiella brevicauda Felt

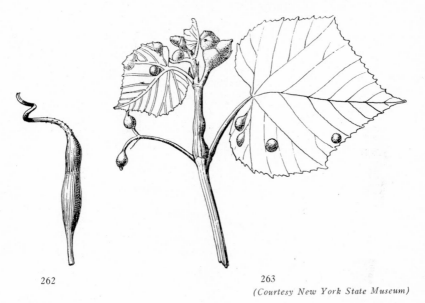

262

263

(Courtesy New York State Museum)

Fig. 262.—Grape tendril gall, *Asteromyia petiolicola.*
Fig. 263.—Grape tomato gall, *Lasioptera vitis.*

Solitary or confluent yellowish-red vein galls, diameter ½ inch, midge, summer.......................................*Cecidomyia sp.*

Circular, pinkish or greenish leaf blisters, diameter ⅛ inch, midge, summer. Pl. 9 (5)...................Grape blister gall, *Cecidomyia sp.*

Conical, reddish or greenish leaf gall, length ¼ inch, midge, summer. Fig. 264...................Grape tube gall, *Cecidomyia viticola* O.S.

Subglobular leaf swelling on lower surface, caterpillar, summer. Pl. 4 (9)
....? *Coleophora sp.*

Wart-like leaf galls, diameter ⅛ inch, aphid, summer. Pl. 3 (5).....
....................Grape Phylloxera, *Phylloxera vitifoliæ* Fitch
Lasiopteryx arizonensis Felt

Leaf pile on under surface on *V. vinifera*, mite, summer...........
....*Eriophyes vitis* Land.
Warty or pouch leaf galls or brownish or whitish leaf pile, mite, summer
....*Eriophyes sp.*
Oval cane galls, length 1 inch, beetle, summer...................
....................Grape cane weevil, *Ampeloglypter sesostris* Lec.

264

(Courtesy New York State Museum)

Fig. 264.—Grape tube gall, *Cecidomyia viticola. (After Beutm.)*

Cissus

Irregular stem gall, length 1 to 4½ inches, midge, summer. Fig. 265...
....*Astrodiplosis speciosa* Felt

Linden Family *(Tiliaceæ)*

The linden or basswood is a favorite with several species of gall insects which may produce numerous swellings upon the twigs and petioles or upon the leaves, the galls of one species being very abundant on the foliage.

Linden, Basswood *(Tilia)*

Irregular twig swelling, length ½ inch, fly, summer. Fig. 266........
.........................Linden bark gall, *Agromyza tiliæ* Coud.

Twig and petiole swellings, diameter ⅙ to ⅓ inch, midge, summer. Fig. 267
.....................Linden twig gall, *Cecidomyia citrina* O.S.[1]
Subglobose, basal, midvein gall, midge, summer..*Colpodia pectinata* Felt[2]
Globose brownish leaf galls, diameter ⅛ inch, midge, summer. Pl. 7 (9)
..................Linden wart gall, *Cecidomyia verrucicola* O.S.
Porricondyla dilatata Felt[2]

265

266

(Courtesy New York State Museum)

FIG. 265.—Shrunken gall of *Asterodiplosis speciosa.*
FIG. 266.—Linden bark gall, *Agromyza tiliæ.*

Top-shaped galls on upper leaf surface, diameter ⅛ inch, mite, summer.
Fig. 268, 269........Linden mite gall, *Eriophyes abnormis* Garm.
Long haired, circular galls, usually near vein, diameter ⅛ inch, mite, sum-
mer.......................*Eriophyes tiliæ* Pag. *var. exilis* Nal.
Light brown pile beside leaf veins...............................
.........................*Eriophyes tiliæ* Pag. *var. liosoma* Nal.
Wrinkled leaves, veins badly twisted..........*Cecidozoon,* undetermined

[1] Rearing may prove the European *Contarinia tiliarum* Kieff. identical.
[2] It is quite possible that the association of these species with the respective galls is due to a merely casual relation.

Mallow Family (*Malvaceæ*)

Several genera in this family are acceptable hosts to gall insects. Cotton, possibly on account of its economic importance, is host to three species and three other plant genera to several gall midges and a small gall-making caterpillar, the latter working in the leaf stem of two related genera.

Abutilon (*A. incanum*)

Elongate, closed sepals, length ¼ inch, midge, summer.............
...................................*Asphondylia abutilon* Felt

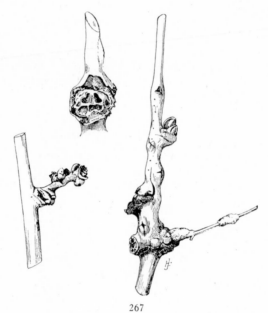

267

(Courtesy New York State Museum)

Fig. 267.—Linden twig gall, *Cecidomyia citrina*.

Elongate leaf stem galls, dimensions 1 by ⅜ inches, caterpillar, summer
...................................*Meskea dyspteraria* Grote

Cotton (*Gossypium*)

Flower buds, spring..........Cotton bud midge, *Contarinia gossypii* Felt
Pocket midrib galls, midge, summer....................*Cecidomyia sp.*
Leaf galls, sometimes deforming foliage, mite, summer.............
...................................*Eriophyes gossypii* Bnks.

Kosteletzkya

Conspicuous, elongate galls in leaf stems, caterpillar, summer.......
...................................*Meskea dyspteraria* Grote

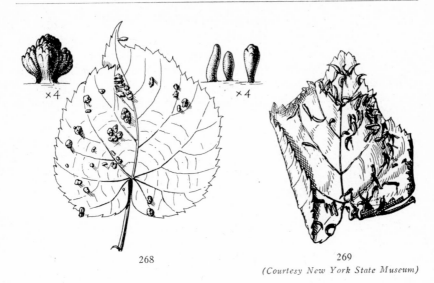

268   269

(Courtesy New York State Museum)

Fig. 268.—Linden mite gall, *Eriophyes abnormis.*
Fig. 269.—Linden mite gall, *Eriophyes abnormis,* presumably this species.

Oval stem gall, length 1½ to 2 inches, diameter ½ inch, midge, summer
....*Lasioptera sp.*

Swamp Rose Mallow *(Hibiscus)*

Reared from seed pods of *H. militaris,* summer....................
........................Three-eyed midge, *Trisopsis hibisci* Felt
Swollen stems, summer. Fig. 270..............................
...................Mallow stem midge, *Neolasioptera hibisci* Felt
Swollen base of leaf petioles and adjacent parts of stem, beetle, summer
....*Apion hibisci* Fall

False Mallow *(Malvastrum)*

Elongate leaf stem gall, caterpillar, summer.....*Meskea dyspteraria* Grote

St. John's Wort Family *(Hypericaceæ)*

St. John's Wort *(Hypericum)*

Axillary bud galls, length ⅙ inch, midge, early fall..*Dasyneura toweri* Felt
Globular stalk swelling, length ¼ to ½ inch, midge, summer........
...................................*Cecidomyia triadenii* Beutm.
Lasioptera virginica Felt
Fine black pile on upper leaf surface, mite, summer........*Eriophyes sp.*

Violet Family *(Violaceæ)*

The lowly violet by no means escapes these insects, it being host for three different gall midges, one a serious pest in commercial violet houses. The violet fruit midge is probably more common than records would indicate, since the deformed fruit, though easily seen, is inconspicuously located. There is also a gall mite which attacks violets.

Violet *(Viola)*

"Plum-like" deformed fruit, length ½ inch, summer and fall. . . . . . .
. . . . .Violet fruit midge, *Dasyneura semenivora* Beutm.

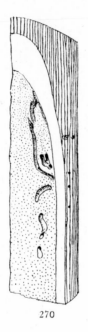 

270   271

(Courtesy New York State Museum)

FIG. 270.—Mallow stem midge, *Neolasioptera hibisci.*
FIG. 271.—Cactus infested with *Asphondylia betheli.*

Globose leaf galls, diameter ¼ inch, mite, summer. . . . .*Eriophyes sp.*
Rolled discolored leaves, *V. odorata*, greenhouse species, winter. . . . . .
. . . . .Violet leaf midge, *Phytophaga violicola* Coq.
Curled, corrugated leaves, *V. pubescens*, midge, summer. . . .*Dasyneura sp.*

Loasa Family *(Loasaceæ)*

Mentzelia

Flower bud gall, midge, summer. . . . .*Asphondylia mentzeliæ* Ckll.

Cactus Family *(Cactaceæ)*

Prickly Pear *(Opuntia)*

Large swollen fruit, midge, summer. Fig. 271..*Asphondylia arizonensis* Felt
Asphondylia betheli Ckll.
Swollen leaves, midge, summer. Pl. 5 (6)......*Asphondylia opuntiæ* Felt

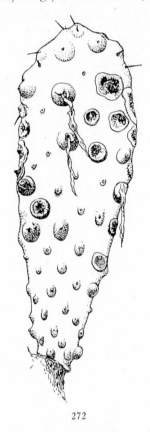

272
273
(Courtesy New York State Museum)

Fig. 272.—Cactus midge, *Itonida opuntiæ*.
Fig. 273.—Bud gall of *Thecodiplosis zauschneriæ*.

Yellowish decayed spots at base of spines, summer. Fig. 272.........
.........................Cactus midge, *Itonida opuntiæ* Felt

Oleaster Family *(Elæagnaceæ)*

Shepherdia canadensis

Oval bud gall, midge, spring..............*Asphondylia shepherdiæ* Felt

Evening Primrose Family *(Onagraceæ)*

Evening Primrose *(Oenothera)*

Enlarged flower buds, caterpillar, summer........*Mompha stellella* Busck

Zauschneria

Rosette gall, midge, summer. Fig. 273.....*Thecodiplosis zauschneriæ* Felt

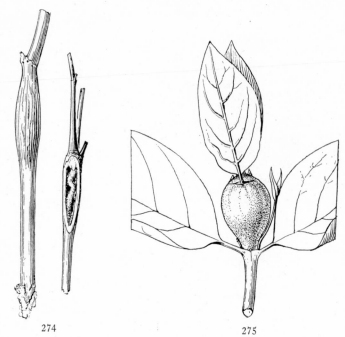

274

275

(Courtesy New York State Museum)

Fig. 274.—Stem gall of *Lasioptera ziziæ*.
Fig. 275.—Dogwood bud gall, *Cecidomyia sp.*

Ginseng Family *(Araliaceæ)*

Wild Sarsaparilla *(Aralia nudicaulis)*

Irregular, crooked, fusiform leaf stem gall, length ½ inch, diameter ⅛ inch, fall, scale insect...........................? *Asterolecanium sp.*

Parsley Family *(Umbelliferæ)*

Black Snake Root *(Sanicle)*

Minute, globose, stem and leaf enlargements, diameter ¹⁄₁₆ inch......
....? *Asteromyia sp.*

Golden Alexanders *(Zizia)*

Fusiform stem gall, length 1½ inches, midge, summer. Fig. 274......
....*Lasioptera ziziæ* Felt

Angelica

Stem swelling, 1½ to 2 inches long, midge, summer.......*Cecidomyia sp.*

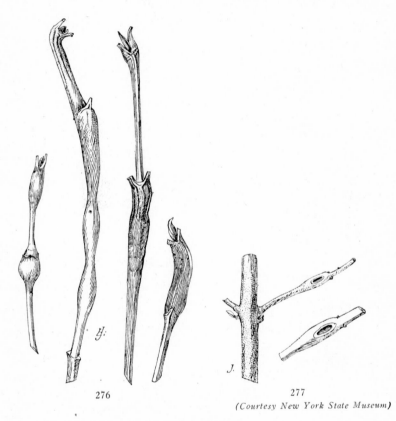

276

277

(Courtesy New York State Museum)

FIG. 276.—Dogwood club gall, *Mycodiplosis alternata.*
FIG. 277.—Dogwood stem gall, *Neolasioptera cornicola.*

Myrtle Family *(Myrtaceæ)*

Eugenia

Deformed fruit, midge.......................*Dasyneura eugeniæ* Felt
Hairy, globose leaf gall, diameter 1/10 inch, midge, summer........
....*Cystodiplosis eugeniæ* Felt

Dogwood Family *(Cornaceæ)*

Cornus or dogwood is acceptable to some five species of gall midges, they producing characteristic bud, leaf and twig deformities and also two species of gall mites. The related black or sour gum is host for two species of gall midges and two gall mites and a bud gall midge has been reared from the western *Garrya*.

Garrya fremontii

Black bud gall, midge.....................*Asphondylia garryæ* Felt

Dogwood *(Cornus)*

Green, red-tinted bud gall, length ¾ inch, midge, summer. Fig. 275...
...........................Dogwood bud gall, *Cecidomyia sp.*
Club-shaped twig gall, length ½ to 1 inch, on *C. florida*, midge summer. Fig. 276...........Dogwood club gall, *Mycodiplosis alternata* Felt
(Previously listed in error as *Lasioptera clavula* Beutm.)
Tubular, curved, green leaf gall, length ⅓ inch, on *C. amomum*, midge, summer..............Dogwood tube gall, *Cecidomyia tuba* Stebb.
Yellowish, purple-margined blister leaf gall, diameter ⅛ inch, on *C. stolonifera*, midge, summer. Pl. 13 (9).....................
......................Dogwood spot gall, *Lasioptera corni* Felt
Irregular stem gall, length ½ to 1 inch, on *C. stolonifera*, midge, summer. Fig. 277, 278....Dogwood stem gall, *Neolasioptera cornicola* Beutm.
Blackish leaf pile, mite, summer.......................*Eriophyes sp.*

Black or Sour Gum *(Nyssa)*

Twig gall, length 2 to 2½ inches, midge, summer.........*Cecidomyia sp.*
Marginal leaf fold, length ⅛ inch, midge, summer.................
.............................*Cecidomyia nyssæcola* Beutm.
Capsule gall, often lobed, mite, summer.........*Eriophyes nyssæ* Trott.
Narrow infolding of leaf margin, mite, summer...........*Eriophyes sp.*

Heath Family *(Ericaceæ)*

The blueberry is host for some five species of gall midges, the fruit, the bud and the leaves being attacked and also a gall wasp and a gall mite, while buds and leaves of the related cranberry are attacked by another species of gall midge. The attractive odorous pinkster supports a bud midge and a scale insect, the latter deforming the twig.

Pinkster, Rhododendron *(Rhododendron sp.)*

Rolled, swollen, yellowish young leaves of Rhododendron, midge.....
............Rhododendron tip midge, *Giardomyia rhododendri* Felt

Bud gall, length ¼ inch, midge, spring. . . . .
. . . . Pinkster bud gall, *Asphondylia azaleœ* Felt

Manzanita (*Arbutus arizonica*)

Possibly the same as the following, aphid. . . . .*? Tamalia coweni* Ckll.

Bearberry (*Arctostaphylos*)

Thickened, reddish, marginal leaf fold, length ¼ to 1 inch, width ⅕ inch, aphid, summer. . . . .*Tamalia coweni* Ckll.

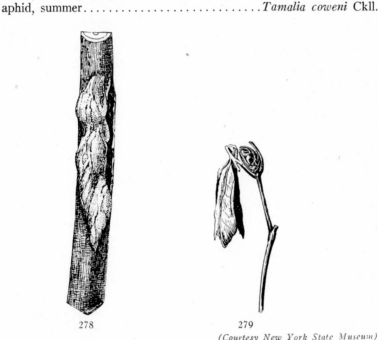

278

279
(Courtesy New York State Museum)

Fig. 278.—Dogwood stem gall, probably *Neolasioptera cornicola*.
Fig. 279.—Pinkster bud gall, *Asphondylia azaleœ*.

Dangleberry (*Guylussacia frondosa*)

Globose leaf gall, diameter ¼ to ½ inch, midge, summer. . . . .
. . . .*Cecidomyia vaccinii* O.S.

Blueberry, Cranberry (*Vaccinium*)

Reared from fruit, summer. . . . Blueberry midge, *Lasioptera fructuaria* Felt
Apical bud gall on blueberry, midge, spring. . . . .
. . . . Blueberry bud gall, *Dasyneura cyanococci* Felt
Injured blueberry tips, midge, summer. . . . .*Contarinia vaccinii* Felt

Valved, midrib leaf gall, length ⅛ inch, on blueberry, midge, summer
.................Blueberry leaf gall, *Dasyneura gaylussacii* Felt

Small, round galls on blueberry leaves, mite, summer........*Eriophyes sp.*

Kidney-shaped stem gall, diameter ½ to 1 inch, on blueberry, gall wasp, summer. Fig. 280...Blueberry stem gall, *Hemadas nubilipennis* Ashm.
Guest flies, *Ormyrus vacciniicola* Ashm.
Guest flies, *Solenozopheria vaccinii* Ashm.

Leaf fold or bud gall on cranberry, spring, summer...............
....................Cranberry midge, *Dasyneura vaccinii* Smith

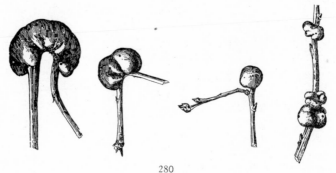

280

(Courtesy New York State Museum)

Fig. 280.—Blueberry stem gall, *Hemadas nubilipennis*. *(After Beutm.)*

Lead Wort Family *(Plumbaginaceæ)*

Sea Lavender *(Limonium)*

Small black spots or leaf pile, mite, summer..............*Eriophyes sp.*

Primrose Family *(Primulaceæ)*

Swamp Loosestrife *(Lysimachia)*

Globose bud gall, length ⅛ inch, midge, spring. Pl. 9 (9)..........
...............................*Dasyneura lysimachiæ* Beutm.

Cyclamen

Loose leaf and blossom deformations, summer...................
....................Cyclamen mite, *Tarsonemus pallidus* Bnks.

Sapodilla Family *(Sapotaceæ)*

Bumelia

Irregular, many-celled twig gall, length 1 to 2 inches, midge, spring. Pl. 41 (4)...............................*Asphondylia bumeliæ* Felt

Ebony Family *(Ebenaceæ)*

Persimmon *(Diospyros)*

Warty leaf gall on distorted foliage, jumping plant louse, summer....
....*Trioza diospyri* Ashm.

Patches of leaf pile, mite, summer.....................*Eriophyes sp.*

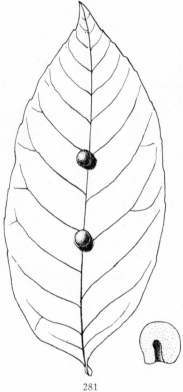

281

(Courtesy New York State Museum)

FIG. 281.—Ash bullet gall, *Cecidomyia pellex.*

Storax Family *(Styracaceæ)*

Symplocos, Horse Sugar

Bladdery enlargement of leaf buds, greenish, white-coated, length 1 to 2
inches, fungus, summer.......*Exobasidium symploci* Ellis & Martin

Olive Family *(Oleaceæ)*

Several gall midges have been reared from ash bud or leaf deformities,
some of these inquilines, a Pysllid deforms the leaves and species of gall

mites transform the flowers into irregular masses or produce swellings upon the leaves.

Ash *(Fraxinus)*

Deformed buds of white ash, midge, spring......................
.........................Ash bud gall, *Dasyneura apicata* Felt
Subglobular leaf gall, diameter ¼ inch, midge summer...........
.................................*Lasioptera fraxinifolia* Felt
Colpodia termeritatas Felt

282

(Courtesy New York State Museum)

FIG. 282.—Ash midrib gall, *Contarinia canadensis.*

Ash bullet gall, midge, summer. Fig. 281.........*Cecidomyia pellex* O.S.
Swollen midrib, length ¼ to ½ inch, midge, summer. Fig. 282......
.....................Ash midrib gall, *Contarinia canadensis* Felt
Dasyneura tumidosæ Felt
Tightly rolled leaves, midge, summer. Fig. 283..................
...............................*Dasyneura fraxinifolia* Felt
Rhizomyia fraxinifolia Felt
Curled, purple-streaked leaves, jumping plant louse, summer. Pl. 15 (3)
........................Ash Psyllid, *Psyllopsis fraxinicola* Forst.
Basal petiole swelling, midge, summer. Fig. 284..................
...................Ash petiole midge, *Phytophaga fraxini* Felt

Lobulate flower masses, mite, summer. Pl. 15 (9)...............
......................Ash flower gall, *Eriophyes fraxiniflora* Felt
Capsule gall on red ash leaves, mite, summer.....*Eriophyes fraxini* Garm.
Pinkish or green capsule leaf or vein galls, mite, summer....*Eriophyes sp.*
Deformed, badly curled leaves produced *Arthrocnodax sambucifolia.* Pl.
5 (1)...*Eriophyes sp.*

Logania Family *(Loganiaceæ)*

Buddleia

Aborted ovary, the flower about twice the normal length, midge, summer
....................................*Asphondylia buddleia* Felt

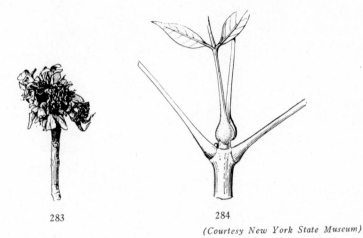

283   284

(Courtesy New York State Museum)

FIG. 283.—Ash bud deformed by *Rhizomyia fraxinifolia.*
FIG. 284.—Ash petiole midge, *Phytophaga fraxini.*

Dogbane Family *(Apocynaceæ)*

Dogbane *(Apocynum)*

Slightly enlarged flower buds, summer.........................
.....................Dogbane flower midge, *Itonida apocyni* Felt
Oval, reddish stem discolorations, midge, summer...............
....................................*Lasioptera apocyni* Felt

Milkweed Family *(Asclepiadaceæ)*

Milkweed *(Asclepias)*

Swollen midrib fold, length ¼ inch, midge, summer, *A. incarnata.*...
....*Cecidomyia sp.*

Brownish, swollen leaves, *A. incarnata,* midge, summer....*Cecidomyia sp.*
Fusiform stem gall, *A. incarnata,* summer. Fig. 285.............
...............Milkweed stem midge, *Neolasioptera asclepiæ* Felt

Convolvulus Family *(Convolvulaceæ)*

Morning-Glory *(Ipomoea)*

Reared from flower buds, midge, summer.......*Schizomyia ipomoeæ* Felt
Camptoneuromyia meridionalis Felt

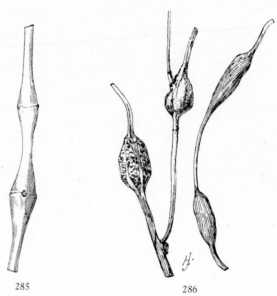

285

286

(Courtesy New York State Museum)

Fig. 285.—Milkweed stem gall, *Neolasioptera asclepiæ.*
Fig. 286.—Bindweed stem gall, *Lasioptera convolvuli.*

Hedge Bindweed *(Convolvulus)*

Fusiform stem gall, length ¾ inch, midge, summer. Fig. 286.......
..................Bindweed stem gall, *Lasioptera convolvuli* Felt

Dodder *(Cuscuta)*

Globose or ovate swellings subtending the inflorescence, diameter ⅛ to ⅕
inch, beetle, summer................*Smicronyx sculpticollis* Casey

Borage Family *(Boraginaceæ)*

Amsinckia lycopsoides

Presumably bud gall, midge, summer.........*Schizomyia macrofila* Felt

Vervain Family *(Verbenaceæ)*

Vervain *(Verbena)*

Aborted ovary and lower corolla tube, length ¼ inch, midge, summer
.....................................*Asphondylia verbenæ* Felt

Cylindric flower stalk swelling, *V. rostrata*, midge, summer.........
.....................................*Lasioptera verbeniæ* Felt

287   288

(Courtesy New York State Museum)

Fig. 287.—Leaf and flower galls of *Rhopalomyia audibertiæ*.
Fig. 288.—Blue curls stem gall, *Stagmatophora sexnotella*.

Oval stem gall, length ¼ inch, midge, summer..? *Lasioptera verbeniæ* Felt
Marginal leaf rolls, summer....Vervain leaf midge, *Itonida verbeniæ* Felt
Frost-like leaf pile, *V. hastata*, mite, summer.............*Eriophyes sp.*

Stachytarpha jamaicensis

Reared from flower, probably a mite gall, midge, summer.........
.....................................*Hyperdiplosis producta* Felt

Clerodendron aculeatum

Flower bud gall, midge, spring............:*Asphondylia attenuatata* Felt

Mint Family *(Labiatæ)*

Gall insects appear to be widely distributed though not particularly abundant upon any one of the large series of plants grouped in the mint family. The more common gall producers are midges, though at least one caterpillar and one gall wasp (a very large proportion of the last occur upon oaks) attack plants belonging in this family.

Audibertia stachyoides

Cylindric leaf, petiole or flower stem gall, length ¼ inch, midge, summer. Fig. 287.........................*Rhopalomyia audibertiæ* Felt

False Pennyroyal *(Isanthus)*

Reniform stem gall, length ¾ inch, caterpillar, summer...........
..........................? *Stagmatophora sexnotella* Chamb.

289

(Courtesy New York State Museum)

Fig. 289.—Catmint gall, *Aylax glechomæ*.

Blue Curls *(Trichostema)*

Reniform stem gall, length ¾ inch, caterpillar, summer. Fig. 288....
............Blue curls stem gall, *Stagmatophora sexnotella* Chamb.

Skull Cap *(Scutellaria)*

Oval stem gall, length ⅓ inch, midge, summer...........*Cecidomyia sp.*

Catmint *(Nepeta)*

Globose leaf petiole or stem gall, diameter ¼ inch, gall wasp, summer. Pl. 38 (1); Fig. 289...........Catmint gall, *Aylax glechomæ* Linn.

Hemp Nettle *(Galeopsis)*

Irregular stem gall, length ¼ to 1 inch, midge, summer...........
..................Hemp nettle gall, *Lasioptera galeopsidis* Felt

Sage *(Salvia)*

Conical or tubular leaf gall, length ½ inch, midge, summer. Fig. 290
......................Salvia leaf gall, *Rhopalomyia salviæ* Felt

Mountain Mint *(Pycnanthemum)*

Root galls, midge, summer.........................*Cecidomyia sp.*

Mock Pennyroyal *(Hedeoma)*

Enlarged flower buds, diameter 1/10 inch, midge, summer...*Cecidomyia sp.*

Wild Bergamot *(Monarda)*

Stem gall, length ½ to 1 inch, midge, summer. Fig. 291...........
................................*Cecidomyia monardi* Brodie

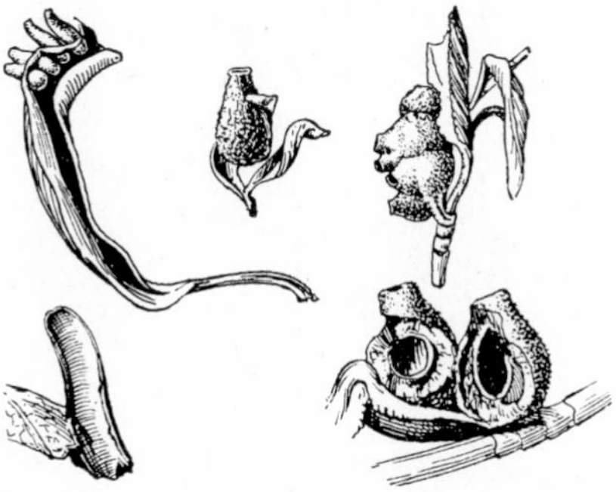

290 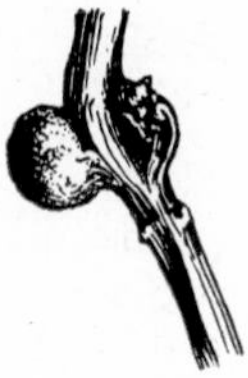 291
(Courtesy New York State Museum)

FIG. 290.—Salvia leaf gall, *Rhopalomyia salviæ.*
FIG. 291.—Monarda stem gall, *Rhopalomyia sp.*

Ovate root-stalk bud gall, length ⅛ inch, midge, summer..*Cecidomyia sp.*

Cunila

Globose bud gall, with a short point apically, diameter ⅛ inch, midge
....*Cecidomyia sp.*

Water Horehound *(Lycopus)*

Subglobular stem gall, length ½ inch, midge, summer. Fig. 292......
................................*Lasioptera lycopi* Felt
Fusiform stem gall, length ¾ to 1 inch, midge, summer. Fig. 293....
................................*Lasioptera mitchellæ* Felt

Mint *(Mentha)*

Terminal bud gall, length ⅛ inch, *M. gentilis*, midge, summer.......
....*Cecidomyia sp.*

Axillary or terminal bud gall, length ⅙ inch, midge, summer........
.................Spearmint bud gall, *Dasyneura aromaticæ* Felt
Loose bud gall, length ⅛ inch, *M. piperitæ,* midge, summer........
...................Peppermint bud gall, *Dasyneura piperitæ* Felt
Pustule leaf gall, diameter ⅛ inch, *M. canadensis,* midge, summer...
....................................*Giardomyia menthæ* Felt
Stem gall, length ¼ to ½ inch, midge, summer. Fig. 294...........
.........................*Neolasioptera menthæ* Felt

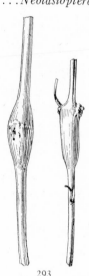

292

293

(Courtesy New York State Museum)

Fig. 292.—Stem gall of *Lasioptera lycopi.*
Fig. 293.—Stem gall of *Lasioptera mitchellæ.*

Horse Balm *(Collinsonia)*

Subglobular, pubescent leaf gall, length ¼ inch, midge, summer......
..............................*Cecidomyia collinsoniæ* Beutm.
Midrib or vein swelling, midge, summer........................
..............................*Cecidomyia collinsonifolia* Beutm.

Nightshade Family *(Solanaceæ)*

Tomato *(Lycopersicum)*

Reared from flowers.......Tomato flower gall, *Contarinia lycopersici* Felt

Horse Nettle *(Solanum)*

Spiny stem gall, length ⅛ to ¼ inch, midge, summer. Fig. 295......
......................Horse nettle gall, *Neolasioptera solani* Felt
Distorted, incurled leaves, margins appressed, summer....? *Lepidopteron*

Irregular swelling of base of leaf and leaf stem, weevil, maker unknown. Pl. 40 (8).

Matrimony Vine *(Lycium)*

Circular or oval, slightly hairy leaf galls, diameter ⅛ inch, on *Lycium chinense, L. halmifolium*, mite, summer.....*Eriophyes eucricotes* Nal.

294

295

(Courtesy New York State Museum)

Fig. 294.—Gall of *Neolasioptera menthæ.*
Fig. 295.—Horse nettle gall, *Neolasioptera solani.*

Figwort Family *(Scrophulariaceæ)*

Only a few genera in this large group are attacked by gall insects, practically all of these being gall midges, one or at most two species occurring upon the same plant. Only one gall mite is represented in the series and another, not a true gall mite, produces loose leaf and blossom deformations.

Toad Flax *(Linaria)*

Irregular stem swelling, frequently crooked, ¼ by ⅛ inch, scale insect, summer...................*Asterolecanium ? fimbriatum* Fonsc.

Snapdragon *(Antirrhinum)*

Loose leaf and blossom deformations, mite, summer..............
......................................*Tarsonemus pallidus* Bnks.

Figwort *(Scrophularia)*

Distorted flower buds, probably predaceous midge, summer........
...............................*Lestodiplosis scrophulariæ* Felt

Bearded Tongue *(Penstemon)*

Stem or branch gall, length ½ inch, midge, summer. Fig. 296......
....*Lasioptera tibialis* Felt

Monkey Flower (*Mimulus*)

Stem gall, midge, summer.................*Neolasioptera mimuli* Felt

Diplacus

Ovoid stem gall, midge, summer..............*Lasioptera diplaci* Felt
Cabbage bud gall, midge, summer, Fig. 297......*Asphondylia diplaci* Felt

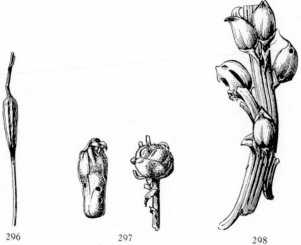

296   297   298

(Courtesy New York State Museum)

Fig. 296.—Gall of *Lasioptera tibialis*.
Fig. 297.—Galls of *Asphondylia diplaci*.
Fig. 298.—Gerardia seed pods infested by *Cecidomyia sp.*

Downy False Foxglove (*Gerardia*)

Larvae in seed pods, midge, summer. Fig. 298...........*Cecidomyia sp.*
Deformed leaf, mite, summer........................*Eriophyes sp.*

Bignonia Family (*Bignoniaceæ*)

Trumpet Flower (*Tecoma*)

Irregularly curled, wrinkled leaves, midge, summer....*Itonida tecomiæ* Felt

Catalpa

Dwarfed shoots and pods, summer..Catalpa midge, *Itonida catalpæ* Comst.

Madder Family (*Rubiaceæ*)

Bedstraw (*Galium*)

Aborted flower buds, diameter ⅛ inch, summer...................

.....................Bedstraw midge, *Dasyneura americana* Felt
Upper leaves with margins inrolled, mite, summer....*Eriophyes galii* Karp.

Buttonbush (*Cephalanthus*)

Twig gall, midge, summer.......................................
..............Buttonbush twig gall, *Rhabdophaga cephalanthi* Felt
Pale or reddish dimples on upper leaf surface, white below, height ⅛ inch,
mite, summer......................*Eriophyes cephalanthi* Cook
Leaf pocket gall, mite, summer.......................*Eriophyes sp.*

Randia aculeata

Thick, fusiform swellings in the hard wood of old stems, length 1 inch,
caterpillar, summer.............*Thyridopyralis gallœrandalis* Dyar

Honeysuckle Family (*Caprifoliaceæ*)

The arrowwood, *Viburnum,* is an obvious favorite with gall makers, there
being nine gall midges recorded from various members of this genus, bud
and leaf galls being more numerous, though one species produces a stem gall.
There are also two gall mites. The elder or *Sambucus* is an acceptable host
to three gall midges, two bud galls, one stem gall and also to a plant mite.
The fauna of the bush honeysuckle, *Diervilla,* closely parallels that of the
elder, though no plant mite has been recorded.

Bush Honeysuckle (*Diervilla*)

Bud gall or enlarged fruit, length ¼ inch, summer................
...........Bush honeysuckle bud midge, *Asphondylia diervillœ* Felt.
Reared from apparently normal stems, summer..................
..........Bush honeysuckle stem midge, *Lasioptera caulicola* Felt

Honeysuckle (*Lonicera*)

Ovate bud gall, ½ to ¾ inches, on *L. subapicata*, midge, summer....
....................................*Rhopalomyia lonicera* Felt
Lobulate bud gall, diameter ¼ to ½ inch, midge,..........*Cecidomyia sp.*
Irregular bud gall, globose or cylindrical, ¾ to 1 inch long, on *L. ciliosa*,
midge, summer ....? *Asphondylia sp.*

Snowberry (*Symphoricarpos*)

Thickened, distorted leaflets, midge, summer....*Thomasia californica* Felt
Fusiform twig gall, midge, summer...................*Cecidomyia sp.*

Arrowwood (*Viburnum*)

Bud gall, length ⅙ inch, midge, spring........................
.................Arrowwood bud midge, *Schizomyia viburni* Felt

Purplish vein swellings, length ¼ inch, summer. Pl. 13 (5)........
...............Purple vein midge, *Sackenomyia viburnifolia* Felt
Purplish discolorations along vein, mite, summer. Fig. 299....*Eriophyes sp.*
Minute blister gall, diameter ⅒ inch, midge, summer. Pl. 9 (7)......
.............Arrowwood blister midge, *Cystiphora viburnifolia* Felt
Circular blister gall, diameter ⅒ inch, on *V. cassinoides*, midge, sum-
mer...*Cecidomyia sp.*

299

300

(Courtesy New York State Museum)

Fig. 299.—Plant mite or *Eriophyes* on *Viburnum*.
Fig. 300.—Arrowwood stem gall, *Neolasioptera viburnicola*.

Pinkish pustule galls, diameter ⅛ inch, on *V. acerifolium*, midge, sum-
mer......................Arrowwood spot gall, *Cecidomyia sp.*
Green, circular leaf mines, diameter ¼ inch, on *V. opulus*, midge, summer.
....*Cecidomyia sp.*
Greenish blister gall, diameter ⅒ inch, on *V. dentatum*, midge, summer.
....*Cecidomyia sp.*
Irregular lobed leaf dimples, on *V. dentatum*, mite, summer..*Eriophyes sp.*
Marginal leaf roll, length ½ inch, on *V. cassinoides*, midge, summer..
....*Cecidomyia sp.*
Irregular stem gall, length ⅒ to ¼ inch, on *V. dentatum*, midge, summer.
Fig. 300......Arrowwood stem gall, *Neolasioptera viburnicola* Beutm.

Elder (*Sambucus*)

Swollen florets, summer. Pl. 13 (7)...........................
................Elder flower midge, *Youngomyia umbellicola* O.S.
Bud gall, diameter ¾ inch, summer. Fig. 301.....................
.......................Elder bud gall, *Asphondylia sambuci* Felt
Marginal leaf roll, whitish or brownish velvet, mite, summer. .*Eriophyes sp.*
Irregular stem gall, length $\frac{1}{10}$ to $\frac{1}{7}$ inch, midge, summer. Fig. 302....
....................Elder stem midge, *Neolasioptera sambuci* Felt

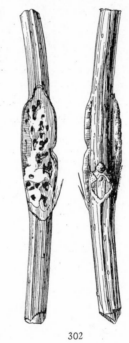

301   302

(*Courtesy New York State Museum*)

FIG. 301.—Elder bud gall, *Asphondylia sambuci.*
FIG. 302.--Elder stem gall, *Neolasioptera sambuci.*

Lobelia Family (*Lobeliaceæ*)

Lobelia

Elongate, stem swelling, length ½ inch, midge, summer...........
....? *Lasioptera sp.*

Gourd Family (*Cucurbitaceæ*)

Melon (*Cucumeris*)

Curled, slightly enlarged tips of muskmelon, summer............
................Muskmelon tip midge, *Contarinia setigera* Lintn.

Curled dying tips of watermelon, summer........................
..................Watermelon tip midge, *Itonida citrulli* Felt

Composite Family (*Compositæ*)

The long series of similar plants grouped in this family prove acceptable hosts to a considerable number of gall insects, the goldenrods, the asters, the wormwoods, the sunflowers and sagebrush being marked favorites, especially of the gall midges.

Ironweed (*Vernonia*)

Probably from a bud gall, midge, summer.....................
..................Ironweed bud gall, *Asphondylia vernoniæ* Felt
Reared from blossoms, summer...............................
.............Ironweed blossom midge, *Youngomyia vernoniæ* Felt
Deformed florets or oval petiole or midrib gall, length ¼ inch, midge, summer. Pl. 41 (1, 2)...................*Lasioptera vernoniæ* Beutm.
Ovate stem or bud swelling....................*Eutreta sparsa* Wied.

Joe-Pyeweed (*Eupatorium purpureum*)

Blossom bud gall, length ½ inch, summer.....................
.............Joe-pyeweed blossom midge, *Dasyneura purpurea* Felt

Thoroughwort, Boneset (*Eupatorium perfoliatum*)

Reared from florets, summer................................
...............Boneset blossom midge, *Contarinia perfoliata* Felt
Reared from florets, midge, summer......*Clinorhyncha eupatoriflorœ* Felt
Oval stem gall, length ½ to ¾ inch, summer..................
...............Boneset stem midge, *Neolasioptera perfoliata* Felt
Brachyneura eupatorii Felt

White Snakeroot (*Eupatorium urticæfolium*)

Flower buds, length ¼ inch, midge, summer. Pl. 11 (1)...........
...............................*Lestodiplosis eupatorii* Felt[1]
Stem galls, length ¾ inch, midge, summer. Pl. 41 (3)...........
...............................*Neolasioptera eupatorii* Felt
Similar stem gall, midge, summer...........*Asphondylia eupatorii* Felt
Oval, yellowish leaf mine, diameter ¼ inch, midge, summer........
....*Cecidomyia sp.*

Climbing Hempweed (*Mikania*)

Internodal stem gall, length ¼ to 2½ inches, fly, summer........*Trypetid*

[1] Predator, not the true gall maker.

Button Snake Root (*Liatris*)

Irregular, apical bud gall, diameter 1 inch......*Asphondylia lacinariæ* Felt

Gum-Plant, Tar-Weed (*Grindelia*)

Apical, ovoid, rosette gall, length 1-1½ inches, on *G. lanceolata*, midge, summer...*Cecidomyia sp.*

Globose, axillary bud galls, diameter ⅛ to ¼ inch, midge, summer....
....*Cecidomyia sp.*

Globose, grayish-white, woolly, sessile stem gall, diameter ⅕ to ½ inch, midge, summer.............................*? Rhopalomyia sp.*

Reared from flower heads, summer. Fig. 303...................
.............Tar-weed blossom midge, *Rhopalomyia grindeliæ* Felt

Blister leaf gall, greenish or blackish, diameter ⅛ inch, summer. Fig. 304.
...............Tar-weed blister midge, *Asteromyia grindeliæ* Felt

 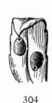 

303   304   305

(*Courtesy New York State Museum*)

FIG. 303.—Tar weed blossom gall, *Rhopalomyia grindeliæ.*
FIG. 304.—Tar weed blister gall, *Asteromyia grindeliæ.*
FIG. 305.—Black gouty gall, *Asteromyia gutierreziæ.*

Gutierrezia sarothræ

Flower bud gall, length ¼ inch, midge, summer...............
................Gutierrezia bud gall, *Rhopalomyia gutierreziæ* Ckll.

Blackened enlargement of slender stems, length ¼ to ⅓ inch, midge, summer. Fig. 305..........Black gouty gall, *Asteromyia gutierreziæ* Felt

Heterotheca subaxillaris

Fusiform stem enlargement, length 1-¾ to 2½ inches, diameter ½ inch, caterpillar, summer.............................*Lepidopteron*

Golden Aster (*Chrysopsis*)

Woolly bud gall, diameter ¾ inch, midge, summer...............
..............Golden aster bud gall, *Rhopalomyia chrysopsidis* Lw.

Goldenrod (*Solidago*)

The goldenrods are quite common flowers, not infrequently giving character in autumn to entire landscapes. The great abundance of several species leads to their being regarded as common and therefore uninteresting. The latter is not the case.

These native and widely prevalent weeds support a highly interesting series of gall insects, most of which have largely escaped attention. The ball gall, a globular stem swelling about an inch in diameter, green, occasionally rosy cheeked like an apple, is common, sometimes occurring on most of the stems in a good sized patch of goldenrod. Rarely two of these galls may be found on one stalk. Frequently most of these swellings are at approximately the same height on the stem. They are most readily seen in winter and the maker, a good sized fly with brown marked wings, may be easily reared in the spring if the galls are gathered and placed in a container, such as a glass jar covered with light netting.

There are more slender stem swellings over an inch long, the home of whitish caterpillars. These gall makers keep the interior walls of their shelters smooth and neat, the castings being packed at the bottom of the cavity. The caterpillars of several moths produce similar shelters in goldenrod stems. These and the preceding are frequently emptied of their living contents by mice and woodpeckers.

A considerable series of gall midges find very satisfactory conditions in the goldenrod. Two of these deform flower buds, one producing a smooth, onion-shaped, frequently red tinted gall, and the other a cylindrical, hairy deformity—both occurring in clusters in place of normal flowers. Another midge specializes in leaf buds, transforming them into small globular masses of deformed leaflets with the center sheltering a stout, yellowish maggot. Still another attacks leaf buds and transforms them into globose leafy shelters containing a number of reddish maggots distributed in oval cells of the fleshy interior. This last midge is so resourceful that it not infrequently attacks the underground buds of subterranean branches or stolens and as a result the shoot pushes up a small, potato-like gall instead of a normal tip. Many of these galls even spit partly open at the time the delicate flies are ready to escape.

Another interesting phase of bud infestation is seen in the goldenrod. The slender, fusiform stem gall produced by a little midge may arise from among the flower cluster, the upper branches and the leaves, indicating that the young maggots establish themselves while these parts are all in the bud and then, by judicious irritation, compel the infested portion to develop the characteristic gall. The maggots of another bud midge sometimes establish themselves between the surfaces of leaves while they are touching or apposed in the bud and as a result the adjacent tissues develop rapidly and form an oval cell between the two surfaces. This injury is not sufficient to prevent a nearly normal development and as a result one may find these leaves still attached at the point of injury, thus providing shelter for the maggots, while other parts are widely separated and the stems or petioles of the two leaves arising from the stalk an inch or two apart. In other words, infestation by the midge has resulted in tying two portions of the leaves together and keeping them in this position in spite of the nearly normal development of the stem and other portions of the affected leaves.

The so-called aster blister galls, noticed elsewhere are also abundant upon goldenrod, the coal black spots in the narrow-leaved goldenrod being especially numerous.

Flower Galls

Greenish or reddish, globular, diameter $\frac{1}{10}$ inch, on *S. canadensis*, midge, summer. Pl. 12 (6)..Beaked flower gall, *Rhopalomyia racemicola* O.S.

Densely pubescent, cylindrical gall, length $\frac{1}{4}$ inch, on *S. canadensis*, midge, summer. Pl. 12 (5); Fig. 306...............................
...................Downy flower gall, *Rhopalomyia anthophila* O.S.

| 306 | 307 | 308 |

(Courtesy New York State Museum)

FIG. 306.—Downy flower gall, *Rhopalomyia anthophila*.
FIG. 307.—Gall of Nun midge, *Asphondylia monacha*.
FIG. 308.—Clarke's goldenrod gall, *Rhopalomyia clarkei*.

Reared from undescribed gall, midge, summer.................
.....................................*Rhopalomyia cruziana* Felt

Apparently normal florets, midge, summer. Fig. 307..............
........................Nun midge, *Asphondylia monacha* O.S.
Asphondylia johnsoni Felt

Bud Galls

Apical bud gall:
Loose, convolute leaf mass, diameter $\frac{1}{4}$ inch, midge, summer....
..............................*Asteromyia convoluta* Felt

Loose, narrow leaf pod on *S. canadensis*, midge, summer.......
...................................*Dryomyia folliculi* Felt

Two or more leaves with adherent edges, length ⅛ to ¼ inch, on
  S. graminifolia, midge, summer.......*Dasyneura flavicornis* Felt
Closely adherent leaf gall, length 1/25 inch, on *S. graminifolia, S. cana-
  densis*, midge, summer........*Camptoneuromyia flavescens* Felt
Loosebud gall, on *S. graminifolia*, midge, summer............
  ....*Dasyneura carbonaria* Felt
White or brownish galls on stem, or subterranean root stalks, diameter
  ⅛ inch, on *S. juncea*, summer, fall.....................
  ....Rootstalk bud midge, *Rhopalomyia hirtipes* O.S.
Cylindric bud gall on rootstalk, length ¼ inch, midge, summer, fall
  ....*Rhopalomyia bulbula* Felt
Elongate, terminal head, length ⅛ inch, midge, summer.......
  .... *Rhopalomyia sp.*

Apical Rosette Galls
Solidago canadensis
Deformed compound head, diameter ½ inch...*Rhopalomyia carolina* Felt
Pyriform gall of closely adherent leaves, length ½ inch, midge, summer
  ....?*Camptoneuromyia flavescens* Felt
Globular, diameter 2 to 2½ inches, midge, summer. Pl. 13 (2).......
  ....Goldenrod bunch gall, *Rhopalomyia solidaginis* Lw.
  Inquiline, *Rhopalomyia albipennis* Felt
  Inquiline, *Oligotrophus inquilinus* Felt
  Predator, *Lestodiplosis sp.*

Solidago canadensis and S. serotina
Numerous small cells, diameter 1¼ inch, midge, summer..........
  ....Goldenrod rosette midge, *Rhopalomyia capitata* Felt
  Rhopalomyia inquisitor Felt

Solidago graminifolia
Loose apical bud gall, diameter ½ to ¾ inch, summer. Pl. 5 (5)....
  ....Nun midge, *Asphondylia monacha* O.S.
  Camptoneuromyia flavescens Felt
  Rhopalomyia lanceolata Felt

Solidago sempervirens
Loose apical bud gall, diameter ½ to ¾ inch, summer............
  ....Nun midge, *Asphondylia monacha* O.S.

Solidago altissima
Rosette gall, length ½ to ¾ inch, fly, summer.................
  . ...Small rosette gall, *Oedaspis polita* Lw.
  Oedaspis atra Lw.

Leaf Galls

Galls Attached to One or at Most Two Leaves and Producing a Marked Deformity

Solidago graminifolia

Fusiform, sessile, ribbed, greenish, red-marked, length ¼ inch, midge, summer.........Goldenrod ribbed gall, *Rhopalomyia fusiformis* Felt

Fusiform, stemmed, green, red-marked gall, length ½ inch, midge, summer ....Goldenrod stemmed gall, *Rhopalomyia pedicellata* Felt

Elongate, blackened, thickened leaflets, length ¾ to 1 inch, midge, summer ....Black blister gall, *Asteromyia ? carbonifera* Felt

Solidago puberla or S. juncea

Oval, greenish, clustered root leaves, length ½ inch, midge, summer ....*Dasyneura radifolii* Felt

Solidago rugosa

Fusiform, sessile, green, red-marked gall, length ¹⁄₁₀ inch, midge, summer. Fig. 308...........Clarke's goldenrod gall, *Rhopalomyia clarkei* Felt

Solidago canadensis and S. serotina

Oval, adherent capsule gall, diameter ¹⁄₁₀ inch, summer. Pl. 5 (4)....
.........................Nun midge, *Asphondylia monacha* O.S.

Probably inquilines {
Camptoneuromyia adhesa Felt
Lasioptera argentisquamœ Felt
Trotteria solidaginis Felt

Blister-Like Leaf Galls with at Most a Slight Thickening and Discoloration

Oval, black gall, diameter ⅙ inch, on *S. graminifolia*, midge, summer ....Black blister gall, *Asteromyia carbonifera* Felt

Grayish-brown, black-margined blister, diameter ⅛ inch, on *S. squarrosa*, midge, summer......................*Asteromyia squarrosœ* Felt

Circular, marginal, golden-gray blister, diameter ⅛ inch, on *S. canadensis*, midge, summer.....Golden lunate gall, *Asteromyia flavoanulata* Felt

Circular, pinkish or rosy blister, diameter ½ inch, on *S. rugosa*, midge, summer..................Rosy blister gall, *Asteromyia rosea* Felt

Oval blister gall, on *S. canadensis*, midge, summer...............
.....................................*Asteromyia socialis* Felt

Elongate, yellowish-brown, blistered area, length 1½ inches, on *S. canadensis*, midge, summer.........................?*Asteromyia sp.*
Predator, *Lestodiplosis triangularis* Felt

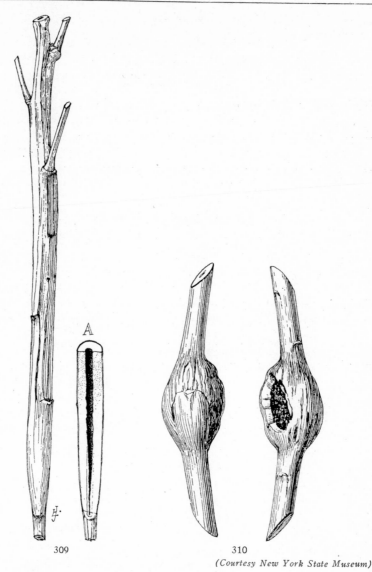

A

309

310

(Courtesy New York State Museum)

FIG. 309.—Goldenrod stem gall, *Lasioptera cylindrigallæ*.
FIG. 310.—Knotty goldenrod gall, *Lasioptera solidaginis*.

Blister gall on goldenrod and aster, diameter ⅛ to ⅙ inch, midge, summer
..............................*Asteromyia albomaculata* Felt
Oval, yellowish or blackish blisters with a darker central nipple, diameter
⅛ to ¼ inch, on *S. rugosa*, midge, summer..................
.......................Reddish blister gall, *Asteromyia rubra* Felt

Semi-oval, marginal, yellowish blister, length ½ inch, on *S. canadensis,* midge, summer......Yellow blister gall, *Asteromyia flavolunata* Felt

Stem and Root Galls
Solidago graminifolia

Fusiform, sessile, ribbed, greenish, red-marked gall, length ¼ inch, midge, summer........Goldenrod ribbed gall, *Rhopalomyia fusiformis* Felt

Fusiform, stemmed, red-marked, greenish gall, length ½ inch, midge, summer............Goldenrod stem gall, *Rhopalomyia pedicellata* Felt

Subglobular, green gall near tip, diameter ¾ inch, midge, summer...
.....................................*Rhopalomyia lobata* Felt

Uniform stem enlargement, length 5 inches, diameter ¼ inch, midge, summer. Fig. 309....Goldenrod stem midge, *Lasioptera cylindrigallæ* Felt

Solidago, Various Species

Irregular, globose, lateral stem gall, diameter ⅛ inch, on *S. occidentalis,* midge, summer.................................*Cecidomyia sp.*

Globose or fusiform eccentric enlargement, length 1¼ inches, on *S. rugosa,* midge, summer. Fig. 310.....................................
................Knotty goldenrod gall, *Lasioptera solidaginis* O.S.

Globose, smooth, brownish, apical, aerial or subterranean galls, diameter 1¼ inches, on *S. juncea,* summer, fall. Pl. 12 (9)............
................Root stalk bud midge, *Rhopalomyia hirtipes* O.S.

Cylindric bud gall, on root stalk, length ¼ inch, midge, summer. Pl. 12 (7)
.....................................*Rhopalomyia bulbula* Felt

Globose stem gall, diameter 1¼ inches, interior pithy, fly, summer. Fig. 311
....................Goldenrod ball gall, *Eurosta solidaginis* Fitch

Oval stem gall, length ½ inch, caterpillar, summer. Pl. 4 (8)........
..............Scarred goldenrod gall, *Eucosma scudderiana* Clem.

Oval stem gall, on *S. sempervirens,* caterpillar, summer...........
.....................................*Gnorimoschema salinaris* Busck

Gall just above or close to ground, on *S. rigida,* caterpillar, summer...
.....................................*Gnorimoschema gibsoniella* Busck

Fusiform stem gall, length 1½ inch, usually near ground, on *S. latifolia, S. cæsia* and *Aster divaricatus,* caterpillar, summer...........
.....................................*Gnorimoschema gallæasteriella* Kell.

Elongate, spindle-shaped stem gall, on *S. canadensis,* caterpillar, summer. Fig. 312 ....
......Elliptical goldenrod gall, *Gnorimoschema gallæsolidaginis* Riley

Ovoid, solitary or clustered root-stalk bud galls, length ¼ inch, midge, summer. Pl. 13 (4)....................*Rhopalomyia thompsoni* Felt

Cylindric, hollow, bud-like gall near surface, length 1 inch, fly, summer
.... Goldenrod root-stalk gall, *Eurosta reticulata* Snow
Fusiform, subterranean bud gall, length 1 to 1½ inches, fly, summer. Pl.
4 (5).............. Goldenrod root-stalk gall, *Eutreta sparsa* Wied.

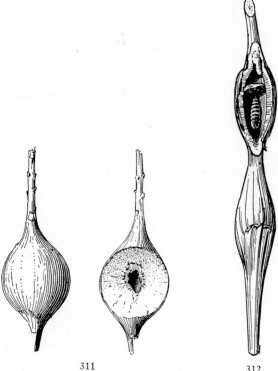

311

312

(Courtesy New York State Museum)

Fig. 311.—Goldenrod ball gall, *Eurosta solidaginis.*
Fig. 312.—Elliptical goldenrod gall, *Gnorimoschema gallœsolidaginis.*

Ovate, potato-like root gall, length ¾ to 1 inch, diameter ½ inch, on *S.
rugosa, S. juncea,* fly, summer............... *Eurosta comma* Wied.
Eurosta elsa Daecke

Rayless Goldenrod (*Bigelovia graveolens*)

Enlarged leaf buds, length ¼ inch, midge, summer. Fig. 313........
.... *Asphondylia chrysothamni* Felt
Purplish, swollen leaf buds with recurved leaflets and thick, gray pubes-
cence, length ½ inch, midge, summer. Fig. 314..............
.... *Rhopalomyia utahensis* Felt

Ovate, woolly, lateral bud gall, length ½ inch, fly, summer. Fig. 315
. . . . *Eurosta bigeloviæ* Ckll.
Oedaspis atra Lw.

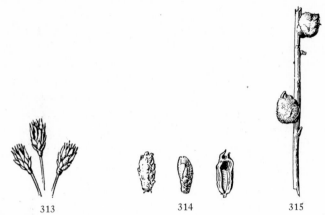

FIG. 313.—Gall of *Asphondylia chrysothamni*.
FIG. 314.—Gall of *Rhopalomyia utahensis*.
FIG. 315.—Gall of *Eurosta bigeloviæ*.

Ovate seed gall or lateral bud swelling, midge, summer. Fig. 316. . . . .
. . . . *Rhopalomyia bigelovioides* Felt
A small bud-like gall, midge, summer. . . . .*Cecidomyia brassicoides* Town.
Cone-like, probably bud gall, midge, summer. . . . .
. . . . *Dasyneura strobiloides* Town.
Slightly swollen leaflet, midge, summer. . . . . . .*Asteromyia chrysothamni* Felt

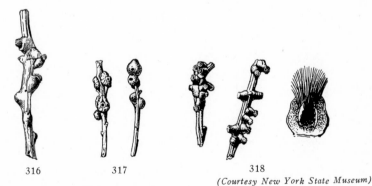

(Courtesy New York State Museum)

FIG. 316.—Gall of *Rhopalomyia bigelovioides*.
FIG. 317.—Gall of *Rhopalomyia glutinosa*.
FIG. 318.—Gall of *Rhopalomyia chrysothamni*.

Globose or fusiform terminal twig swelling, length ½ to 1 inch, gall wasp, summer. Fig. 319....................*Aylax chrysothamni* Beutm.

Globose, green or brown stem swelling, diameter ⅛ inch, midge, summer. Fig. 317...............Lecanoid gall, *Rhopalomyia glutinosa* Felt

Conical stem or oval bud gall, with a variable amount of cottony fibers protruding, dimensions, ¼ to ½ inch, midge, summer. Fig. 318..
.............................*Rhopalomyia chrysothamni* Felt

Hollow stem gall, midge, summer...........*Rhopalomyia bigeloviæ* Felt

Cylindric, brown, ribbed stem gall, height 1/10 inch, midge, summer....
....*Cecidomyia sp.*

Oval, subcortical cell, length ⅛ inch, midge, summer......*Asteromyia sp.*

Globose, probably bud gall, diameter ¼ inch, on *B. plattensis*, midge, summer.....................................*Cecidomyia sp.*

Aster Blister Galls

This name is applied to peculiar discolored swellings found upon the leaves of aster and goldenrod in particular, though a few occur upon the foliage of other plants. They are usually oval, flattened thickenings in the leaf surface some one-quarter to one-half inch in diameter and appear like a fungous growth. The resemblance is so close that a number of botanists were deceived in earlier years, and those leaf blisters are to be found in certain botanical collections labeled as species of fungus. In reality, the swellings are produced by maggots of the aster leaf-blister midges, insects so closely dependent upon plants that they breed only in these peculiar swellings, which are confined very largely to the leaves of aster and goldenrod. The close interrelation of insect and plant is so marked that there are some twenty-seven species of blister leaf midges living in these galls.

The oval black tar-like swellings, sometimes thickly spotting the leaves, on the narrow leaved goldenrod are among the more common leaf blisters. Aster leaves are frequently disfigured by similar galls, though upon this plant they are frequently yellowish, occasionally yellowish white and sometimes margined with purplish red. It is easy, by breaking open the swellings toward the end of the summer, to find the yellowish jumping maggots responsible for the thickening of the leaf.

Aster

Flower or Bud Galls

Aborted flower head, on *A. patens*, summer.......................
.......................Nun midge, *Asphondylia monacha* O.S.

Stunted flower heads, on *A. paniculatus*, midge, summer............
.............................*Rhopalomyia asterifloræ* Felt

Axillary bud gall, diameter ⅛ to ½ inch, on *A. lateriflorus*, midge, summer. Pl. 13 (1)....................*Rhopalomyia lateriflori* Felt

Flower buds of *A. undulatus* deformed. Pl. 13 (3)......*Rhopalomyia sp.*

Fusiform, frequently clustered, subterranean stem or root stalk gall, length ½ inch, midge, summer.................*Rhopalomyia weldi* Felt

Ovate, axillary bud gall, length 1/10 to 1/6 inch, midge, summer......
....*Rhopalomyia sp.*

Blister Leaf Galls

Circular, yellowish-white, diameter 1/10 to 1/8 inch, on *A. macrophyllus*, midge, summer.........................*Lasioptera clarkei* Felt

Narrowly oval, yellowish-brown, length 1/6 inch, midge, summer.....
.................................*Asteromyia dumosæ* Felt

Circular, brownish-yellow, wrinkled, diameter 1/8 inch, midge, summer
.................................*Asteromyia waldorfi* Felt

Oval, yellowish, shiny, diameter 1/4 inch, midge, summer...........
.................................*Asteromyia nitida* Felt

Oval, pinkish blotches, diameter ½ inch, on *A. divaricatus*, midge, summer
.................................*Asteromyia divaricata* Felt

Yellowish or brownish oval galls, diameter 1/4 inch, on *A. paniculatus*, midge, summer....Red-tinted blister gall, *Asteromyia paniculata* Felt

Oval, blackish gall, diameter 1/6 inch, on *A. undulata*, possibly the same occurs on *Ionactis lineariifolius*, midge, summer. Pl. 5 (7)......
.................................*Asteromyia reducta* Felt

Oval, greenish-yellow or papery-white, diameter 3/4 inch, on *A. lævis*, midge, summer..............Papery blister gall, *Asteromyia læviana* Felt

Oval, sooty-yellow, white beneath, length 1 inch, midge, summer....
.................................*Asteromyia flavomaculata* Felt

Circular, yellowish-white, dark margined, diameter 1/8 inch, on *A. lateriflorus*, midge, summer...................................
..............Aster leaf blister gall, *Asteromyia asterifoliæ* Beutm.

Oval green swellings, length 1/12 inch, midge, summer............
.................................*Asteromyia vesiculosa* Felt

Circular, yellowish or brownish, diameter 1/8 inch, on *A. cordifolius*, midge, summer...........................*Asteromyia sylvestris* Felt

Ovate, greenish or yellowish-green, diameter 1/4 to ½ inch, midge, summer
.................................*Asteromyia sp.*

Stem or Branch Galls

Pustulate swellings, diameter 1/8 inch, midge, summer.............
.................................*Asteromyia pustulata* Felt

Oval twig gall, length 3/4 inch, on *A. novæ-angliæ*, midge, summer....
.................................*Rhopalomyia astericaulis* Felt

Fusiform stem or branch gall, length ½ inch, midge, summer. Fig. 320
.................Aster stem gall, *Neolasioptera ramuscula* Beutm.

Fusiform, greenish-brown stem swelling near leaf base, length ½ inch, on *A. infirmus*, midge, summer. Fig. 321....*Neolasioptera albitarsis* Felt

Fusiform stem gall, length 1 inch, on *A. umbellatus*, caterpillar, summer ....*Gnorimoschema gallœdiplopappi* Fyles

Fusiform stem gall, usually near ground, length 1½ inch, on *A. divaricatus, Solidago latifolia, S. cæsia*, caterpillar, summer............. ....*Gnorimoschema gallœasteriella* Kell.

Ovate, sessile, brownish, white-haired, length ¼ inch, on *A. crassulus*, midge, summer....................*Rhopalomyia crassulina* Ckll.

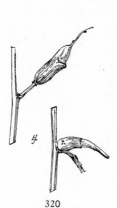

319

320

(Courtesy New York State Museum)

Fig. 319.—Gall of *Aylax chrysothamni*. (*After Beutm.*)
Fig. 320.—Aster stem gall, *Neolasioptera ramuscula*.

Spindle-shaped stem or root galls, length ½ inch, on *A. multiflorus*, caterpillar, summer.................*Gnorimoschema subterranea* Busck

Acamptopappus sphaerocephalus

Gall-like swellings on tips of branches, caterpillar, summer......... ....*Gnorimoschema octomacullela* Chamb.

Hymenoclea salsola

White woolly stem galls, diameter ½ inch, midge, summer.......... ....*Rhopalomyia hymenocleæ* Felt

Horseweed, Bitterweed *(Erigeron canadensis)*

Inconspicuous blister mine, midge, summer. Fig. 322..............
..............Horseweed blister midge, *Asteromyia modesta* Felt

Fusiform stem gall, length 1 inch, midge, summer. Pl. 40 (4); Fig. 323
..............Horseweed stem midge, *Neolasioptera erigerontis* Felt

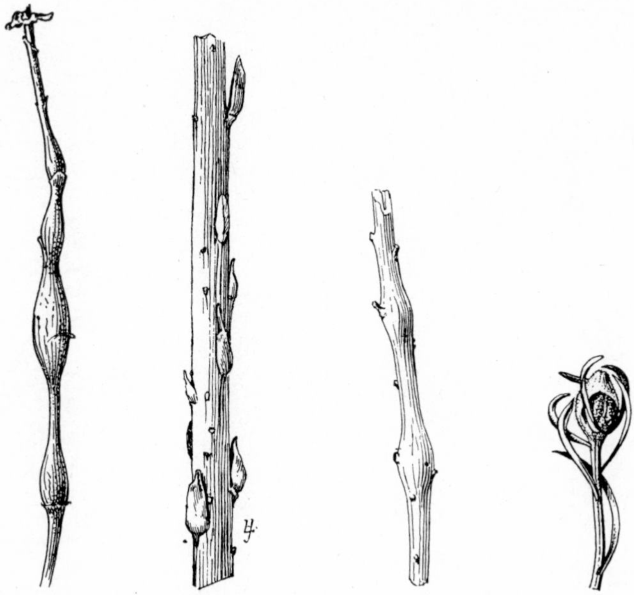

321   322   323   324

(Courtesy New York State Museum)

FIG. 321.—Aster stem gall, *Neolasioptera albitarsis.*
FIG. 322.—Horseweed blister gall, *Asteromyia modesta.*
FIG. 323.—Horseweed stem gall, *Neolasioptera erigerontis.*
FIG. 324.—Gall of *Rhopalomyia erigerontis.*

Apical bud gall, length ½ inch, on *E. fragilis,* midge, summer. Fig. 324
...............................*Rhopalomyia erigerontis* Felt

White-Topped Aster *(Sericocarpus asteroides)*

Apical, greenish bud gall, summer.............................
.....................? Nun midge, *Asphondylia monacha* O.S.

Groundsel Tree *(Baccharis pilularis)*

Flower bud or leaf gall, single or clustered, lobulate, greenish or reddish-
brown, diameter ¼ to ¾ inch, midge, summer.............
...............................*Rhopalomyia californica* Felt

Lobulate bud gall, midge, summer...................*Rhopalomyia sp.*

Globose, apical twig gall, diameter ¼ to ½ inch, midge, summer....
....*Cecidomyia sp.*

Stem gall, midge, summer.................*Rhopalomyia baccharis* Felt

Stem gall, caterpillar, summer.......*Gnorimoschema baccharisella* Busck

Irregular stem swelling, "potato gall," length ½ to 1½ inches, diameter ½ inch, midge, summer.........................*Asphondylia sp.*

Irregular, pustulate leaf swelling, diameter 1/10 inch, mite, summer....
....*Eriophyes sp.*

Ericameria

Rosette galls, leaflets recurved, length ½ inch, midge, summer. Fig. 325
...............................*Rhopalomyia ericameriæ* Felt

325    326    327

(Courtesy New York State Museum)

FIG. 325.—Gall of *Rhopalomyia ericameriæ*.
FIG. 326.—Rosinweed flower gall, *Aylax laciniatus*. (*After Beutm.*)
FIG. 327.—Rosinweed stem gall, *Aylax silphii*. (*After Beutm.*)

Everlasting, Lady's Tobacco *(Antennaria)*

Corm-shaped bud gall, length ⅓ to ½ inch, summer.............
.............Everlasting bud midge, *Asphondylia antennariæ* Whlr.

Elongate bud galls, leaflets scarcely recurved, length ⅛ to ⅕ inch, midge, summer........................*Rhopalomyia antennariæ* Whlr.

Globose, white, woolly masses, summer.........................
......................Woolly bud midge, *Rhopalomyia pilosa* Felt

Cudweed *(Gnaphalium)*

Narrowly ovate, white, woolly bud gall, midge, summer...........
...........................Cudweed bud gall, *Asphondylia sp.*

Rosinweed *(Silphium)*

Ovate, frequently clustered flower galls, length ⅙ inch, gall wasp, summer.

Pl. 38 (6); Fig. 326....Rosinweed flower wasp, *Aylax laciniatus* Gill.
Irregular, apical, green stem swelling, length 1¼ to 6 inches, gall wasp,
  summer. Pl. 37 (9); Fig. 327..............................
.....................Rosinweed stem wasp, *Aylax silphii* Gill.
(*leavenworthi* Bass.)

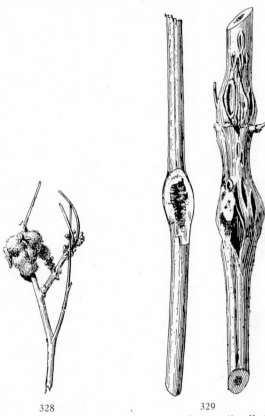

328   .   329
(*Courtesy New York State Museum*)

FIG. 328.—Gall of *Paradiplosis partheniicola.*
FIG. 329.—Ragweed stem gall, *Neolasioptera ambrosiæ.*

In apparently normal stems, gall wasp, summer. Pl. 38 (5)........
....*Aylax rufus* Gill.
Aylax gillettei Kieff.
Parthenium

Woolly gall, diameter ⅕ inch, midge, summer. Fig. 328............
..............................*Paradiplosis partheniicola* Ckll.
Marginal, hairy, variable leaf rolls, mite, summer.........*Eriophyes sp.*

Iva

Enlarged stems, gall diameter $\frac{3}{16}$ inch, length 1-1½ inches, midge, fall
.... *Lasioptera sp.*
Globose, pubescent, yellowish or greenish pouch galls on upper leaf surface,
mite, summer.................................... *Eriophyes sp.*

Ragweed *(Ambrosia)*

Probably from a stem gall, gall wasp, summer....................
.... Ragweed stem wasp, *Aulacidea ambrosiæcola* Ashm.
Stems of giant ragweed, midge, summer. Fig. 329................
.... Ragweed stem midge, *Neolasioptera ambrosiæ* Felt
Subglobose branch or stem gall, diameter ⅓ inch, fly, summer.... *Trypetid*

Franseria dumosa

Oval, apical bud gall, whitish, diameter ⅓ inch, midge, summer.....
.... ?*Diarthronomyia sp.*
Oval stem gall, length 1 inch, diameter ¾ inch, caterpillar, summer...
.... *Lepidopteron*

Cone-Flower *(Rudbeckia)*

Deformed, enlarged florets, midge, summer.. *Cecidomyia rudbeckiæ* Beutm.
Subglobular apical bud gall, diameter ⅙ inch, midge, summer. Pl. 5 (2)
.... Cone-flower gall, *Asphondylia conspicua* O.S.
Nodula stem gall, midge, summer...................... *Cecidomyia sp.*
Apparently from a nearly normal stem, summer..................
.... Cone-flower stem midge, *Lasioptera rudbeckiæ* Felt

Lepachys

Deformed flower bud, midge, summer. Pl. 41 (8)................
.... *Asphondylia ratibidæ* Felt
Irregular stem swelling, summer.................. *Eutreta sparsa* Wied.

Sunflower *(Helianthus)*

Sunflower seeds, apparently normal, summer....................
.... Sunflower seed midge, *Lasioptera murtfeldtiana* Felt
Asphondylia globulus O.S.
Subglobular leaf gall, diameter ¼ inch, midge, summer. Pl. 10 (5)...
.... Sunflower bullet gall, *Trishormomyia bulla* Felt
Globular or spherical stem galls, diameter ½ to 2 inches, midge, summer,
also reared from seeds. Pl. 5 (3)..........................
.... Sunflower purse gall, *Asphondylia globulus* O.S.
Stem gall undescribed, midge, summer....... *Asphondylia conspicua* O.S.

Stem gall, on *H. divaricatus,* midge, summer.....................
....................................*Cecidomyia thurstoni* Brodie

Fusiform stem gall, length 1½ inches, summer. Fig. 330..........
.....................Sunflower stem midge, *Lasioptera weldi* Felt

Stem gall undescribed, midge, summer.........*Neolasioptera trimera* Felt

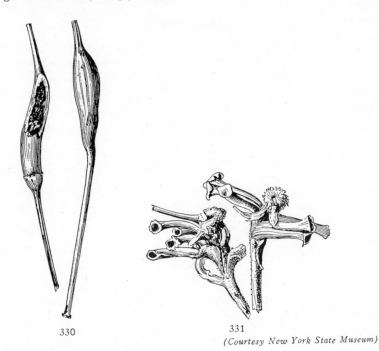

330

331

(Courtesy New York State Museum)

Fɪɢ. 330.—Sunflower stem gall, *Lasioptera weldi.*
Fɪɢ. 331.—Tubular bud gall, *Trishormoyia helianthi.*

Spindle-shaped stem gall, length 1⁄10 inch, on *H. tracheliifolius,* caterpillar,
summer...............................*Bucculatrix fuscicola* Braun

Ovate stem swellings, frequently roughened, diameter ¾ inch, on *H. tubero-
sus,* fly, summer.............Several *Diptera* and possibly a *Cecid*

Helianthus strumosus

Flower heads, apparently unmodified, midge, summer.............
...............................*Asphondylia helianthiflorœ* Felt

Tubular, axillary bud gall, length ½ to 1 inch, midge, summer. Fig. 331
.................Tubular bud gall, *Trishormomyia helianthi* Brodie

Reared from undetected gall, midge, summer.....................
....................................*Neolasioptera helianthi* Felt

Actinomeris alternifolia

Globose bud gall, midge, summer.........*Cecidomyia verbesinæ* Beutm.

Bur Marigolf *(Bidens)*

Slender, fusiform stem gall, length ½ inch, midge, summer. .*Lasioptera sp.*

Sneezeweed *(Helenium)*

Apical rosette gall, length ⅒ inch, midge, summer. Pl. 40 (3)......
.............................*Asphondylia autumnalis* Beutm.
Tunneled pith, midge, summer........................*Cecidomyia sp.*

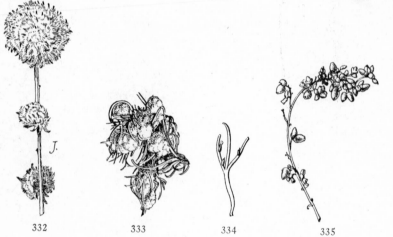

332   333   334   335

(Courtesy New York State Museum)

FIG. 332.—Woolly wormwood gall, *Rhopalomyia alticola.*
FIG. 333.—Gall of *Diarthronomyia floccosa.*
FIG. 334.—Gall of *Diarthronomyia californica.*
FIG. 335.—Gall of *Diarthronomyia betheliana.*

Yarrow *(Achillea)*

Florets apparently normal, summer..............................
..............Yarrow flower midge, *Clinorhyncha millefolii* Wachtl.
Ovate flower bud gall, white pubescence, length ¼ inch, midge, summer
..............................?*Rhopalomyia millefolii* H.Lw.

Chamomile *(Anthemis)*

Larvae in flower heads, midge, summer................*Cecidomyia sp.*

Chrysanthemum

Swollen stems, leaf stalks or deformed buds containing oval, frequently

coalescent cells, each with a length $\frac{1}{10}$ inch, midge, summer. Pl. 10 (4)
............Chrysanthemum midge, *Diarthronomyia hypogœa* H.Lw.

Loose leaf and blossom galls, mite, summer....*Tarsonemus pallidus* Banks

Wormwood *(Artemisia)*

Artemisia californica

Irregular, lobulate, woolly, lateral bud masses, individual galls, diameter $\frac{1}{6}$ inch, midge, summer..............*Diarthronomyia floccosa* Felt

Subconical, thin-walled, brownish or reddish leaf galls, length $\frac{1}{10}$ inch, midge, summer.................*Diarthronomyia californica* Felt

Artemisia caudata

Oval, woolly, apical or lateral bud galls, diameter $\frac{1}{2}$ to $\frac{3}{4}$ inch, midge, summer.......Woolly wormwood gall, *Rhopalomyia ? alticola* Ckll.

336   337

(Courtesy New York State Museum)

FIG. 336.—Gall of *Diarthronomyia occidentalis*, on *A. heterophylla*.
FIG. 337.—Gall of *Diarthronomyia artemisiæ*, on *A. tridentata*.

Artemisia forwoodii (? canadensis)

Globular, woolly galls, diameter $\frac{1}{2}$ inch, midge, summer. Fig. 332....
...............Woolly wormwood gall, *Rhopalomyia alticola* Ckll.

Artemisia frigida

Fusiform flower or leaf bud galls, length $\frac{1}{6}$ inch, also on *A. filifera*, midge, summer. Fig. 335.................*Rhopalomyia betheliana* Ckll.

Artemisia gnaphalodes

Irregular, lobulate, whitish, pubescent gall, diameter $\frac{1}{2}$ inch, midge, summer............................*Rhopalomyia gnaphalodis* Felt

Artemisia heterophylla

Ovate, thin-walled, oblique leaf galls, length $\frac{1}{25}$ inch, also in apparently normal flower buds, midge, summer. Fig. 336...............
..............................*Diarthronomyia occidentalis* Felt

Artemisia sp.

Deformed flower heads, length $\frac{1}{2}$ inch, midge, summer............
..........Wormwood flower midge, *Rhopalomyia coloradella* Ckll.

Bud galls, presumably, midge, summer.......*Asphondylia artemisiæ* Felt

Globose deformed buds with black, densely crowded filaments, mite, summer...*Eriophyes sp.*

Ovate masses of linear leaves, on branchlets, length $\frac{3}{4}$ inch, mite, summer
....*Eriophyes sp.*

Subconical, short-wooled, yellowish-gray, axillary bud gall, length 1 inch, fly, summer.......................................*Trypetid*

Globose, axillary, grayish-white, woolly bud gall, diameter $\frac{1}{4}$ to $\frac{1}{2}$ inch, fly, summer.......................................*Trypetid*

Sage Bush (*Artemisia tridentata*)

Oval bud-like flower gall, the size of a pea, midge, summer.........
................................*Rhopalomyia tridentatæ* Rubs.

338   339

(Courtesy New York State Museum)

Fig. 338.—Gall of *Diarthronomyia occidentalis*, on *A. tridentatæ*.
Fig. 339.—Wormwood flask gall, *Rhopalomyia ampullaria*.

Ovate, hard, thick-walled, yellowish-brown bud gall, length $\frac{3}{4}$ inch, fly, summer .... *Trypetid*

Many lobed, irregular, white, thickly haired gall, diameter $\frac{3}{4}$ inch, midge, summer..............................*Rhopalomyia navasi* Tav.

Flask-shaped leaf gall, length $\frac{1}{6}$ inch, midge, summer. Fig. 339.....
...............Wormwood flask gall, *Rhopalomyia ampullaria* Felt

Oval, grayish or almost black, solitary or clustered gall on the underside

of the leaves, length ¾ inch, midge, summer. Fig. 338..........
...........................*Diarthronomyia occidentalis* Felt

Globose leaf bud or rosette gall or bladdery leaf gall, diameter ⅛ to ½
inch, midge, summer. Fig. 337.......*Diarthronomyia artemisiœ* Felt

Subglobular, brown, spongy, apical gall, diameter 2 inches..........
....*Cecidomyia sp.*

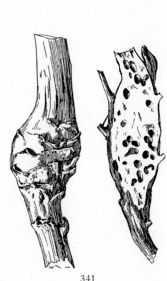

340   341

(*Courtesy New York State Museum*)

FIG. 340.—Dandelion stem gall, *Aylax taraxaci.* (*After Beutm.*)
FIG. 341.—Lettuce tumor gall, *Aulacidea tumida.* (*After Beutm.*)

Fireweed (*Erechtites*)

Infesting flowers, midge, summer....................*Asphondylia sp.*

Irregular stem gall, 1½ by 1 inch, gall wasp, summer.....?*Aulacidea sp.*

Irregular stem enlargement, length 1 to 1½ inches, on *E. hieracifolia*, midge,
summer.......................................*Lasioptera sp.*

Groundsel, Ragwort, Squaw-Weed (*Senecio*)

Flower heads, presumably unmodified, midge, summer...........
.............................*Rhopalomyia cockerelli* Felt

Reared from heads, on *S. douglassi,* midge, summer.............
.....................................*Asphondylia bea* Felt
Stem gall undescribed, midge, summer........*Lasioptera arizonensis* Felt

Saltbush *(Tetradymia spinosa)*

Fusiform, woolly, stem enlargement, length 1½ inches, on *T. spinosa,*
caterpillar, summer...........*Gnorimoschema tetradymiella* Busck
Ovate bud gall, on *T. comosa,* midge, summer. . *Phytophaga tetradymia* Felt

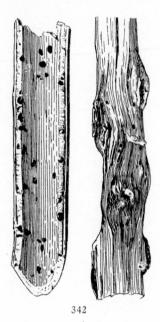

342   343
(Courtesy New York State Museum)

Fig. 342.—Gall of *Aulacidea podagræ.* (*After Beutm.*)
Fig. 343.—Gall of *Antistrophus pisum.* (*After Beutm.*)

Burdock *(Arctium)*

Yellowish larvae in burrs, midge, summer......... ....*Cecidomyia sp.*

Malacothrix? (spinosus)

Gall-like swellings in the stem, beetle, summer...*Anthonomus ligatus* Dietz

Cat's Ear *(Hypochæris)*

Irregular, multilocular stem swellings, length 1 to 2 inches, gall wasp, summer..............................*Aulax hypochoeridis* Kieff.

Dandelion (*Taraxacum*)

Oblong, irregular, polythalamous or midrib swelling, length 1 to 2 inches, summer. Pl. 38 (2); Fig. 340..............................
......................Dandelion gall wasp, *Aylax taraxaci* Ashm.

Elongate, polythalamous swelling of midrib, fly, summer...........
....................................*Agromyza youngi* Mall.

Lettuce (*Lactuca*)

Irregular stem gall, diameter ⅞ inch, midge, summer.............
.....................Lettuce stem midge, *Lasioptera lactucæ* Felt

Rounded, irregular stem swelling, length 1 to 3 inches, gall wasp, summer. Pl. 37 (8); Fig. 341.....Lettuce tumor gall, *Aulacidea tumida* Bass.

Apical, club-shaped, bent or twisted stem swellings, length 3 inches, gall wasp, summer.........................*Aulacidea annulata* Kins.

In pith, sometimes a stem swelling, gall wasp, summer. Pl. 3 (6); Fig. 342
....................................*Aulacidea podagræ* Bass.

In thin-walled cells in pith, gall wasp, summer..................
................................*Aulacidea harringtoni* Ashm.
Aulacidea abdita Kins.

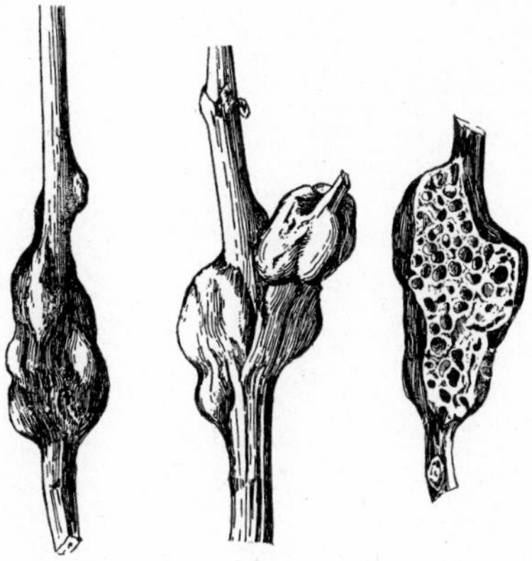

344

(Courtesy New York State Museum)

FIG. 344.—Gall of *Aulacidea nabali*. (*After Beutm.*)

Microseris

Irregular stem swelling, within dense, whitish, spongy, the central larval cell divided into several areas, length ¾ to 1¼ inches, diameter ½ to ¾ inch, gall wasp..............*Aylax microseris* McC. & Egb.

Sow Thistle (*Sonchus*)

Reared from stems, gall wasp, summer........................
.....................Lettuce tumor gall, *Aulacidea tumida* Bass.

Encelia

Leafy bud gall, length ½ inch, midge, summer..*Asphondylia enceliæ* Felt
Conical lateral bud gall, length ¼ inch, midge, summer...........
.................................·....*Rhopalomyia enceliæ* Felt

Lygodesmia

Oval or pea-like stem galls, diameter ¼ to ½ inch, gall wasp, summer.
Pl. 38 (3); Fig. 343.................*Antistrophus pisum* Walsh

Rattlesnake-Root *(Prenanthes)*

Flat, purplish leaf gall, length ¹⁄₁₀ inch, midge, summer...........
.................................*Cystiphora canadensis* Felt
Irregular, polythalamous, basal stem swelling, diameter ⅕ to ½ inch, gall
wasp, summer. Pl. 20 (9), Fig. 344.........*Aulacidea nabali* Brodie
Apical, club-shaped, frequently bent or twisted stem swellings, length 3
inches, gall wasp, summer...............*Aulacidea annulata* Kins.

Cockle burr *(Xanthium sp.)*

Galls on branch tips of *Xanthium speciosum,* gall midge...........
..................*Cockle burr bud gall, Asphondylia xanthii* Felt
Reared from the roots of *Xanthium sp.,* gall midge..............
..................*Cockle burr root gall, Mycodiplosis radicis* Felt

BIBLIOGRAPHY

There are numerous publications, many of them miscellaneous, upon the plant galls and gall insects of America. The author has given an extended bibliography in his "Key to American Insect Galls," New York State Museum Bulletin #200, 1918. The following is limited to the more important works which have appeared subsequently:

1920   KINSEY, ALFRED C. New Species and Synonymy of American Cynipidæ. *Am. Mus. Nat. Hist. Bull.*, Vol. 42, p. 293-317, plates 20-27.

1920   ———— Life History of American Cynipidæ. *Am. Mus. Nat. Hist. Bull.*, 42, p. 319-357, plates 28-31.

1920   ———— Phylogeny of Cynipid Genera and Biological Characteristics. *Am. Mus. Nat. Hist. Bull.*, Vol. 42, p. 357a-402, 1 plate.

1921   WELD, LEWIS H. American Gallflies of the Family Cynipidæ Producing Subterranean Galls on Oak. *U. S. Nat. Mus. Proc.*, Vol. 59, #2368, p. 187-246, plates 28-37.

1922   KINSEY, ALFRED C. New Pacific Coast Cynipidæ. *Am. Mus. Nat. Hist.*, Vol. 46, p. 279-295, 1 plate.

1922   ———— Studies of Some New and Described Cynipidæ. *Indiana University Studies*, Vol. 9, Study #53, p. 1-171.

1922   McCRACKEN, ISABEL and EGBERT, DOROTHY. California Gall Making Cynipids. *Stanford Univ. Pub., Univ. Ser., Biol. Sci.*, Vol. 3, No. 1, p. 1-70.

1922   WELD, LEWIS H. Notes on American Gallflies of the Family Cynipidæ Producing Galls on Acorns, With Descriptions of New Species. *U. S. Nat. Mus. Proc.*, Vol. 61, #2440, p. 1-32, plates 1-5.

1922   ———— Notes on Cynipid Wasps with Descriptions of New North American Species. *U. S. Nat. Mus. Proc.*, Vol. 61, #2439, p. 1-291, 1 plate.

1923   KINSEY, ALFRED C. The Gall Wasp Genus Neuroterus. *Indiana University Studies*, Vol. 10, Study #58, p. 1-150, figures 1-63.

1925   FELT, E. P. Key to Gall Midges (A Resume of Studies I-VII, *Itonididæ*) *N. Y. State Mus. Bull.*, #257, p. 1-239, plates 1-8, figures 57.

1926   WELD, LEWIS H. Field Notes on Gall-Inhabiting Cynipid Wasps With Descriptions of New Species. *U. S. Nat. Mus. Proc.*, #2611, Vol. 68, p. 1-131, plates 1-8.

1929   KINSEY, ALFRED C. The Gall Wasp Genus Cynips, A Study on the Origin of Species. *Indiana University Studies*, Vol. 16, Studies #84, 85, 86, p. 1-577, figures 1-429.

1934   WELLS, B. W. Galls and "Galls." *Elisha Mitchell Scientific Society, Journal*, Vol. 50, p. 65-74.

1936   KINSEY, ALFRED C. The Origin of Higher Categories in Cynips. *Indiana University Publications,* Science Series, Entomological Series #10, p. 1-334, figures 164.

1937   ———— New Mexican Gall Wasps *(Hymenoptera, Cynipidæ). Rev. de Entomologia,* vol. 7, fasc. 1, p. 39-79.

1937   ———— New Mexican Gall Wasps *(Hymenoptera, Cynipidæ). Rev. de Entomologia,* II, vol. 7, fasc. 4, p. 428-471.

1938   ———— New Mexican Gall Wasps *(Hymenoptera, Cynipidæ). Indiana Academy of Science,* vol. 47, p. 261-280.

INDEX